Gen Sir
3.00

E. Newton Harvey

"MELANCOLIA" by Albrecht Dürer (1514)

This superlative engraving has been chosen as a frontispiece for the book because it expresses the main theme so well and in charming symbols. According to Erwin Panofsky, the mature, learned, and pensive Melancolia "typifies Theoretical Insight which thinks, but cannot act"; while the "ignorant infant, making meaningless scrawls on his slate and almost conveying the impression of blindness, typifies Practical Skill which acts but cannot think." Theory and practice are not "together," but "thoroughly disunited; and the result is impotence and gloom." Displayed strewn about are the tools of science: a sphere and a geometric solid, as well as a magic square (representing mathematics: both geometry and arithmetic), an hourglass for the measurement of time, a pair of dividers for the measurement of space, and a balance. The rainbow and the comet signify the phenomena of nature. The tools of the practical man are likewise in disarray: a block plane, a hammer and nails, a saw, a millstone, and a ladder. The history of our civilization since Dürer's time is in large measure the guidance and direction given to blind Practical Skill by Theoretical Insight, the revolution in the sphere of practical action resulting from scientific thought and experiment.

ALBRECHT DÜRER'S "MELANCOLIA"

(*see preceding page*)

SCIENCE,
SERVANT OF MAN

A Layman's Primer for the Age of Science

I. Bernard Cohen

INSTRUCTOR IN THE HISTORY OF SCIENCE
AND GENERAL EDUCATION, HARVARD UNIVERSITY

With Illustrations

Little, Brown and Company · *Boston* · 1948

Published August 1948
Reprinted January 1952

Published simultaneously
in Canada by McClelland and Stewart Limited

PRINTED IN THE UNITED STATES OF AMERICA

Foreword

BY HARLOW SHAPLEY

THE FURIOUS ANTICS of iron atoms in the atmosphere of a star may seem so remote from travel schedules, and the shapes of microscopic animals that have been dead half a billion years so unrelated to the cost of living, that you may be impatient with the labors and technicalities of the astronomer and the geologist. But appearances, and the shopworn jests about impractical professors, have betrayed you. The sun's atoms and the tiny fossils are not remote. The aeronautical companies, as well as the navies of the world, are much concerned with the electronics in solar gases ninety-three million miles away; and the astute businessmen in one of the greatest of industries have invested millions of hard practical dollars in the micro-paleontology of foraminifera in the fossiliferous strata of Paleozoic times. (Please pardon the long technical words, but I use them deliberately to suggest that a quiet academic lane is often the best road to the market place.)

An investment in knowledge of fossils, as shown in Chapter 14 of this volume, aids the development of oil fields, increasing the yield of gasoline, and cutting the cost to the consumer.

The atomic vibrations in the corona of the sun, originally explored just because astronomers wanted to increase their knowledge of the structure of stars, are associated with the radio reflecting layers in the earth's atmosphere (Chapter 16); they are therefore connected with the failures, at times, of those layers to transmit properly the guiding radio signals that make long distance flying safe.

Many such instances of the passage from thought to action, from pure research to its surprising applications, from the quiet, almost aimless explorations in the study and laboratory to the making of entirely new industries and to the creating of new aspects of better living — many such examples are happily described by Dr. I. Bernard Cohen in the chapters of this book. He tells stories that make one cheerful about the human mind. He describes the ingenuity of the men who turn to important human uses some of the small bits of curiosity-satisfying observation and some of the fragments of logical deduction that come out of the workshop of the free investigator.

The great governments, notably England, Russia, and the United States, have in different degrees recognized that social progress, as well as national safety, will depend in the future more than ever on the degrees to which the people and governments support scientific inquiry and application. There is a growing appreciation of the fact that unhampered basic research is more important than the applications.

Although it appears difficult for some politicians and short-visioned operators in agriculture and industry to see the need of freedom for the investigator to choose his field of study and to follow his own inspiration, that concept is now acknowledged by the government of the United States. The significance to America at this time of basic research is specifically stated in the legislative proposals of the past year or two. But the question *What is the good of it?* frequently obstructs attempts to get generous support for scientific training and research from governmental agencies, and often from industry.

Dr. Cohen, at the request of the National Science Fund of the National Academy of Science, sets out to answer that question in the present volume. He succeeds, and at the same time answers many related questions, such as: *How are discoveries made?* and *What spirit moves the scientist, who sometimes looks for "practical" ends but more often does not?*

It seems to me that the legislators, the government bureau chiefs, the university trustees, and the officials in nearly all large business concerns, could profitably look to the stories here presented of hybrid corn, of electronics, and of the antibiotics that bring new hope for the defeat of human maladies. They might think over the daily experiences of modern life — travel, eating, communications, entertainment, and business activities — and discover that most of them have immediate connections with the work of the little-recognized scientific investigators of the past and with the scientifically trained technicians who make the steps from thought to action.

The epoch of the impoverished, overworked scientists, who struggle in their weary spare hours for the physical and mental welfare of mankind, should be near its end. The people and the governments of the world cannot wisely afford to go without the not-yet-known treasures which deliberate thought and basic research can eventually bring to the civilization.

I shall not be entirely happy about this Foreword unless I return to that phrase, *What is the good of it?* "Good" and "Practical" are words that are too often used loosely as synonyms, and too often given restricted meanings. A research is not good and practical only if it adds to material wealth or physical joys, to new thrills or a longer life. A research is practical also when it provides a thought or a tool that leads to further exploration. A research is practical if it enlarges and enriches the spiritual content of human life and knowledge. The concepts of Newtonian gravitation, of Darwinian evolution, of Mendelian inheritance, of Einsteinian relativity, have indeed provided some noteworthy uses in engineering, plant breeding, and atomic energy utilization; but their greatest human contribution has been in the realms of philosophy, religion, and the social behavior of mankind. In such less tangible fields man transcends his biological environment.

Science is indeed the servant of man, and can do even finer service if fully utilized; but much of its greatness lies in its providing for the meditator as well as for the actor.

Preface

> Science can be interpreted effectively only for those who have more than the usual intelligence and innate curiosity. These will work hard if given the chance and if they find they acquire something by so doing.
>
> — VANNEVAR BUSH (1940)

THE WRITING of this book was undertaken because it deals with what I consider to be one of the most important problems of our age: the relation of scientific discovery to our daily lives and to our well-being and national security. In our day we can no longer afford to be silent partners in the scientific enterprise; we can be intelligent citizens of the scientific age only if we participate to some extent in the scientific enterprise, pervaded by the spirit of science and cognizant of scientific accomplishments. Of course, we cannot all be scientists. But the obligation lies on each of us to understand both the nature of the processes by which science advances and the way in which practical applications of those advances are made to change and expand our world.

Those of us who are not scientists talk of science, or listen to talk of science, in terms of great generalities. We take references to examples which we do not fully understand and toss them back and forth. We accept the description "miracle" of each scientific innovation, although the words "science" and "miracle" belong to totally different activities. Sometimes we turn away from the discovery of a new law of life or law of the universe, or a new phenomenon, because our lack of understanding and experience does not enable us to discern the exciting consequences immanent in the account of it.

Many excellent books are in print that acquaint their readers with the discoveries of modern science, the philosophical significance of some scientific achievements, the methods of science, and the advances in the practical arts. This is, I believe, the first attempt to study the practical consequences of scientific research by means of selected case histories. I have attempted to describe some of the greatest scientific achievements of our era, showing the steps whereby in each case knowledge grew and developed. By the study of such case histories, drawn from many different fields of research, evidence is brought forth towards certain general conclusions which may be thought of as signposts for our future attitudes and conduct. But the method of case histories has an additional advantage: it gives the reader, vicariously, a measure of the actual experience of those who work in the laboratory to discover new principles, as well as those who put them to use. By this experience, it is hoped that the reader may come to understand not only the significance of the achievements, but also how they came about, and what their relationship is to the economic, cultural, and social implex of which they are a part.

I have had the great privilege of discussing each of the chapters with specialists within whose province each lies. In addition, each chapter was read in manuscript by at least one established authority in that field. In many instances, the critical reader was the very person whose work has been described. As a historian of science, I must admit that this has been a new experience; most history must be written without the aid of the chief characters!

At the end of the book I have acknowledged my indebtedness to the many scientists who have helped me with various portions of the manuscript. But I should like to record special gratitude here to the National Science Fund (National Academy of Sciences), its first chairman, Dr. William J. Robbins, and its secretary, Mr. Howland Sargeant, for their part in suggesting that I undertake this task. Especially to Mr. Sargeant and to Dr. Harlow Shapley, Director of the Harvard Observatory and present chairman of the National Science Fund, am I grateful for continued and extended kindness throughout all stages of the writing of this book. The John F. Milton Fund of Harvard University awarded a grant during the years 1942–1944, but for the aid of which the book could never have been written.

I. Bernard Cohen

Contents

Illustrations

PART ONE
The Nature of the Scientific Enterprise

In recent years scientists have grown self-conscious, perhaps because they have only lately become of age. They realize that they are now part of the drama of human history, and they look to the professional historian for background and perspective.

— JOHN F. FULTON (1932)

CHAPTER I

The Scientific Education of the Layman

> Science is the soul of the prosperity of nations and the living source of all progress. Undoubtedly the tiring discussions of politics seem to be our guide — empty appearances! What really leads us forward is a few scientific discoveries and their application.
> — LOUIS PASTEUR (1822–1895)

SCIENCE TODAY is everybody's business.

Every aspect of the life of twentieth-century man has been affected by the scientific discoveries in the laboratory: man's health, his wealth, what he eats, what he grows, what he wears, the tools he works with, the products he manufactures, the way he manufactures them — and so, on and on.

The very fabric and framework of the world we live in has been altered by science. The handle of our toothbrush is made of some form of synthetic plastic, its bristles may be made of nylon, and the purity of the dentifrice itself is owing to scientific labor. When we are ill we feel much more secure than our grandparents did because we know that the fruits of scientific discovery are available to the physician who attends us. To take but one example, pneumonia, once the scourge of old age, is now rendered relatively impotent by the use of sulfa drugs and penicillin. Even before we become ill and need a physician, preventive medicine assures us a more healthy existence than was possible say one hundred and fifty years ago. Our water systems are kept uncontaminated because scientists have discovered which diseases may be transmitted by polluted water, and how to keep water pure. Vaccination has all but eliminated the threat of smallpox throughout a large part of the civilized world, while discoveries in nutrition have taught us how to eat more healthful meals.

All the conveniences of modern life are largely owing to the by-products of a scientific research. When we flick on a switch and flood a dark room with illumination, when we use a sewing machine or a vacuum cleaner, or an electric motor in a factory, we may give thanks to such scientists as Michael Faraday and Joseph Henry whose scientific discoveries made possible our electric power system and the electric motor. The telephone, radio, talking movies, new and efficient fuels for motorcars, photoelectric "eyes" which open doors, new fibers such as nylon and rayons, coal-tar dyes which give color to all of our clothing, materials for bleaching cotton and wool, new forms of plants which are resistant to disease and give superior yield, insect-killing sprays such as DDT, and weed-killing compounds such as 2,4–D — and so on down an almost interminable list of applications of scientific discovery.

The advent of the atomic bomb throws into stark relief the impact of science on our lives. So does the possibility of some horrible form of biological warfare. One or the other, or both simultaneously, may spread throughout the world diseases which we cannot control, destroy our food supply as it grows in the ground, pulverize our cities to dust, and wipe out the lives of millions of human beings. Who can doubt the potency of science?

During the war, our government spent enormous sums of money on research which yielded important military innovations such as methods of using blood plasma, microwave radar, the proximity fuze, and, of course, the atomic bomb. Those who wish to see how our scientists and engineers made effective use of the wartime expenditures may consult President James Phinney Baxter's *Scientists Against Time,* which recounts the history of research during World War II. The success of that program has convinced the last doubters of the "obvious" lesson that *scientific research pays dividends in a very practical way*. We are thus led to draw the conclusion that it would be profitable to support scientific research in peacetime, and on a large scale.

The late President Roosevelt was impressed as a layman by the brilliant achievements of wartime research carried out under the direction of the Office of Scientific Research and Development, headed by Dr. Vannevar Bush, President of the Carnegie Institution of Washington. Looking ahead to the days of peace, he wrote a letter to Dr. Bush in 1944 which began as follows:

DEAR DR. BUSH:

The Office of Scientific Research and Development, of which you are the Director, represents a unique experiment of teamwork and co-operation in co-ordinating scientific research and in applying existing scientific knowledge to the solution of the technical problems paramount in war. . . .

There is . . . no reason why the lessons to be found in this experiment cannot be profitably employed in times of peace. The information, the techniques, and the research experience developed by the Office of Scientific Research and Development and by the thousands of scientists in the universities and in private industry, should be used in the days of peace ahead for the improvement of the national health, the creation of new enterprises bringing new jobs, and the betterment of the national standard of living.[1]

President Roosevelt asked for Dr. Bush's recommendations on the following four questions: 1. What could be done, consistent with military security, to make known to the world at large the advances in knowledge made during the war? 2. What could be done to organize a program for continuing the work done in medicine and related science, in the war against disease? 3. How could the government aid the research activities of public and private organizations? 4. Could a program be proposed for discovering and developing scientific talent in American youth?

Dr. Bush obtained the assistance of a considerable number of the leading scientists in the United States, divided into four committees, each investigating one of the President's questions. Their findings, together with a summary and conclusions by Dr. Bush, were submitted to President Truman in July 1945, in the form of a booklet entitled *Science, the Endless Frontier*. This report * is an important document in the history of American science, and it should be read by everyone who is interested in the future of science in this country. It strongly recommended a program of federal support for scientific research, and together with independent findings by senatorial investigations, notably those of a committee headed by the

* Available from the Superintendent of Documents, U. S. Government Printing Office, where it is listed as "Emergency Management Office, Pr32.413:Sci2" — price 30¢.

Honorable Harley Kilgore of West Virginia, it formed the basis of discussions in the Congress. In the spring of 1947, a bill was finally passed establishing a National Science Foundation; but it was vetoed by President Truman because of certain administrative features.

In the meanwhile, an independent study of the problem was made by the President's Scientific Research Board (John R. Steelman, Chairman), whose conclusions were submitted to President Truman on 27 August 1947, in the form of a pamphlet entitled *Science and Public Policy: A Program for the Nation.* This report, like its predecessor, stressed the need for a federally financed program of scientific research. It declared unequivocally: "The Federal Government should spend about $50 million for support of basic research outside of its own laboratories in 1949. From that point, grants for basic research should increase rapidly until they reach an annual rate of at least $250 million by 1957."[2]

In some form or other, we are about to embark on a program of unprecedented large-scale expenditure of public funds for the support of scientific research. Since these funds come from taxes, and since their expenditure is controlled by our elected representatives in the Congress, the thoughts and actions of every man and woman will influence the future course of scientific programs in America. To a considerable extent we are already sponsoring fundamental research with Federal funds under the aegis of the Atomic Energy Commission.

Each of us has thus a new burden of citizenship not shared by previous generations: a new responsibility that calls for a secure understanding of the scope, nature, and effect of the scientific enterprise. To the extent that our voice will be heard, each of us has thus become a lay administrator of science. For example — if a sufficiently large number of people will write letters to their Congressmen and Senators to the effect that the expenditure of many millions of dollars for studying distant nebulae is an obvious case of "boondoggling" at a time when we should balance the budget, support of that particular research program may be withdrawn.

No one has yet raised an objection to the expenditure of millions and even billions of dollars for scientific research, because almost everybody knows that science produces useful and tangible results. We know that our future security as a nation depends on the military strength and superiority which scientific research will make possible. We want to make sure that cures will be found for the diseases we still fear — cancer, arthritis, various heart ailments — and also the common cold.

There is no possible doubt that scientific research will produce for us the practical and useful things we desire, but it will do so *only if we who may control the directions of its progress will make a serious effort to understand its true nature.* We must not think, for example, that the expenditure of $50,000,000 a year for so-called "cancer research" is a guarantee that a cure for this disease will be found in, say, 5 years. Nor can we, in a larger sense, demand that our scientists make "useful" discoveries, susceptible of immediate application to pressing problems, rather than make so-called "academic" investigations of "useless" abstractions. Science consists to a large extent of an attack upon the unknown: how can a man foretell whether his work will eventuate in something that can be applied or not *before he even knows what he is going to discover?* Who knows which branch of apparently useless scientific research will provide the key to unlock the cancer problem?

Many paths that have led to important scientific discoveries have been devious, full of false starts and dead ends, or apparently barren or sterile for many years until, suddenly and deceptively sporadically, there is a full measure of achievement. Too many times has the apparently abstract research, far removed from any possible practical use, yielded a rich return — we no longer dare to say that any field of scientific endeavor will not provide the practical innovation for tomorrow's technology or the cure for today's disease.

One conclusion that will emerge from studying the case histories in this book is that the useful things we expect to get as payment for our support of scientific research are *not end-products at all,* but rather *by-products of the search for fundamental truth* — which is science. Only a program of research aimed at increasing knowledge — even if apparently for its own sake alone — will provide in the end the cures for disease and the easier, better, and more secure lives that the fruits of science will make possible.

The scientific education of the layman takes on today a new and profound significance that was absent a few years ago. The purpose of this book is to prepare the layman for his new post of lay administrator of science, enabling him, by a study of case histories, to obtain guides for action with regard to the following topics: what science does, what science can do, how science does it, how every citizen must act so as to make sure that science does it best.

ᕙ   ᕙ   ᕙ

As a historian of science, I am constantly struck by the fact that the average reader of the eighteenth century had a much better grasp of the full meaning and significance of the science of his day than a similar person has in ours. The English poets of the eighteenth century, for example, were not only familiar with the principles of Newtonian mechanics and optics but — as Miss Marjorie Nicolson has so well demonstrated in her recent book, *Newton Demands the Muse* — they integrated Newtonian ideas into their actual poetic writings, and even constructed esthetic canons in Newtonian terms. The educated layman of that day — whether poet, philosopher, statesman, merchant, or dreamer — was able to learn his science by reading popular books by great masters.[3]

Foremost among the scientific primers for the eighteenth-century layman was Leonhard Euler's *Letters to a German Princess,* written for the instruction of the Princess of Anhalt-Dessau. This book was so extraordinarily good that it continued in vogue for almost a hundred years, being reprinted thirty-five times and appearing in nine languages — French, Russian, German, Dutch, Swedish, Danish, Italian, English, and Spanish — from the time it was first printed in 1768 until the last edition was printed in New York in 1858.[4] This extraordinary book was distinguished for its easy flow of language and graceful style (as befitting the education of a princess), the niceness with which the points were illustrated, and the mastery of the subject by the author — one of the foremost mathematicians of his age. Another book equally characterized by its beautiful style and technical competence was Count Algarotti's *Newtonianism for the Ladies,* published in Italian, French, and English.[5]

Voltaire's *Elements of Sir Isaac Newton's Philosophy* [6] is today as splendid an introduction to Newtonianism, for scholars and students of the history of ideas, as it was to its eighteenth-century readers. His book reveals that famous author's gift for scientific exposition in the great French tradition of making available to laymen the discoveries of science in terms to be understood by all. The tradition probably begins with Fontenelle, a great stylist of the seventeenth century, famous in the annals of literature, who was also the Secretary of the French Royal Academy of Sciences. His *Conversations on the Plurality of Worlds* discussed the principles of Copernican astronomy, and the discoveries of Galileo, against a background of moonlit gardens and enchanting boudoirs. This great French tradition continues to our own day, although without the garden and the boudoir, in the writings of expositors like Henri Poincaré and Louis de Broglie.

Among the English writers of the eighteenth century, the most important was probably Henry Pemberton, whose *View of Sir Isaac Newton's Philosophy* [7] bore the stamp of authority in so far as the author had been selected by "great Newton" himself to superintend the publication of the third edition of the latter's masterpiece, *Mathematical Principles of Natural Philosophy* — the famous *Principia*. Pemberton's book appealed to laymen interested in science such as Jonathan Edwards because, in addition to informing his readers about scientific principles, he also indicated "the simple and genuine Products of the Philosopher . . . disengaged from the Problems of the Geometrician." [8]

In order to understand why these books were so successful, we must reinvoke the nature of the times. Experimental science, as we know it today, was then hardly more than a century old. Newton himself was born within a year of Galileo's death. [9] The "new science" had discovered many important truths, but it was Newton who obtained the first great scientific synthesis; he had shown mankind how a few simple laws of motion and attraction, together with the secondary laws mathematically derived from them, could account almost completely for the motion of both terrestrial objects and celestial bodies. A book expounding the principles of Newtonian mechanics and astronomy was also something more; it made available to its readers for the first time an explanation of the mechanism of the heavens, thereby both elucidating the fundamental laws by which the Creator had assured the governance of the universe and also demonstrating the relation of man to the Cosmos. No wonder that Cotton Mather — remembered today as a New England clergyman connected with the witchcraft trials, but also author of *The Christian Philosopher,* the first book on science for the layman written in America — declared that Newton is our "perpetual dictator."

What chiefly excited the poets and princesses of the eighteenth century was that the human mind, through its rational processes and aided by experiment and observation, had finally comprehended what hitherto always had been called the "eternal mysteries" of nature, never to be fully grasped. As the century progressed, interest in science grew by leaps and bounds. Courses were offered for the layman, including experiments and demonstrations. One of the pioneers in this field in England was J. T. Desaguliers, descended from a French Huguenot refugee family, who himself made notable contributions to science and who was the author of a poem entitled *The Newtonian System of the World — the Best Form of Universal Government.*[10] In France a similar program was instituted by the Abbé Nollet, and the accompanying illustration shows the ladies of the court engaged in the study of science under his tutelage. So widespread was the interest in science that it was profitable for lecturers to come from the British Isles to America. One such was Dr. Adam Spencer, who lectured in New York and Philadelphia on scientific subjects with elaborate apparatus for demonstrations. It was this same Spencer who aroused Franklin's interest in electricity, and thus started him off to a distinguished scientific career.[11] Franklin's own book on electricity was widely read by both scientists and laymen, and was recommended by Diderot, editor of the famous *Encyclopedia,* as a model book. In this instance the recommendation was only in part due to the important new facts and principles the book contained and the careful elucidation of the method of scientific inquiry; in addition, as Sir Humphry Davy told his students, "the style and manner of his publication on electricity are almost as worthy of admiration as the doctrine it contains. . . . Science appears in his language in a dress wonderfully decorous, the best adapted to display her native loveliness."[12]

N. le Sueur Invenit

R. Brunet fecit.

Frontispiece to Abbé Nollet's Essai sur l'électricité des corps (*Paris, 1746*), *showing the ladies of the French Court studying experimental physics. The lady on the right is drawing sparks from a charged, pointed, insulated conductor — i.e., from the nose of a young boy suspended from the ceiling. Reproduced from the copy in the Harvard Library.*

But eighteenth-century man was also informed by the Baconian spirit, and he knew that practical benefits of all kinds would follow close on the heels of the new knowledge. Lord Francis Bacon, known to us today chiefly for his *Essays,* was a contemporary of Galileo, and wrote extensively on the subject of scientific method. "Fruits and works," he declared, were "sponsors and sureties" for the truth of science. And he further pointed out, in terms very much like those of the modern pragmatist, that "truth and utility are the very same things," but "works themselves are of greater value as pledges of truth than as contributing to the comforts of life." [13] The reason for this point of view seems clear. If the discoveries made by science pertain to the real world about us, then they must find application in that same real world. In a pre-scientific age, one might devise orbits in which imaginary creatures might move in any way one pleased; but, in a scientific age, the orbits must be those of real bodies such as planets. Furthermore, if a "scientific law" about the motion of planets is to have any validity, it must be susceptible of application to the motion of the planets themselves; it must, for example, enable us to predict with reasonable accuracy where a given planet will be at some future time.

      ❧   ❧   ❧

In contrast to the speculations of the Greek philosophers and the medieval theologians, the fundamental principle of modern science is that every theory must be based upon observations and experiments; and that, if it does not conform to further observations and experiments, it must be either modified or replaced. This is the sense in which we must construe Newton's famous motto, *Hypotheses non fingo.* "I frame no hypotheses" — that is, I am not concerned with the "essences" or "quiddity" of things, with hypothetical or metaphysical statements that are neither based on, nor logically deduced from, experiments, and that are not susceptible of experimental verification. In this spirit he began his treatise on *Opticks* with the classic statement, "My Design in this Book is not to explain the Properties of Light by Hypotheses, but to propose and prove them by Reason and Experiments." [14] Writing in a similar vein, the late Professor Walter B. Cannon stated: "What the experimenter is usually trying to do is to learn whether facts can be established which will be recognized as facts by others and which will support some theory that in imagination he has projected. But he must be ingenuously honest. He must face facts as they arise in the course of experimental procedure, whether they are favorable to his theory or not. In doing this he must be ready to surrender his theory at any time if the facts are adverse to it." [15]

Since modern science deals with the data of the real external world, each advance in scientific knowledge must necessarily enlarge our control of the world around us. This was the sense in which Bacon uttered his famous dictum that the roads to knowledge and to power lie close together; they are in fact intertwined. The educated layman of the eighteenth century had learned this lesson well and knew that the pursuit of science would yield many useful or practical innovations. But he also knew — and perhaps even better than we do — that primarily science is a way of looking at the external world and uncovering its fundamental truths.

Today a book on science for the layman can no longer discuss a single field of activity — say celestial mechanics — and at the same time present the scientific view of the universe in all of its aspects. Science has become so complex and so highly compartmentalized that the best books for the layman can deal with but a single branch of knowledge. The average reader is thus not at fault for having little feeling for the life of science as a whole. The very particulate nature of his reading — acquainting him with the fission of U-235; the manufacture of nylon from coal, air, and water; the way in which penicillin was discovered by chance; and the use of "plant hormones" for killing weeds — has introduced him to a series of apparently unconnected scientific achievements, mostly those that have led to the useful and tangible end products which affect his daily life.

Must we then resign ourselves to the sad conclusion that twentieth-century man can never gain an understanding of the science of his times, in the sense that eighteenth-century man did? I don't believe so. The scientific view of the world, and all that goes on in it, is of course much more complex than that of several centuries ago, and to that extent no single individual — be he scientist or layman

— can ever hope to achieve a full view of all fields of knowledge. Even the professional scientist, when he ventures outside of his own narrow specialty, is a layman, although in a very special sense which we will discuss in just a moment.

Yet a more limited — but equally sound — basis of understanding is possible today. The success of the many books on atomic energy, on the antibiotics, and on chemical technology, demonstrate that we can inform ourselves about what has been going on in these fields of science. But each story will be significant only if it can be treated as a case history in our understanding of the scientific enterprise as a whole.

I do not expect that the layman will ever be able to achieve a full synthesis of scientific knowledge. Indeed, it is greatly to be doubted whether even the most accomplished scientist of today can achieve that goal of synthetic knowledge that Herbert Spencer set himself a little less than a century ago.[16] Nevertheless, we must ask of the layman that he acquaint himself with *certain broad principles of scientific development;* that he learn *under precisely what conditions important scientific discoveries are made,* and *in just what way the practical applications of science come about.* The layman's goal of getting the maximum number of useful end products out of science will depend, as we shall presently see in detail, to a very large degree on his *sympathetic understanding of the scientific enterprise as a whole.*

In the Terry Lectures delivered at Yale in 1946, which have been published under the title *On Understanding Science, an Historical Approach,* President James B. Conant addresses himself at some length to the fundamental problem of the scientific education of the layman. In his experience, a successful investigator in any field of experimental science always approaches a problem in pure or applied science, even in an area in which he is quite ignorant, with a special point of view — it is this point of view that President Conant designates as "understanding science." For such a person, understanding science depends on a "feel for science," and is wholly "independent of a knowledge of the scientific facts or techniques in the new area to which he comes."[17] The layman, by and large, does not have this point of view because of his *fundamental ignorance of what science can or cannot accomplish and of the way in which science goes about its fundamental task.*

President Conant points out that the remedy "does not lie in a greater dissemination of scientific information among non-scientists." (Of course, in order to understand science, a certain amount of information is obviously necessary. One must know some of the language and facts with which scientists continually deal; and the layman who merely wishes information may find it quite readily available in a large number of excellent books dealing with this or that subject, many of which will be found listed in the Guide to Further Reading at the end of this volume.) President Conant argues that, by an analysis of case histories of scientific development, the student will be able to learn the principles whereby scientific advances have been made, principles he denotes as the "tactics and strategy of science." In terms of particular examples, or case histories, he would "show the difficulties which attend each new push forward in the advance of science, and the importance of new techniques; how they arise, are improved and often revolutionize a field of inquiry . . . illustrate the intricate interplay between experiment, or observation, and the development of new concepts and new generalizations; in short, how new concepts evolve from experiments, how one conceptual scheme for a time is adequate and then is modified or displaced by another." [18] In this point of view, it does not matter very much which particular scientific examples are employed, nor from which period in the history of science they are chosen. The choice of one example as opposed to another must be dictated by two possible considerations: (1) the ease with which it is intelligible to the lay student, and (2) the particular developmental principles of science that it illustrates. Since no one would question that the paths to scientific discovery are the same now as they were in the preceding several centuries, an example from the eighteenth century may serve to illustrate a particular point as well as, if not better than, one from the twentieth century; with the obvious advantage that the materials are easier to grasp because little previous factual knowledge is required "either as regards the science in question or other sciences, and relatively little mathematics." Then too, "in the early days one sees in clearest light the necessary fumblings of even intellectual giants when they are also pioneers; one comes to understand what science is by seeing how difficult it is in fact to carry out glib scientific precepts." [19]

 ᕋᕌ   ᕋᕌ   ᕋᕌ

President Conant's ideas apply to the topic with which this book is concerned because the fundamental problems of the scientific education of the layman are the same no matter whether the layman in question is a college student who does not plan to major in one of the scientific fields or a layman whose education will be continued by his reading. This Primer for a Scientific Age aims at giving the lay reader some insight not only into the ways in which scientific discoveries are made but also into the developmental processes by which they have been applied to affect the innermost corner of our daily lives and most cherished beliefs. Many other books have been written on the subject of the applications of scientific discoveries; yet none of them has been conceived in the spirit of the present one — namely, to study the *living principles behind each such application,* and to base whatever generalizations may be made on specific, intelligible case histories. I believe this is the first attempt to analyze in detail the ways in which the practical innovations based on science are related to the search for fundamental scientific truths of which they are the by-product; I hope it may contribute to the foundations of the sociology of science and a true understanding of the place of science in our society and civilization.

Unlike the eighteenth-century popularizer, his twentieth-century counterpart has the obligation to educate his readers for scientific citizenship, not merely to inform. Since every layman will make his opinion felt, either about some particular scientific program, or the research enterprise as a whole, which his taxes will support, he will need education so that his opinion will not be narrow or uninformed. To this job, the present book is dedicated.

But before we turn to a study of our case histories we must make clear what a discovery is, how it is made, what conditions determine its being incorporated into the main body of science, under what conditions it may be applied to a useful end. Likewise, we need to know something about the nature of the scientific enterprise in the large, what the types of scientific activity are, and how they are related one to the other. Let us therefore turn to the first of these important questions: *What are the conditions of scientific discovery?*

CHAPTER 2

Conditions of Scientific Discovery

> Medical history, as it is commonly written and
> taught, is a chronicle of achievements, recording
> who did what, and when. It is thus that the medical
> historian glorifies the deed and neglects the motivat-
> ing idea. . . . The history of the human race, in
> all its manifold phases, can be adequately under-
> stood only in terms of the inception, growth, and
> development of ideas.
>
> — IAGO GALDSTON (1937)

THE EDUCATED layman and the scientific administrator both need to
know well the conclusions to be derived from the history of science
with regard to the conditions under which scientific discoveries are
made. What factors within science itself cause investigators to follow
this or that path? Or, in a deeper sense, wholly apart from the external pressures which society at large exerts on all men — scientists
or non-scientists — is there any logic to the seemingly haphazard
progress of science? We shall try to illuminate this important topic
by two examples, one from recent history and the other from the
eighteenth century: the discovery of penicillin and the discovery of
the electric current and the electric battery.

Many centuries ago, before modern medicine was born, a host of
learned and wise men sought for a universal healing agent. Then a
knight, or a soldier, or an ordinary citizen could go forth with im-
punity, carrying a "guaranteed" cure-all in his pocket or pouch, one
that would heal all types of wounds in short order and cure whatever disease might afflict him. Save for the stroke of the "grim
reaper" that would bring him face to face with his Maker, he would
be able to survive both the ravages of sickness and the wounds of
battle.

Various such elixirs were thought to have been discovered, some by honest and sincere men, and others by the rankest charlatans. The most famous was undoubtedly the "powder of sympathy" of that extraordinary character in English history, Sir Kenelm Digby, whose "epitaph," written by Richard Farrar in 1665, begins:

Under this Tomb the Matchless Digby lies;
Digby the Great, the Valiant, and the Wise;
This Age's Wonder for His Noble Parts;
Skill'd in Six Tongues, and Learn'd in All the Arts.

When in Florence as a boy, he learned the secret of a powder which could promote, even at a great distance, the healing of a wound. He used it first when a friend was wounded while trying to separate two duelers. Digby was called for. When he arrived, he asked for the bandage which had been used to tie up the friend's cut. This he placed in a basin of water in which he dissolved the "secret powder." So long as the bandage remained in the solution, the friend "felt a pleasing freshness" in the wounded part, but whenever Digby removed the bandage, the friend complained of feeling worse. Digby claimed in this way he cured the wound in three days.[1]

The use of such devices as the "powder of sympathy" and the prevalent belief in their efficacy affords an example of the credulity of the seventeenth century. Faced with the great death toll exacted by wounds and disease and the apparent helplessness of the medical men who, ignorant of the causes of disease, were unable to effect cures, people at large hoped that some simple, if "magic," device existed that would free them from the ever-present specter of death.

The search for such a curative agent may be likened to other great searches: the quest of the Holy Grail, the search for a Fountain of Youth, and the continued seeking by the alchemists for a principle by which they could combine sulphur and mercury and transmute them into gold. The honest and sincere alchemists never found gold, but their ancient profession continued into modern times. Isaac Newton, who discovered the "rationale of the universe," believed in alchemy. The alchemist of old has left to our society a positive legacy. The facts uncovered by him in his alchemical putterings in the "witches' kitchen" were in part responsible for making possible a true science of chemistry. In token of that debt, the very name "chemistry" derives in a direct line from "alchemy."

A less fortunate bequest from the old alchemist and his *Hexenküche* is the popular picture of the scientist in his laboratory as a man of "magic" in a place of mysteries. This misleading picture of the modern scientist is printed indelibly in our minds by the scenes in motion pictures and the advertisements in newspapers and magazines. When a scientist in an advertisement holds a tube of tooth paste ("*scientifically* pure") or a package of cigarettes ("*proved* to be less harmful by *laboratory* tests") he wears the long white coat which is the supposed mark of his profession and which replaces the long gown covered with stars of the alchemist or the magician and astrologer of bygone days. Only the pointed conical cap is missing.

The laboratory shown on the screen of the movie palace contains great retorts which bubble and steam in a manner calculated to arouse feelings of awe and mystery, just as huge caldrons in smoke-filled rooms served to impress the observers of hundreds of years past when they visited the magic kitchens of the alchemist. Yet the glamorous laboratory with its bubbling and fuming is rarely found in places where scientists are at work, save perhaps in a few isolated cases in the field of organic chemistry, where the maze of intricate glassware is at once beautiful and arresting.

        ᕮᕮ   ᕮᕮ   ᕮᕮ

Some of us hope to appear as neophytes of the scientific order, if not quite hierophants. We learn magic words — never mind what they mean — such as paradichlorobenzene, and when we go to the store we are not outside the pale; we do not have to ask for "anti-moth flakes," but utter the magic word that marks us as a member of the circle of the elect, even if only the very outermost of all possible circles. How much practice must go into the perfect pronunciation of such marvelous and complicated "magic" words!

The new words are added to our vocabulary with great rapidity nowadays. ("Fission" has replaced "abacadabra.") And sometimes we get them a little mixed up. Thus it is common to hear people talk about the "sulphur" drugs — because everybody knows of sulphur, whereas "sulfa" is strange and too like the familiar word to be kept distinct.

The announcement of the sulfa drugs inflamed the imagination of radio commentators and writers. How wonderful that chemists working on dyes derived from coal tar had produced those magic powders which seemed to surpass by far the "powder of sympathy" of old Kenelm Digby. It was almost as if old desires of the race, bred in the bone as it were, would after all be vindicated. All diseases, ailments, and injuries were to succumb to the new substances!

Miraculous as the sulfa drugs seemed to be, they had, nevertheless, to be used with great care in order to prevent any untoward after-effects. Then too, it turned out that all diseases could not be cured by them, even though the list of those which could was very impressive. By contrast, penicillin seemed an even greater miracle. Nontoxic, it could apparently be taken in unlimited quantities without deleterious effects on the patient. Furthermore, the very way in which penicillin was discovered seemed almost calculated to increase lay wonder, to ensure penicillin's being in the class of "miracles" of modern scientific discovery.

Surely all the world knows by now that one day a "mysterious something" landed in the dish in which Alexander Fleming was growing a bacterial culture. It came out of the air — by pure chance — so to speak. He had been growing such cultures for years, but one day in one of his dishes this wonderful something landed. Fleming did not throw away the contaminated dish, but studied it, only to discover that the unexpected growth had great powers of destroying disease germs. And then, as if the "miracle" were not complete, he discovered that the mysterious gift of the winds and the air was not a strange or even a rare species. It was simply a form of bread mold, the general group of which are called Penicillia, because the spore head appears brush-shaped when viewed under the low-power microscope, and the Latin word for brush is *penicillus*.

The story has been presented to the public so many times in such a dramatic manner that it may be too late now to change our ideas about the discovery of penicillin. Yet this type of presentation is actually an ironic distortion of the whole scientific process. It corrupts our understanding of how discoveries which are useful for our health and material well-being are actually made and become available to us.

By representing the scientist as a magician, and placing his person and his achievement on a plane far above the rest of human society, we effectively deny to ourselves any participation, even a vicarious one, in the scientific enterprise. Granting that the nature of modern science is very complex, and that a true understanding of many aspects of modern science demands a deep knowledge of mathematics which most of us do not have, I still believe that it is possible for the average layman to appreciate the human values of science, to learn how scientific discoveries are made, how they are put to use, and how they actually affect our lives. Such an understanding requires of each layman an educative effort, but it is one that is rewarding in giving him, among other things, a surer grasp of the nature of the world in which he lives.

"Science" and "miracle" are two mutually exclusive words, standing for two opposite and manifestly distinct experiences of the human spirit. We confuse them, or use them together, at great peril to our understanding. Indeed, I think it is no exaggeration to say that there is a ring of hollow mockery in the expression, "We live in an age of science," so long as we continue to describe each new advance in science in terms of "miracle," or "magic."

Each of us has a vital stake in the advance of science. Take the medical field alone: the dread cancer may strike in our family tomorrow. Does a friend have an incurable disease? Does one have parents suffering from arthritis? Or heart trouble? Do we want to cure a crippling paralysis? Or even a common cold? These are primary concerns. In the other sciences we have interests no less urgent. But if we think of science as magic, we can only wait for the magical to come about. If, on the other hand, citizens of a scientific era, we understand what really happens in the course of a discovery, we participate in the enterprise and can aid in making further useful discoveries possible.

∾   ∾   ∾

Let us re-examine the story of penicillin — without miracles — and thereby investigate more thoroughly the conditions of scientific discovery: what determines when a scientific discovery will be made, and also when it will find a useful application.

Recalling how Alexander Fleming made his discovery, one is tempted to ask a number of questions: Suppose Fleming *had* thrown the dish away? What then? Or, suppose he had not seen it himself, but had an assistant whose job it was to examine the cultures and who had found one contaminated. (This is something that happens almost every day and usually the contaminated dish *is* thrown away.) Or what if that *particular* dish had not become contaminated, but another dish with another culture growing in it, one that was not affected by the penicillium mold? Or, the contamination might have been another type of mold, one that has no effect on cultures; what then?

It is barely possible that today penicillin would not yet have been discovered. Yet, it is just as likely that the action of the mold would have been noticed by somebody else at some other time, and that a different chain of human events would have led to the discovery.

In any event, we must not allow ourselves to be misled by the apparently "miraculous" aspects of Fleming's great discovery. As we shall see in just a moment, it was a long trail, indeed, from Fleming's observation to the production of a practical antibiotic to be used in the war against disease. For a period of about ten years, Fleming's discovery lay almost forgotten except by Fleming himself. Then with a special kind of logic, it insisted on being used. This is not an uncommon course of events in the history of science. With an ebb and flow very much like the ocean tides, very often discoveries are made, then apparently ignored, then found again and incorporated into the living stream of science, and put to use. But, in the meantime, and as a necessary condition for the acceptance of a discovery and its integration into the corpus of scientific knowledge, certain changes must occur in the atmosphere or environment of science itself.

We shall discuss the story of penicillin from three points of view: Fleming's chance observation, Florey's completion of it some ten years later, and all that had occurred in the meanwhile.

When, in 1928, Fleming observed what had happened in his culture dish, he wrote in his notebook: "It was astonishing that for some considerable distance around the mold growth the staphylococcal colonies were undergoing lysis. What had formerly been a well-grown colony was now a faint shadow of its former self. . . ."

Lysis is the process of disintegration or solution. Fleming added: "I was sufficiently interested to pursue the subject. The appearance of the culture plate was such that I thought it should not be neglected." [2]

Bread molds are common and there are many members of the family of Penicillia. *P. camemberti* and *P. roqueforti* give the distinctive character to camembert and roquefort cheese; *P. expansum* destroys stored apples, and *P. digitatum* oranges. [3] They look so much alike that Fleming first thought his mold was *P. rubrum;* it later turned out to be *P. notatum.*

Fleming was a medical doctor who had become interested in the subject of infections generally during his army service in the first World War. In the years following, he had continued to keep interested in this subject and had discovered a test for syphilis, as well as an enzyme named *lysozome.* Found in human tears and also in egg whites, *lysozome* proved to have bacteria-killing powers, but unfortunately, it only destroyed the useful or harmless varieties, and had no effect whatever on the disease producers. He discovered the action of *P. notatum* in 1928 and 1929 and embodied the results of his investigations concerning it in what has been described as a "clear, scholarly little paper" in the *British Journal of Experimental Pathology* of June 1929. For ten years, the subject was apparently forgotten, except by Fleming himself, who kept alive the original strain of penicillin-producing Penicillium, which he used to obtain clear cultures of resistant strains of bacteria.

Why was there a lag of ten years? That is a most important question, and closely allied with it is another one. Why after ten years was penicillin put to use at all? Fleming had manifested his faith in the clinical possibilities of penicillin * and had suggested that it "may be an effective antiseptic for application to, or injection into, areas infected with penicillin-sensitive microbes." [5] Nevertheless, a period of some ten years *had to elapse* before penicillin was finally added to the tools of the physician.

In order to understand why there was such a time lag, we need to investigate the change in the scientific environment to which we have just referred, and which I should like to call the "total scientific

---

* Fleming had given the name "penicillin" to filtrates from the broth on which he grew the mold and which contained an antibacterial substance, although in more recent times this name is restricted to "dried preparations of the active principle." [4]

situation." To do so in this case, we must pause for a moment in our telling of the story of penicillin and retrace some of the major steps in the history of medical thought in the last hundred years or so. We must go back in time to a period before that described by Dr. Iago Galdston in the sentence, "We of the twentieth century are germ conscious." Today we accept as fact that "germs" or micro-organisms are in a causal relation to disease; and, "because we grant this, we are willing to daub iodine on a bruise or cut, submit to diphtheria immunization, to typhoid vaccination, and so on." [6] But a hundred years ago, many eminent and sensible physicians would have scoffed at the idea that specific germs cause specific diseases. And some, like the great Lister, founder of antiseptic surgery, held that there was only one kind of germ which, depending on the medium, could change into any type of disease-producing organism. Others held that there was no connection at all between germs and diseases, and that the germs associated with particular diseases were not the causative agents at all, but merely scavengers "drawn to the afflicted body as buzzards are to carrion." In the course of the second half of the nineteenth century, owing mainly to the labors of Pasteur on the one hand and of Henle and Koch on the other, it became firmly established that a particular germ or micro-organism is the "cause" of a particular disease. This is the so-called "germ theory" of disease and we must note that it does not cover all disorders of the human organism, but only infectious diseases. Cancer, for example, is a most egregious exception.

Those who established the "germ theory" of disease developed methods of fighting disease — by using vaccines, toxins, and anti-toxins,* which would cause the affected animal or human being to

---

* Originally the word "vaccine" referred to the matter obtained from a cow, containing the virus of cowpox (or vaccinia); today it is used in a more general sense to denote a suspension of sensitized, attenuated, or killed, bacteria which is injected into human beings or animals to induce an immunity to that particular bacterium, or its toxin. (The discovery of the general principle of vaccines is discussed in the following chapter, pp. 37–38.) The word "toxin" denotes the specific poison derived from a micro-organism; in sufficient quantity and concentration, the toxin itself can produce the effects of the disease, even if the micro-organism usually associated with the disease is not present. If the toxin, say of diphtheria, is injected into the body of a healthy person, first in very small quantities, and then in increasing doses, that person will build up an immunity to the disease. The serum from the blood stream of such a person will then contain antitoxin, and may be denoted antitoxic serum. Von Behring, in 1890, showed that antitoxic serum, obtained from a horse that had been inoculated with diphtheria toxin, could be used to fight diphtheria in a patient's body. Preventive and curative medicine today makes use of all three principles: vaccines, toxins, and antitoxins.

develop antibodies to fight the disease-producing micro-organisms.

At the end of the nineteenth century and the beginning of the twentieth, a revolutionary theory was born, that of chemotherapy, or the idea that diseases might best be fought by developing chemical agents which could be introduced into a diseased organism and which would destroy the disease-causing parasitical micro-organism without affecting the host organism, i.e., the diseased animal or human being. The founder of that science is, properly speaking, Paul Ehrlich, discoverer of salvarsan, a purely chemical agent that would cause a cure of syphilis.

Ehrlich died in 1915, predicting the birth of a great new era in medicine, one in which a host of new chemicals would be found, capable of destroying disease-producing micro-organisms without harming the patient. Yet, despite such a roseate prediction, by the year 1935, just before the announcement of the so-called sulfa drugs, Professor C. H. Browning, one of Ehrlich's co-workers, counted the total rewards of chemotherapy to date: "Four distinct anti-malarials — six groups of trypanocidal compounds — an almost miraculous spirocheticide (salvarsan) — and many new antiseptics."[7] This was surely not the fulfillment of the golden age that Ehrlich had predicted was on its way. And an interesting aspect of the state of things is that all of the advances listed by Browning are limited to diseases caused by protozoa (tiny "animals"), while the more common and more numerous diseases — such as tuberculosis, pneumonia, typhoid, the pus-producing infections (such as staphylococcus and streptococcus), and gonorrhea — are caused by bacteria (parasites which are tiny "plants"). These doldrum years caused most experimenters to give up the earlier ideal of Ehrlich. The year after Fleming published his first paper on penicillin, the general opinion of most medical men was that expressed in the *Münchener Medizensche Wochenschrift:* "Ehrlich's ideal to effect the destruction of all the parasites of a disease by means of an internally administered chemical agent, innocuous to the host, has shown itself on biological grounds to be unattainable."[8]

If chemotherapy had seemed to lead to a dead end, so did another current in the warfare against disease — microbial antagonism. In the course of nineteenth-century research, bacteriologists had come to recognize that some microbes kill others. While studying the disease anthrax, Pasteur and his co-worker Joubert found that the bacillus causing this disease often failed to act when contaminated with "common bacteria." Pasteur suggested, therefore, that this observation might "perhaps justify great hopes from a therapeutic point of view." Further investigation indicated that few pathogenic microbes would long survive in the ground, and Pasteur logically concluded that the normal microbial population of the soil must destroy them. He later found that the air-borne micro-organisms perform the same function.

This addition was the result of a "happy accident," reminiscent of Fleming's discovery of the action of *Penicillium notatum*. A bottle of boiled urine, in which Pasteur had been growing a culture of anthrax bacilli, became contaminated by exposure to air and was soon swarming with other and unwanted microbes. The customary reaction would have been simply to throw the contaminated mixture away. But in this instance, for some unexplained reason, the vessel not only was kept overnight, but was examined the next day. To his great surprise, Pasteur found that all trace of the anthrax bacilli had disappeared; and his logic told him that the contaminating microbes must have been responsible.

Pasteur had no luck in trying to use this important discovery. He inoculated a chicken with anthrax bacilli; and at the same time he introduced into the chicken a great collection of air-borne microbes. The chicken died, and he turned to other and apparently more rewarding work.[9]

But others continued to investigate this subject. As knowledge accumulated, it became apparent that when microbes live together, in some cases they grow in harmony or "friendship," while in others one destroys the other. Hope grew that antibiosis — the antagonism of one microbe for another — might provide a means of fighting disease and, indeed, this point of view seemed to find justification when the secretion, "pyocyanase," of the bacteria *Bacillus pyocyaneus,* was isolated and found to be the agent whereby that bacteria inhibits the growth of other micro-organisms. Pyocyanase was manufactured commercially and even used clinically, but its apparently unpredictable behavior (it sometimes cured an infection and at other times failed utterly) caused it to be abandoned. Despite the activity of many research workers, by the mid-thirties of the twentieth century, the idea that some microbes might be used to fight other microbes in disease, although encouraged by much evidence accumulated since the time of Pasteur, had not as yet produced so much as a single reliable and trustworthy cure.

∾   ∾   ∾

By the middle of the fourth decade of the twentieth century, the 1930's, therefore, the failure to find a satisfactory antibiotic * was just as marked as the apparent failure of chemotherapy. While bacteriologists and research doctors were, as a result, turning back to the more orthodox and time-tried procedures of serums, antitoxins, and vaccines, Gerhard Domagk announced (in 1935) the action of "prontosil," a product of German research in dye chemistry, in protecting mice against otherwise fatal doses of streptococcus germs. Soon afterwards, the active part of prontosil was found by the French investigators to be the substance "sulfanilamide." The family of sulfa drugs was quickly increased to include, among others, sulfathiazole and sulfapyradine. The wondrous cures wrought with the new drugs soon passed the bounds of the wildest imaginations of a few years earlier. The newspapers described the latest product of scientific research in terms of the usual headline — MIRACLE! — and men's thoughts about chemotherapy were stimulated perhaps even more than they had been by Ehrlich's startling pronouncement many years earlier.

One of the most significant features of the new sulfa drugs was their effectiveness against diseases caused by bacteria (microscopic "plants") as well as those caused by protozoa (microscopic "animals"). As a matter of fact, they mark the first chemotherapeutic agents discovered by man *to be effectively used in diseases caused by bacteria.*

Yet many disease-causing micro-organisms were not affected by the sulfa drugs, including those responsible for typhoid and paratyphoid, African sleeping sickness, tularemia, tuberculosis, Rocky Mountain spotted fever, as well as other diseases of both plants and animals. The war against disease went on. The success of the sulfa drugs

---

* The term "antibiotic" has been proposed by Dr. Selman A. Waksman as a generic name for all substances produced by micro-organisms that have chemical properties that cause them to inhibit the growth of other micro-organisms (such as those which cause disease) or even kill them.

accelerated research. Men in laboratories all over the world turned with renewed hopes and increased courage to the job of conquering the diseases of bacterial origin.

∾   ∾   ∾

A "noticeable quickening" was evident in the research for antibacterial agents produced by microbes. The first signal success was announced by Dubos in 1939, just four years after Domagk's announcement of prontosil. René J. Dubos was born and brought up in France and studied at the National Institute of Agronomy in Paris, from which he was graduated in 1921. After graduation, Dubos took a position as assistant editor of an agricultural journal published in Rome. In 1924 an international congress of soil scientists was held in Rome, and the delegates included Dr. Jacob C. Lipman of the New Jersey Agricultural Experimental Station, who had been influential in starting the department of soil microbiology there under the direction of Dr. Selman A. Waksman. Dubos inquired of Dr. Lipman whether he might work under him, and in the fall of that year he came to America. Dubos enrolled in the Rutgers graduate school at New Brunswick, where he completed his doctorate and worked under the direction of Dr. Waksman, a Russianborn graduate of Rutgers of 1915, who had inaugurated a division of soil microbiology at the New Jersey Agricultural Experiment Station, and who is known today as the discoverer of the antibiotic substance "streptomycin."[10]

The problem to which Dubos was set by Waksman was to investigate the action of the microbes of the soil in decomposing cellulose. Cellulose is the chief constituent of the cell walls of plants. Every year *more than a ton* of leaves, stalks, and other cellulose material, falls *on each acre* of forest land in the United States, and a considerable amount of it is digested by microscopic organisms.[11]

At the same time, unknown to Dubos, Dr. O. T. Avery was working at the Rockefeller Institute on an apparently unrelated problem dealing with a method of attacking the pneumococcus: the microorganism causing pneumonia, but which is protected from the action of the leucocytes, colorless or white corpuscles in the blood stream, which would destroy the pneumococcus were the latter not coated with a gummy protective layer.[12]

Dr. Avery hoped to find some agent capable of destroying this layer, thus permitting the leucocytes of the body to attack the pneumococcus. He thought that Dubos's experience with soil micro-organisms capable of digesting cellulose might lead him to the discovery of a similar micro-organism capable of digesting the coating of the pneumococcus germ. Dubos joined the Rockefeller Institute in 1927 and obtained from his friend and teacher, Dr. Waksman, samples of soil rich in microbes. After years of research Dubos discovered that when these soil-borne microbes were deprived of their normal cellulose food supply, some of them could adapt themselves to a new diet, and use the coating of the pneumococcus germ for food in place of the customary cellulose. His next step was to separate from the altered soil bacteria the enzyme, or secretion whereby it produces its action. After obtaining a quantity of enzyme, he found that this substance itself would dissolve the protecting covering of pneumococcus germs. Once its external protection was gone, the pneumococcus germ could be effectively destroyed.

In 1931, Dubos knew that he had found a substance that seemed to be very effective against one pathogen, or disease-causing organism, and he naturally wondered whether or not it might be equally effective against others. He felt he had a clue in the action of the so-called "Gram stains." (This was a method invented in the late nineteenth century by the Danish bacteriologist, Hans Christian Gram. When bacteria are stained with a dye in a special way, and then treated with alcohol and washed with water, some of them will retain the dye or stain and are denoted "Gram-positive," but others will not hold the dye and are denoted "Gram-negative.")

Dubos believed that the ability to retain the dye, even after alcohol and water washings, must be due to some particular characteristic of cell construction. He decided to concentrate his attention on Gram-positive micro-organisms — streptococcus, staphylococcus, and pneumococcus germs. After filling his tumblers with soil rich in bacteria, Dubos waited, as before, until the microbes in the soil had exhausted the available food supply. Then he introduced as a source of nourishment a collection of the three above-named Gram-positive micro-organisms, in sterile water. Once again there resulted strains of soil microbes which could subsist on a diet wholly composed of these germs. The strain which adapted itself best he identified as *Bacillus brevis* — common soil bacteria! Once more, Dubos and his associates undertook the long and tedious job of separating the enzyme from the bacteria. A pure powder was obtained in 1939; Dubos called it "gramicidin" in honor of the Dane, Gram, who had invented the staining process which had proved so helpful. Subsequent work in the following year by Dubos and his associate, R. D. Hotchkiss, revealed that this powder actually contained *two* antibacterial substances, one of which they continued to call "gramicidin" and the other "tyrocidine," because the group to which *Bacillus brevis* belongs was at one time called Tyrothrix. The "parent substance" of gramicidin and tyrocidine became known as "tyrothricin."

Dubos wrote: "Although the Gram staining technique was introduced as a purely empirical procedure for the detecting of bacterial cells in infected tissues, it has now been recognized to divide the bacterial world into two general groups which differ profoundly with reference to many structural and physiological characteristics. The differential susceptibilities of the Gram positive and Gram negative species to gramicidin is obviously the result of some fundamental difference in cellular structure or metabolism between the two groups of organisms, and illustrates the significance of comparative bacterial physiology in the problems of chemotherapy." [13]

The first large-scale use of tyrothricin occurred in 1940, when the Walker-Gordon Laboratory discovered that sixteen of some one hundred prize cows to be exhibited at the World's Fair in New York had become infected with mastitis, a contagious and inflammatory condition of the udder. The agents causing this disease may be varied, but in this case were a form of a streptococcus. When sulfanilamide failed, the veterinarians decided to try the new drug, tyrothricin, and it proved to be successful in most cases. The importance of curing this disease may be seen from the fact that streptococcal mastitis used to cost some millions of dollars a year in diseased cows that could not be cured.[14]

Tyrothricin was the first antibiotic to receive very widespread clinical attention, and was furthermore the "first microbially-produced [antibiotic] substance to be crystallized, or reduced to a pure state. Dubos proved that such chemotherapeutic agents as his were not only theoretically possible, but actually obtainable in practicable quantities." [15]

Within a compass of four years (1935–1939) the general attitude of medical men and research scientists underwent an amazing re-orientation. Domagk's discovery of the sulfa drugs seemed to vindi-cate Ehrlich's idea of chemotherapeutic agents, and the millennium of chemotherapy that Ehrlich had predicted appeared to be finally at hand. Dubos's great discovery of another germ-killing substance, produced by one type of bacteria but able to destroy many others, renewed in men's hearts the hope of finding still more such "magic bullets."

One of the scientists so motivated was Australian-born Dr. Howard Walter Florey, who had investigated the substance pyocyanase, a secretion of the bacteria *Bacillus pyocyaneus*, which was dis-covered in 1899 to have weak germ-killing properties. Florey, by his own account, next gave his attention to Fleming's lysozome, because of his interest in "the problem of natural immunity." The investiga-tion of the properties of this "powerful natural antibacterial agent" continued until lysozome was finally purified and "its nature and mode of action as a carbohydrate-splitting enzyme were estab-lished." [16] At some time in 1938, during the course of this work which was being conducted by a research team of which Florey was the leader, Florey and the refugee chemist Ernst Chain — let us allow them to tell the story in their own words — "concluded that it might be profitable to conduct a systematic investigation into the chemical and biological properties of antibacterial substances produced by micro-organisms. Though the existence of such substances had been clearly established in many cases, very little was known at the time about their chemical and biological properties, and it was hoped that a systematic study might lead to the preparation of new com-pounds of biological interest. By great good fortune one of the first to be investigated was penicillin, which, despite the unfavorable ac-count in the literature of its chemical properties, showed interesting biochemical and biological characteristics." [17]

The splendid research team, led by Florey and Chain, went to work on penicillin in the new atmosphere of 1938–1939, so different from that of 1929. The change in the total scientific situation was so great that whereas formerly practically no one had been interested in penicillin, now a great research team was actually looking for a substance, such as penicillin, to which to devote their varied talents. In 1939 it was only natural that penicillin should be investigated; in 1929 the likelihood of such action was of small probability if not of utter impossibility. That such indeed was the case is revealed by the beginning of that now classic report on penicillin which appeared in the leading British medical journal, *Lancet,* in August 1940, signed by Chain and Florey, and also by their co-workers, A. D. Gardner, M. A. Jennings, J. Orr-Ewing, and A. G. Sanders. That report begins:

In recent years, interest in chemotherapeutic effects has been almost exclusively focused on the sulphonamides and their derivatives. There are, however, other possibilities, notably those connected with naturally occurring substances. It has been known for a long time that a number of bacteria and molds inhibit the growth of pathogenic micro-organisms. Little, however, has been done to purify or determine the properties of any of these substances. The antibacterial substances produced by *Pseudomonas pyocyanea* have been investigated in some detail, but without the isolation of any purified product of therapeutic value.

Recently Dubos and his colleagues (1939, '40) have published systematic studies on the acquired bacterial antagonism of a soil bacterium which have led to the isolation from its culture medium of bacterial substances active against a number of Gram-positive micro-organisms. . . .

Following the work on lysozome in this laboratory it occurred to two of us (E. C. and H. W. F.) that it would be profitable to conduct a systematic investigation of the chemical and biological properties of the antibacterial substances produced by bacteria and molds. This investigation was begun with a study of a substance with promising antibacterial properties produced by a mold and described by Fleming (1929).

It must be borne in mind that there were great and almost insuperable difficulties in the path of the development of penicillin as a therapeutic agent. Three British scientists, Clutterbuck, Lovell, and Raistrick, endeavored to isolate the active part of the mold product in 1932 but had been discouraged by its apparent instability. Not only did penicillin itself have to be isolated, but a simple and quick quantitative test for the presence of the substance had to be found. Furthermore, in the early days the production of penicillin was on *such a minute scale* that the experimenters were limited in their research. Thus the first attempted cure, despite a most auspicious beginning, failed because there was not at hand enough penicillin to continue the treatment. The obstacles to be overcome before penicillin could even be tested in experimental cases of disease were therefore so very great that the *research workers had to be very well convinced that their road would lead to a useful destination for them to undertake the investigation at all.* For this reason, *the time had to be ripe,* or, in our terminology, *the total scientific situation had to be propitious for the realization of the potentialities of penicillin.*

By this time the reader should be able to appreciate that the vast difference between the scientific environment in 1928–1929 and that of 1938–1939 was to a large degree responsible for the time sequence in the discovery of penicillin. This aspect of the story is far from unique and could be illustrated by any number of case histories taken from the last three centuries. Let us examine one that occurred in the closing years of the eighteenth and opening years of the nineteenth century.

∽ ∽ ∽

The electric current was discovered toward the latter part of the eighteenth century when an Italian doctor and anatomist, Luigi Galvani, observed that the leg of a dissected frog would twitch under certain special conditions. The circumstances of the discovery are that one of Galvani's assistants, frequently presumed to be his wife, happened to touch the inner crural nerve of the dissected frog with the point of his scalpel and observed the violent convulsions of the leg. We need not go into the details of Galvani's many careful experiments, by means of which he followed up the chance observation; but, in the end, he showed that the essential feature of stimulating the frog was a chain of two different metals, joined together at their free ends, and completed into a circuit through the moist muscles and nerve of the frog.[18]

Galvani thought that the twitching was due to the circulation of an "animal electricity" — just like ordinary electricity, save that it resides in animals — which may be released under the special circumstances of a "conducting arc" made of two different metals. But his contemporary, a professor of physics at Pavia, Alexander Volta, although at first agreeing with Galvani, later came to an entirely different point of view, one which led to an understanding of what had really taken place.

Volta first showed that, contrary to the speculations of Galvani, the nerve was not a necessary part of the circuit. The effect could be produced by two metals and a moist muscle. He later found out that if two metal plates, say zinc and copper, are each supported by an insulating handle and brought into close contact for a moment, then their separation produces a remarkable effect. One of the metals, zinc, becomes positively electrified or charged, and the other, copper, negatively electrified.

Volta was able to make this important discovery because he was a most skilled experimenter and because he had at his disposal a new instrument which he had devised — a most delicate electroscope, or electrometer, connected to a condenser, by means of which he could detect and compare extremely small electric charges.

Volta's next step was to "intensify" the electric effect he had obtained from placing two insulated metal surfaces of different metals in contact with each other. This he did in two different ways — first, by making cells composed of a zinc and a copper disk separated by a piece of moist cloth or leather that had been wet with salt water; secondly, by placing a strip of copper and zinc in a cup of water to which a few drops of acid had been added. By placing a series of zinc, cardboard, and copper sandwiches together, he made the famous "Voltaic Pile." And by linking a number of cups together he created the renowned "Crown of Cups." (See plate.) These experiments of Volta produced the first electric battery, and we have been building batteries in the same way ever since. In this way, there was made available to man, for the first time, a means of obtaining a steady electric current at relatively low tension or low voltage, and for a considerable period of time; in contrast to the rapid discharges hitherto available. The practical nature of the discovery of a method for producing a steady electric current does not need, I am sure, to be enlarged upon. Yet, it is important to emphasize that this discovery began in the investigations of an

Italian anatomist who one day observed a "mysterious" twitching of a frog's leg.[19]

The story of the electric current is related to the story of penicillin, because the major facts in this case had both been noticed and described in publications long before Volta and Galvani began their work. The Dutch naturalist, Swammerdam, had some years earlier described the curious effect of the twitching frog's leg when two different conductors made a conducting arc with a moist nerve and muscle. Likewise, the curious effect of placing two different metals in contact had been pointed out by a German, Sulzer, who had drawn attention to the tingling sensation that arises when one touches to the tongue two different metal disks.

Why was it that the observations of Sulzer and Swammerdam did not lead to a fruitful result, whereas Galvani's observation did? We can never hope to find a direct answer to such questions which we pose to History. Various factors are involved, including the psychological state of the experimenter and many others. But there *was* a vast difference between what we have called the total scientific situation which existed at the time of Sulzer's and Swammerdam's observation and the time of Galvani's. The whole world in the meanwhile, lay and scientific, had become aware of the new subject of electricity which, as a science, had advanced enormously. The invention of the condenser and the design of electrostatic machines for generating electric charges had made possible large-scale demonstrations for the education and entertainment of the public at large, and electrical performances were in a sense as popular a form of entertainment in the 1740's, 1750's, and 1760's as the movies are today. No gentleman interested in science was without an electrical machine, and even an anatomist such as Galvani had one on his dissecting table.

The work of many "electricians," such as Benjamin Franklin, had in the meanwhile elevated electricity to an eminent state of scientific theory, whereas, at the beginning of the eighteenth century, electricity was not a science at all, but merely a collection of curious and apparently unrelated facts.

Thus, at the time Galvani made his observation, the scientific world, like the lay world, was to a large degree "electricity conscious." Franklin's one-fluid theory of electricity had made it possible to talk

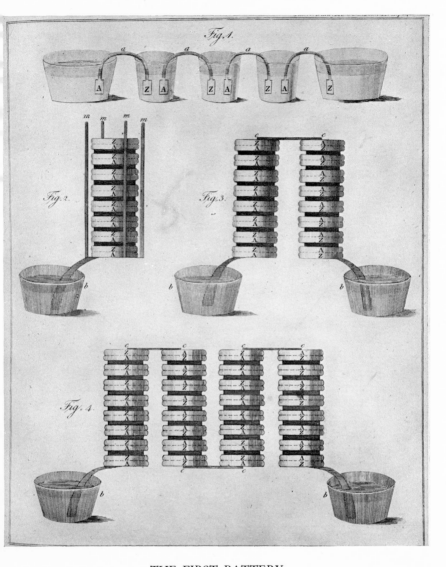

THE FIRST BATTERY

Volta's crown of cups may be seen at the top of the page, Fig. 1, while Figs. 2, 3, and 4 show various forms of his pile. This plate accompanied Volta's famous paper, "On the electricity excited by the mere contact of conducting substances of different kinds," in the Philosophical Transactions *for 1800. Reproduced from the copy in the Harvard Library.*

simply and understandingly about all sorts of electrical phenomena, to correlate, interpret, and integrate the known facts and to predict new ones. In this new total scientific situation, the resolution of Galvani's observation to its electrical quintessence, by his own efforts and those of Volta, was no more remarkable than any other scientific advance. Yet to have achieved this resolution fifty years earlier would have truly been, in the literal sense of the word, a "miracle."

No chain is stronger than its weakest link and, to the extent that each advance of science is inextricably linked to others, our progress in the sciences can be no more secure than any single part of the chain. In the case of penicillin, Florey knew of Fleming's earlier discovery, lysozome, and, in fact, had studied this substance before turning to Fleming's other discovery, penicillin. Here we see the weak link in the chain, the tenuous thread that linked together the investigations of these two great men, Fleming and Florey. The element of chance in Fleming's original discovery, and in Florey's knowing about that discovery, is sufficiently important to merit a full investigation; it forms the subject of the next chapter.

CHAPTER 3

The "Happy Accident"
and Its Consequences

In order to succeed in advancing the experimental science of biology it is not enough to follow a good working method; one must possess certain moral qualities, at least to a certain degree, and one must make an effort to develop them more and more.
— MAURICE ARTHUS (1921)

IN THE LAST chapter we have looked briefly into the question of the total scientific situation which determines to a very large degree not only directions of scientific research, but also, as we illustrated by the history of penicillin and the electric current, whether a particular discovery will exist, so to speak, in a vacuum — or be incorporated into the living stream of science.

This investigation raises another fundamental and very interesting question. When is a "discovery" made? For example, if we denote by penicillin the therapeutic agent which we use today for a multitude of diseases, shall we say that it was "discovered" by Fleming in 1928, or by Florey, Chain, and their co-workers ten years later? The Nobel Prize award for this important discovery was given jointly to Fleming and Florey and Chain, in wise recognition of the fact that without Fleming's observation, Florey and Chain would not have been provided with the raw materials essential to their part of the discovery; and also taking into account that, had Fleming made his observation and had Florey and Chain not done their share, the discovery would not have been completed. At some halfway point between 1928 and 1938, say 1933, would it have made any sense to say that penicillin had been "discovered"? Obviously not. This reemphasizes the point we made earlier — namely, that a scientific discovery can never be discussed intelligently without some knowledge of the background from which it came.

❧   ❧   ❧

It is frequently pointed out that a significant aspect of the discovery of both penicillin and the electric current was the fact that in both discoveries chance played a very large role. Fleming and Galvani both made their important discoveries as the result of what is sometimes denoted a "happy accident," which means that the scientist in question made an important discovery while looking for something else. Such chance discoveries are so frequent an occurrence in the history of science that many writers have been led to conclude that the development of science is entirely erratic, depending wholly on the beneficence of the goddess, Fortune.

In discussing such "happy accidents," a sentence of Louis Pasteur is frequently quoted: "In the realm of observation, chance favors only the prepared mind." One of Pasteur's own most important discoveries, the principles of vaccines in fighting disease, was made by chance; and we can perhaps better understand Pasteur's famous dictum if we describe that discovery.

He had been studying chicken cholera during the years 1880–1882 and by chance he happened to inoculate some laboratory hens with an old culture of the disease rather than the customary fresh one. Instead of dying, as chickens usually did when inoculated with a culture of cholera microbes, these hens became ill and then recovered. When, some time later, they were re-inoculated with a fresh culture — one that was strong enough to kill an ordinary chicken — these hens continued to remain perfectly healthy. Thus did Pasteur discover the famous principle of vaccines whereby a germ culture is "attenuated" by exposing it to air, heating it, or even killing it, before it is injected into a living animal or human being, which then develops the natural antibodies which render it immune to later attacks of the same disease. Like Fleming and Galvani, Pasteur made this discovery while looking for something else.

Pasteur followed up the chance observation. He studied the situation thoroughly, in order to determine *why* the hens did not succumb to cholera. Rather than dismissing the unusual event as "odd," or "strange," and going on with other work, he seized upon the occasion and made an important and wholly unexpected discovery. But in exactly what sense his mind was prepared to make the most of the "happy accident," as contrasted for example to another experimenter who might have had the same experience and have passed it by, we are not yet in a position to say. Let us first consider another example.

An important discovery made by chance was that of the great French physiologist, Claude Bernard, a contemporary and friend of Pasteur. Some time about the middle of the last century, Bernard wanted to test an idea of his that the impulses which pass along nerve fibers set up chemical changes that produce heat. In his experiment he first measured the temperature of a rabbit's ear, and then surgically severed the nerve which delivers impulses to the ear. He expected, in accordance with his theory, that the ear, now deprived of nerve impulses and of a source of heat, would become cooler than the normal ear on the other side of the rabbit's head. To his astonishment, however, he found it to be considerably warmer.

We know today that, in the course of this experiment, Claude Bernard had disconnected the blood vessels of the ear from the influences of the nerves which normally keep them *contracted;* after the operation, the warm blood from the internal organs of the rabbit flushed through the enlarged blood vessels in a much faster flow than normally, thereby causing the ear to rise in temperature. The late physiologist, Walter B. Cannon, who discussed this example in a study devoted to the role of chance in discovery, draws from it the conclusion: "Thus by accident appeared the first intimation that the passage of blood into different parts of the body is under nervous government — the most significant advance in our knowledge of the circulation since Harvey's proof, more than 300 years ago, that the blood does, indeed, circulate."[1]

Like Pasteur, Claude Bernard followed up an unusual and totally unexpected experimental result and was led to a significant discovery.

Yet another striking example of an accidental discovery comes from the field of allergy, what the physiologist calls "anaphylaxis." It commonly comes about as a result of an initial exposure to some substance which later becomes poisonous to the body. Many people had noted the phenomenon in an incidental way, before it was brought to the attention of the scientific world in the latter part of the nineteenth century by Charles Richet.

Richet was studying the effect of an extract prepared from the tentacles of a sea anemone, and wanted to learn the toxic dose of such an extract upon a laboratory animal. He found that if animals which had survived the toxic dose were given a much smaller dose, as little as one tenth of the original, some time later, the effect was promptly fatal. This discovery of so-called "induced sensitization" was so astonishing that, as Richet tells us himself, he could hardly believe it was a result of anything he had done. According to his own testimony, he discovered induced sensitization *in spite of himself,* by studying and reinterpreting his unusual experimental results.[2]

Richet's example provides a key. Not only must the successful experimenter follow up the lead given to him by a "happy accident," but he frequently must make the discovery "in spite of himself." No matter what his preconceptions were, he must overcome them and follow the course suggested by the observed facts. Preparedness, in Pasteur's sense of the word, simply implies a quality of receptivity on the part of the mind of the experimenter — one that allows him to recognize, accept, use, rather than reject, an experimental datum he did not expect or which he finds to contradict his original theory or hypothesis.

The great French physiologist, Maurice Arthus, who made his own discoveries in the field of allergy by chance, wrote a philosophical paper on the subject of scientific discovery, wherein he declared:

At the origin of many scientific discoveries there was an observation made by chance which the experimentalist grasped, dissected, interpreted, and discussed in order to wrest from it the secret it concealed. . . . But chance, in biology at least, does not grant its favors to all and sundry. It seems to require from its protegés one quality, scientific curiosity. He who possesses that mental attitude is not content with looking casually at the facts that turn up, and with giving them without further inquiry any kind of interpretation, the first that occurs to him. No, he examines the fact with sustained attention, repeats his examination as often as is needed to distinguish between the constant peculiarities and the variable elements. He describes, analyzes, measures, controls, criticizes, interprets and in order to justify his interpretation, conceives an experiment that will demonstrate its worth or emptiness.[3]

The mind's preparedness to grasp a chance observation and to carry it through to its logical conclusion certainly depends to a very great extent on the factor of curiosity. Had Pasteur not been curious enough to want to find out why certain hens survived a lethal dose of cholera microbes, he would never have discovered the principle of vaccines. But, one might argue with equal validity, if Pasteur had not been endowed by nature with an unusual amount of native curiosity, he would never have become a scientist at all! For, in the last analysis, curiosity about the supposed "secrets of nature" is probably the chief motivation of all scientific research. Pasteur's statement about the "prepared mind" may simply be another way of saying that in the field of observation chance favors the scientists with the best native endowment for research — curiosity to impel them onward, and the genius necessary for the completion of a discovery. On one occasion Pasteur spoke of "preparedness" for discoveries in terms of "patient studies and persevering efforts."

Isaac Newton declared that the idea of universal gravitation came to him while he was sitting in his garden drinking tea, and that it was occasioned by seeing an apple fall from a tree.* Countless numbers of men had sat in gardens and had seen apples fall, and a good many, we may be sure, had wondered why and how apples fell *toward* the earth and not *away from* the earth. Why did the idea of universal gravitation come to Newton and to no others? Not only, it seems clear, because he was more curious than they, nor even only because Isaac Newton was one of the most brilliant minds in science that the world has yet produced.

Newton once declared that if he was able to see farther than others, the reason was that he stood on the shoulders of giants. This statement provides an important clue. Newton's achievement was made possible only because he had at hand the results of such scientists as Galileo, Kepler, Huygens, Descartes, and Fermat — to mention but a few of the giants on whose shoulders Newton stood. Had he lived two hundred years earlier, and before the times had been prepared for his own great discoveries, he would never have been able to make the great synthesis: no mind, even in science, can stand wholly alone. And if Newton had lived two hundred years

* Frequently dismissed as an "apocryphal legend." We now have evidence that Newton apparently told the story of the apple to his contemporaries.[4]

later than he did, he would not have made the great discoveries either. Someone else would have made them already, although perhaps in a different form. After all, as the great Laplace wrote a century after Newton's work, there is only one law of the cosmos and only one man can discover it!

Such an interpretation in no way belittles either Newton's great genius or the significance of what he accomplished; he will ever remain one of the greatest scientists the world has produced, and one of the most original, creative thinkers of all time. Our interpretation shows the difference between science, on the one hand, and an activity like composing music, on the other. Albert Einstein has pointed out that even if he himself had never lived, we would still have had some form of the Theory of Relativity; but if Beethoven had never lived, we would *not* have had an "Eroica Symphony." [5]

      ♪   ♪   ♪

As a last example to complete our analysis, let us look at the discovery of x-rays. This case history is better documented than most, and is very revealing. It affords a clear example: a great many scientists who all observed simultaneously a curious and undesired effect, while but one of them, Roentgen, had the curiosity to follow the effect through to its cause and achieve the epoch-making discovery.

X-rays were discovered with the aid of a so-called "Crookes tube" —a glass tube filled with gas at very low pressure, and containing two electrodes which may be attached to an electrical source. Such tubes were in every physicist's laboratory in the closing years of the nineteenth century. Under most conditions, these tubes produced not only a glow discharge inside, but gave rise to x-rays as well.

X-rays manifest themselves either by causing a fluorescence (or glow) if they strike the proper material, or by activating a photographic plate or photographic film. As most of us know, x-rays have a very great penetrating power. They can thus affect a fluorescent screen, a photographic plate, or a roll of photographic film, even if it be shielded from the x-ray source by some material that is opaque to ordinary light — for example, black paper, cardboard, wood, a thin sheet of metal, and so on.

If a photographic plate or a piece of photographic film is exposed to a source of ordinary light, whether the sun or an electric light bulb, it undergoes an over-all blackening. If we place an opaque object, such as a coin or a key, on a piece of unexposed film in a dark room, and then briefly turn on the light, when the film is developed and fixed it will be blackened only in the exposed portion; the part of the film that was under the coin or the key, and which was shielded from the light, will be clear. In this way we can get a shadowgraph, or photogram, much like the old-fashioned silhouette but in reverse.

The usual cardboard dark slide, which prevents unexposed films or plates from becoming fogged or blackened by ordinary light, is not impervious to x-rays, which usually pass through it just as if it weren't there at all. Hence, if anyone produces x-rays anywhere in the vicinity of an unexposed photographic plate in the usual type of plateholder, it will become fogged and show a partial blackening on development. In the same way, unexposed plates or films, even though wrapped in light-proof black paper or tinfoil and further protected by a double or triple cardboard box, will become fogged if they are kept for even an instant near an active source of x-rays.

Many physicists at the turn of the last century had the experience of finding their plates fogged because, as we now know, they were kept near a Crookes tube and were affected by the x-rays it produced. One such, interestingly enough, was Sir William Crookes himself, after whom the famous tube was named.

Lord Rayleigh tells us that "It was a source of great annoyance to Crookes that he missed the discovery of the x-rays. According to the account he gave in my hearing, he had definitely found previously unopened boxes of plates in his laboratory to be fogged for no assignable reason and, acting I suppose in accordance with the usual human instinct of blaming someone else when things go wrong, he complained to the makers [of the plates], who naturally had no satisfactory explanation to offer. I believe it was only after Roentgen's discovery that he connected this with the use of highly exhausted vacuum tubes in the neighborhood." [6]

Another and very similar example concerns the first x-ray photograph ever to be made. A. W. Goodspeed, of the University of Pennsylvania, and a friend named W. N. Jennings were photographing electric sparks and brush discharges on an evening in 1890. After they had completed some experiments, and while the table was still littered with the experimental and photographic apparatus, including the loaded plateholders, Goodspeed brought out some Crookes tubes and demonstrated them to his friend, Jennings. When the latter developed the plates next day, he discovered two opaque disks superimposed on the tracings of the spark. Six years later, after the discovery of x-rays had been announced, the photographic plates were re-examined and it was discovered that the disks were the first x-ray photograph to be made — made, indeed, *six years before the discovery of x-rays!* [7]

Of all those who observed the fogging of photographic plates or films, or the fluorescence of certain materials, only Roentgen investigated the cause of the phenomenon and discovered the existence and nature of x-radiation.[8] The discovery was in the air — at the very finger-tips of dozens of scientists who might have made the same discovery. "The seeds of great discoveries are constantly floating around us," the famous American physicist Joseph Henry once wrote, "but they only take root in minds well prepared to receive them."[9]

∾   ∾   ∾

I take it that this statement of Joseph Henry, like that of Pasteur, is intended to describe a mental condition favorable to the experimenter's taking advantage of a chance observation and following it through to its logical conclusion. Sir William Crookes never traced the fogging of his photographic plates to its source, but another English man of science, it was said, knew that Crookes tubes were apt to fog photographic plates anywhere near them. From this he only drew the moral that *such plates should always be stored elsewhere.*[10]

A similar instance was brought to my attention by a distinguished faculty member of the University of Wisconsin. During the first World War, he was one of a group working in the United States Army in the study of infections, particularly streptococcus. They grew many cultures over a period of time and observed that such cultures frequently became contaminated. In many cases they found that this contamination effectively destroyed the streptococcus which they wanted to study. The contaminant producing this unwanted effect was identified as a mold of the Penicillium family. Like the English scientist who made sure that plates would never be stored near a Crookes tube, these bacteriologists thenceforth took especial pains to prevent their cultures from becoming contaminated with bread mold.[11]

On more sober reflection, Pasteur's dictum on the "prepared mind" is easily subject to misconstruction. One must ask, "Prepared by what and by whom?" Does Pasteur's statement imply that by diligent effort the mind can prepare itself and then, being prepared, would capture the occasion and the inspiration? I doubt it. The negative of this statement is probably more accurate — to wit: the unprepared mind *will certainly miss both the inspiration and the occasion.*

Science is in a continual state of flux, and ideas change from year to year, month to month, and sometimes even day to day. Scientists, being human, are subject to all the frailties that the word "human" implies. Although, in their scientific activity, they may differ from most other human beings in the rigid way in which they adhere to the facts of experimental evidence, nevertheless, they may disagree among themselves as to the interpretation of facts. Like other human beings, they are prone to preconceptions and fixed ideas, which they will not abandon until such notions are completely undermined by the weight of experimental testimony.

It is a rare scientist who is willing to desert his preconceptions, and depart, for even a moment, from the customary approach in order to resolve a chance experiment or observation into its full quintessence. A man who will seek the cause of an unsuspected or undesired effect, typified by Roentgen in the case of x-rays, may be said to be "prepared" only to the extent that he is ready to grasp the occasion when it presents itself — either because his innate curiosity impels him onward or for some other reasons that as yet we do not fully comprehend.

One of the most famous instances of grasping the occasion is provided by the work of the distinguished American physiologist, William Beaumont, who, during the early part of the nineteenth century, had as a patient a Canadian trapper, part of whose stomach wall had been shot away. Beaumont recognized immediately that here was an unusual opportunity to make experiments directly on a human stomach. He fully grasped the occasion; and his experimentation, consisting of withdrawing juices from the stomach under various conditions, and dropping through the fistula, or hole, a piece of food attached to a string so that he could pull it out and observe what had happened to it, marked a great step forward in our knowledge of the chemistry and physiology of the digestive process.[12]

Roentgen was in this respect far superior to his many fellow scientists, each of whom *could have made* the discovery but *did not*. Yet it seems perfectly clear that if Roentgen too had missed the occasion, then surely, since so many physicists were working with Crookes tubes, someone else would have made the discovery very shortly afterwards. It was in the air, so to speak; "floating around us," as Joseph Henry put it; or, in still another form of expression, *the total scientific situation was propitious to its discovery*.

Men as such are the immediate instrumentalities in the achievement of chance discoveries. There is no question about that. But they can only be effective in a propitious atmosphere — an atmosphere that must be propitious in its intellectual or ideological interests. All the forces that make up the total scientific situation must be right; and their effect may be likened to a satisfactory nutritional medium wherein the accident arises and the men are nourished. Men of genius are always required for important scientific discoveries, but they may be helpless if they live at the wrong time.

～　　　　～　　　　～

An example which we shall discuss in more detail in a later chapter (7) illuminates this topic further. Soon after Volta's discovery of the battery had made possible the development and use of large steady electric currents, many physicists sought for a relation between electricity and magnetism. That the man who first found experimentally that an electric current produces a magnetic effect did so by accident at the end of a lecture on the subject of electricity is inconsequential. What is much more significant is the fact that the materials were at hand to make such a discovery. Every scientist had a battery and was looking for the effect. The total scientific situation was such that the minds of almost all physicists were turned to the same problem.

If the total scientific situation is such that the atmosphere is propitious for a given discovery to be made, it frequently happens that several men will make the discovery independently in different parts of the world. This is another common occurrence in the history of science. To cite a few examples — in the seventeenth century Isaac Newton and G. W. Leibniz independently developed the differential calculus; in the nineteenth century the Englishman, John Couch Adams, and the Frenchman, V. J. J. Leverrier, independently predicted the planet Neptune; the German, Lothar Meyer, and the Russian, Ivan D. Mendeleieff, independently worked out the periodic classification of the chemical elements; and the Englishman, Joule, and the Germans, Helmholtz and Mayer, independently discovered the theorem of the conservation of energy just about one hundred years ago.

∽   ∽   ∽

What we have been exploring in this chapter, which supplements the last one, is the way in which *a discovery must fit the times*. The total scientific situation is determined not only by elements within science itself but also by external factors. Some of these are social in nature. The social goal of finding a curative agent at a time when the clouds of war are on the horizon is surely not to be discounted in the motivation of Florey and Chain. Likewise, the stimulation of wartime urgencies was a most powerful factor in completing the last stages necessary to the development of atomic energy in the form of the bomb. It is not surprising that Dutch geneticists improved the cinchona plant for the production of quinine in the East Indies where malaria, for which quinine is used, was a common disease. Nor was it entirely a matter of coincidence that the interest of the Honorable Robert Boyle in the seventeenth century was directed toward pumps at a time when such instruments were being used to a hitherto unprecedented degree in English mines.

Not only a discovery but even an invention must fit the times in a very special way. This may be illustrated by a story from the latter part of the eighteenth century, that of James Watt and the steam engine. As a young man, Watt was a mechanic in Glasgow with the title of "Mathematical Instrument Maker to the University." One of his first jobs was to repair a Newcomen engine, an early form of the steam engine used for pumping water out of mines, and this experience convinced Watt of its poor quality and the need of improving it.[13]

The steam engine works by allowing steam to enter a cylinder where it pushes a piston, thereby doing work. In the Newcomen engine, the cylinder was cooled with water, so that the steam which had pushed the piston forward would condense, and the pressure of the air would then push the piston back again into the cylinder. One of the first things that Watt noticed was the fact that, at the beginning of a stroke, the cylinder which had been cooled by water had not had time to be heated again and was, therefore, never hot enough for effective work. How was he to overcome this problem and to dispense with the loss of heat due to alternate heating and cooling?

The first step taken by Watt was a comparison of the volume of a given quantity of steam with that of the water from which it had been generated. By a series of careful experiments he discovered that the volume relation was approximately 1800 to 1. Next he decided to measure how great a quantity of steam would be required to make a given quantity of water boil. He passed steam through a caldron of water, which became hotter and hotter as more and more steam was passed through it, and eventually boiled. He discovered that a certain amount of steam condensing into water will raise *six times* its own weight of water from normal temperature to the boiling point. Was this possible? He took his problem to the professor of chemistry at the university, Joseph Black, who had been working, not only on this very problem, but on others in thermodynamics related in various ways to steam. Black had discovered independently the same phenomenon that Watt brought to his attention. The explanation he elaborated is the one we still accept today. It embodies the principal of "latent" heat, which states that if a quantity of water at the boiling point is changed into steam at the very same temperature, a certain definite amount of heat is required. This amount of heat is apparently "lost," because it does not produce a rise in temperature but merely causes a change of state — from water to steam. It is not truly lost, however, but merely becomes "latent," and it reappears again when the steam condenses into water. This remarkable discovery showed Watt that relatively large quantities of heat are involved in the change of state from water to steam and steam to water, and he applied this knowledge to the design of a superior steam engine in which a separate condenser was supplied for converting the steam back into water.[14]

This story illustrates how the advance in the steam engine depended upon the discovery of a new scientific principle and could not have been accomplished at a time and place other than that which was propitious to the undertaking. Fifty years earlier, Watt could never have come upon the new knowledge of heat just being developed by Black.

But, the way in which Watt's invention fitted the time does not end there. Even with the advantage of the new principles, the success of Watt's invention depended on his being able to make accurate cylinders. He had great difficulty at first in finding mechanics capable of making the parts of his engine with sufficient skill, and upon one occasion he congratulated himself that one of his cylinders *lacked but three eighths of an inch of being truly cylindrical.* Had his steam engine been designed earlier, we are told, "it is quite unlikely that the world would have seen the steam engine a success until this time [the end of the eighteenth century], when mechanics were just acquiring the skill requisite for its construction."[15] The steam engine fitted the times because of the economic need for such an instrument; but also because the scientific principles for its successful invention were just being discovered; and because the purely mechanical skills developed by technologists, independent of scientific thought, had reached the point at which the machine could be successfully made.

Even in our own time many discoveries are made possible to the scientist because of new materials made available to him by industry. To cite but one example which is fairly typical, Professor P. W. Bridgman's innovations in high-pressure research have been greatly aided by the availability of a very hard material produced by industry and known as tungsten carbide.

〜   〜   〜

A most illuminating example of the effect of the times on the direction of thought is provided for us in a hypothetical case by Dr. Ernest O. Lawrence, inventor of the cyclotron. Let us suppose, says Dr. Lawrence, that about one hundred years ago or more, the physicists of the world had been asked to devote their attention to the production of a superior method of illumination. The course of their investigations would have been dictated by the total scientific situation that then obtained. The investigators would have studied various types of fuels, the design of chimneys in lamps, various characteristics of wicks, and so on. It is wholly unthinkable that any of them would have seriously given thought to such curious phenomena as the twitching of frog legs, the action of acids on metals, the effect of waving wires in front of magnets, or any of the other phenomena which have given rise to the practical use of electricity and have made possible the electric light.[16]

In a lecture given before the City Philosophical Society in London in 1816, on the subject of "Oxygen, Chlorine, Iodine, and Fluorine," Michael Faraday declared: "Before leaving this substance, chlorine, I will point out its history, as an answer to those who are in the habit of saying to every new fact, 'What is its use?' Dr. Franklin says to such, 'What is the use of an infant?' The answer of the experimentalist would be, 'Endeavor to make it useful.' When Scheele discovered this substance it appeared to have no use, it was in its infantine and useless state; but having grown up to maturity, witness its powers, and see what endeavors to make it useful have done." [17] This very interesting statement refers to the element chlorine, which had been shown to be a chemical element in 1810 by Faraday's teacher, Sir Humphry Davy. The use to which Faraday referred was in the manufacture of bleaching powder by the method introduced by Charles Tennant of Glasgow in 1798,[18] which had developed into a large and prosperous industry. We shall discuss later (in Chapter 7) the great innovation in the textile industry which these bleaching powders represent.

Franklin uttered the famous statement quoted by Faraday in 1783 when he was in Paris as minister plenipotentiary for the American Colonies. During that year he witnessed the various balloon ascents made in France for the first time. Some of those present queried what use a balloon might have, and Franklin replied, "What good is a newborn baby?" This image was a natural enough one, as Mr. Carl Van Doren in his splendid biography of Franklin points out, since there was at that time in his own house at Passy a little baby two weeks old, Ann Jay, daughter of John Jay.

Franklin's statement may be amplified by a letter which he wrote on 30 August of that year to his good friend, Sir Joseph Banks, President of the Royal Society of London of which Franklin was a Fellow: "The Multitude separated, all well satisfied & much delighted with the Success of the Experiment, and amusing one another with Discourses of the various Uses it may possibly be apply'd to, among which were many very extravagant. But possibly it may pave the Way to some Discoveries in Natural Philosophy of which at present we have no conception." [19]

Franklin's wisdom was as sure in the field of science as it was in the field of politics. We have no idea, when a baby is born, as to whether it will be wise or foolish, tall or short, nor whether it will achieve a life that the world will remember or pass away mute and inglorious. All we know is that it will grow up into a man, and be molded by the environment in which it lives. In the same way each discovery will pave the way to many new ones and to practical applications "of which at present we have no conception," because no one can guess what changes in the total scientific situation or the scientific environment will occur in the distant or even the immediate future.

CHAPTER 4

The Spectrum of Scientific Activity

> While the line of demarkation between pure and
> applied science is never sharp — we are dealing
> with a wide continuous spectrum, as it were — . . .
> From considerable experience I should say that
> while, of course, there is no difference in methodol-
> ogy or techniques, as to goals there is as much dif-
> ference as between red and blue.
>
> There is only one proved method of assisting the
> advancement of pure science — that of picking men
> of genius, backing them heavily and leaving them
> to direct themselves. There is only one proved
> method of getting results in applied science — pick-
> ing men of genius, backing them heavily, and keep-
> ing their aim on the target chosen.
> —J. B. CONANT (1945)

SCIENCE — never mind the definition in the dictionary — is a point of
view that insists on a rational explanation, based on experience, of the
data of external world; and it implies, as we must state again and
over again, a way of learning truths concerning the universe around
us by experiments and observations.

In the preceding chapter we saw that even chance was sometimes
a road to knowledge: the scientist obtaining an important finding
while searching for something else. The ways by which we travel
on our search for truth are various and innumerable: the discovery
of information in a hitherto uninvestigated area by the use of a new
instrument; a new concept which arises from experiments or observations and, in turn, suggests new experiments or new observations;
the reinterpretation of existing data in the light of a new idea; the
development of more refined and more exact methods of observation; the fructifying effect of advance in one area of science upon
another; the introduction of mathematical techniques; the general
progression from qualitative description to quantitative analysis and

synthesis. . . . This brief enumeration is meant to be suggestive and is, therefore, far from exhaustive. Examples can be produced to illustrate scientific developments chiefly owing to any one of the items on the list, or any combination of them taken two at a time, three at a time, and so on.

The simple truth of such a statement may explain why P. W. Bridgman declares that actually there is no such thing as *a* scientific method. In so far as there is any method to science at all, it is nothing more than "to do one's damnedest with one's mind, no holds barred." To Professor Bridgman what distinguishes science from other "intellectual enterprises in which the right answer has to be found is not the method but the subject matter."[1]

The subject matter of science consists entirely of that which is to be found in the real or material world: our earth, the chemical substances that exist on it and their reactions with each other, the atmosphere surrounding the earth, the forms of life which inhabit it, the material of which it is composed; the other bodies in space, their action on the earth and on each other, and the radiation traveling between them — and similar matters. Those who work in industrial laboratories on the development of new machines, new products, or new methods of manufacture, use the same tools and concepts as the so-called "pure" scientists who discover new and important truths in the university laboratories.

In this chapter we will consider the two categories of scientific research-activity — the "pure" or "fundamental," on the one hand, and the "applied," on the other. But, before turning to that "spectrum" of scientific activity, let us first examine a quite different classification, one that is revealing of the nature of science itself.

One distinguishing characteristic of the whole scientific enterprise is that research is undertaken to find something new: something that was never known before, or never before known so well, or so exactly, or in that particular context. But some experimental work partakes of a slightly different character and may be a repetition of someone else's work, in order to check or substantiate it, or to enlarge upon it.

A considerable scientific activity is the collection, and systematization, of simple facts: for example, the determination of constants. Every liquid boils at a temperature which depends upon the pressure. At ordinary atmospheric pressure near sea level, water boils at approximately 100° C., a temperature sufficiently high to cook vegetables and meats, and make coffee. But if we climb a high mountain where the atmospheric pressure is considerably less, we find that water in an open vessel boils at a much lower temperature, so low in fact that it will no longer make coffee, nor will it cook potatoes.

The other end of the scale may be symbolized by the household pressure cooker. This instrument cooks its contents at a rapid rate because a high pressure develops inside, and the temperature of the steam formed and trapped within it (the temperature of boiling water and steam are the same at any given pressure) are "superheated" above the normal point for ordinary atmospheric pressure.

For scientific work and industrial use, tables of data, of which the temperature of boiling water at various pressures is but a simple example, are in constant demand. A vast army of scientists does nothing else than compile such data. This forms a part of what is usually known as "background" research. Other forms of "background" research include the establishment of standards for drugs and vitamins, the relation between one system of units and another, and the collection and description of plants and animals, geological formations, oceanographic and meteorological data, properties of materials, such as the heat conductivity of various metals, their tensile strength, and so on through a long list.

Closely allied to this kind of research are the techniques which create new chemical compounds and determine their physical and chemical properties, or those which compute each year the ephemerides, or tables of the heavenly bodies for the use of navigators and astronomers. This type of research may not seem very exciting to the lay reader. Yet the man who discovers a new chemical compound, or a new plant, experiences the same thrill of discovery as the creator of a new theory. Furthermore he has the satisfaction that his work will be the very basis and foundation, if not the actual building blocks, of the scientific work of the future. He is a pioneer.

When Newton uttered his famous apothegm about standing on the shoulders of giants, he told only half the truth. Every important scientific advance is made possible not alone by the prior work of the *great* men, whose contributions stand out so boldly that none can miss seeing them; there is also a vast and unnumbered collection of small facts, each patiently collected by a man, or a group of men, who may have devoted a whole lifetime to the job. The "tough-minded" theorist who, throwing precaution to the winds, makes a bold synthesis or proposes a daring new theory which may usher in a new age of man, is able to do so because a whole army of patient and "tender-minded" gatherers of knowledge have collected for him the raw materials out of which his world-shaking hypothesis is fashioned.

This is the sense in which the statement is often made, "In science, nothing is ever lost." Every contribution, big or small, profound or insignificant, whether a simple law or a grand generalization or just the description of an unknown plant, serves as nourishment for the living body of science.

                ᔕᔕ   ᔕᔕ   ᔕᔕ

But surely, the reader will ask, is there not a vast difference between the type of work represented by the man who computes the elements of the moon's orbit year after year in the office of the *Nautical Almanac* and that of the man who first worked out a law governing the moon's motion, or who found a refinement of, or correction to, the existing law? Between the astronomical book-keeper who makes nightly records of stellar luminosities or meteor trails, and the man who attempts to find the laws governing the behavior of variable stars or who applies the data concerning meteors to the study of conditions in the earth's upper atmosphere? The difference is one in degree of effect.

Some work is of a broad and general character, affecting a whole branch of a science, or perhaps a whole science, or even all of the sciences. In this category we would place the grand generalizations about nature, such as the law of universal gravitation, the quantum theory, the theory of relativity, the theory of evolution, modern genetics, and so on.

Sometimes, even the results of an experiment or an observation may have important consequences, and are in marked degree of contrast to the single grains of truth added to the storehouse of knowledge: to be used, together with many others, in some later synthesis. As examples of the latter, we would list what we have described as "background research," a hitherto unknown plant or animal, a new constant, a more exact determination of an old constant, and so on.

Here are a few examples of experiments and observations with important consequences: Oersted discovered the important effect of an electric current on a magnet, and thereby established a new branch of science, electromagnetism. Michelson and Morley performed a series of famous experiments which proved that the velocity of light is constant under all conditions and thereby shook the foundations (later to crumble entirely) of our traditionally held notions concerning the nature of time and space. Fleming discovered the action of penicillin on disease-producing organisms and laid the foundation for a future revolution in clinical medicine.

Such new effects, discovered by experimentalists, are of far greater importance than finding the constants of some chemical compound. The reason is that they produce a change in existing concepts and theories in science, or because they mark the beginning of a whole new branch of science. Under this category we must also include the invention of new instruments of research such as the cyclotron, the electron microscope, the ultra-centrifuge, and the method of staining biological tissues for study under the microscope.

We thus naturally classify scientific work according to *the degree whereby it affects scientific thought and procedures;* according to *the amount by which it changes the foundation or structure of science itself.* We may well call this the *fundamental* character of the research. Some work is of a more fundamental character than other work simply because it exerts a greater effect on the existing structure of science, because it affects a broader area, or because within its narrow area of applicability it has a deep and penetrating effect.

॰॰   ॰॰   ॰॰

As we stated earlier, the usual classification of scientific research has nothing whatever to do with the scale determined by the "fundamental" character of the inquiry or the result. Rather, a distinction is commonly made between "pure" science and "applied" science. However useful this latter dichotomy may be, it leads to misunderstandings if we do not exercise the greatest care. The normal antonym of "pure" is "impure" or "mixed," surely not "applied." Indeed, in seventeenth-century England, according to the great *Oxford English Dictionary,* writers on scientific subjects actually spoke of "mixed" science as opposed to "pure," and did not write about "applied" science at all.[2]

Thus Wilkins wrote in 1648 that pure mathematics was "to handle only the abstract quantity," while "that which is mixed doth consider the quantity of some particular determinate subject."[3] This distinction continued on into the nineteenth century. A work of 1858, for example, referred to "pure physicians" who practised only medicine, and "pure surgeons" who practised naught but surgery. To these were added the equivalents of the "mixed" category, the "surgeon apothecaries" or "general practitioners."[4]

Dr. Johnson of literary fame wrote in the *Rambler* in 1750 of "the difference between pure science which has to do only with ideas, and the application of its laws to the use of life."[5] The first reference to "applied science" as such is apparently to be found in Charles Babbage's *On the Economy of Machinery and Manufactures* published in 1832, a plea for the improvement of the state of British science and its further application to useful purposes. Babbage does not use the word "pure" in relation to science, but writes only: "The applied sciences derive their facts from experiment, but the reasons on which their chief utility depends come more properly within the province of what is called abstract science."[6]

As the nineteenth century progressed, Louis Pasteur entered the lists: "No, a thousand times no; there does not exist a category of science to which one can give the name applied science. *There is science and the applications of science,* bound together as the fruit to the tree which bears it." Pasteur also referred to "applied science," *considered apart from science itself,* as "a most improper expression."[7]

⁂

Let us follow Pasteur's lead. The applications of scientific discovery are the fruit (the useful harvest) of the tree of knowledge. Poor as the expression may be, let us call scientific activity which leads to new truths *fundamental research,* keeping in mind that some of it produces results that affect the foundations of knowledge in a much more fundamental way than the rest. The purpose of this book is to show the layman how scientific discoveries that have been truly fundamental in this sense have also been the well-springs of practical innovations. The latter are produced by those whose aim has not been so much to advance knowledge as to apply it for useful purposes, an activity we may denote "applied" research.

As we shall see presently, those who are engaged in the pursuit of fundamental scientific research or "pure" science also provide the raw materials which are used in "applied" research. But we shall see that even those who are interested in "applied" research, in making or providing useful or practical things, sometimes also make contributions to knowledge or to "pure" science; but these are rarely, if ever, of as "fundamental" a character as the most important achievements of "pure" science.

There is no sharp line of demarcation between pure and applied science, or between fundamental and applied research, but this does not imply that they are the same. They differ in the outlook of the man engaged in the work, the goal he sets himself, and the final result — as greatly as the discovery of the fundamental law of universal gravitation differs from the plotting of the trajectory of a bullet.

In the quotation at the beginning of this chapter, President J. B. Conant has likened the relationship to a wide, continuous spectrum.[8]

If we allow the light of the sun on a carbon arc to pass through a glass prism, we will find that the light is broken up into light of many colors, as in the rainbow, forming a spectrum. At one end, we have red light, and then orange, yellow, blue, green, and finally violet. This is called a *continuous* spectrum, because the closest examination can never decide, except in a purely arbitrary way, where one color leaves off and the next one begins; there is a continuous gradation from one into the other. So it is with pure and applied scientific research.

To see the spectrum of scientific research more vividly, let us look briefly at the kinds of work in which scientists are daily engaged.

❧   ❧   ❧

Most of the scientific work done in the United States falls into the "applied research" end of the spectrum, as the following table[9] will make clear. Except during the war years, the greater part of the research budget was expended by industry.

Comparison of National Research and Development Expenditures, 1930–1945

(*Excluding Atomic Energy*)

Millions of dollars expended

Year	Total	Federal Government	Industry	Universities	Other*
1930	166	23	116	20	7
1932	191	39	120	25	7
1934	172	21	124	19	8
1936	218	33	152	25	8
1938	264	48	177	28	11
1940	345	67	234	31	13
1941–1945 (average)	600	500	80	10	10

Percentage of total expenditures

Year	Federal Government	Industry	Universities	Other*
1930	14	70	12	4
1932	20	63	13	4
1934	12	73	11	4
1936	15	70	11	4
1938	18	67	11	4
1940	19	68	9	4
1941–1945 (average)	83	13	2	2

* State Governments, private foundations and research institutes, including non-profit industrial institutes.

A large proportion of industrial research is devoted to the application of known principles and is classified by the various industrial concerns as "applied research *and development*." Considerable time and money is spent in improving existing products and the processes for manufacturing them; and a great many of the people employed by industry are engaged in this most practical part of applied research, which we call development. This is the activity that consists largely in taking the new processes developed in the laboratory and trying them out on a small scale, in what is known as a "pilot" plant, in order to eliminate "bugs" before the process is put into large-scale commercial application. The new developments are tested on a small scale before mass production is undertaken, because experience has shown that many problems occur in large-scale production which are not at all apparent on the laboratory scale.

Sometimes, during pilot-plant operation, the research workers discover that certain specific information — constants of boiling point, pressure relations, and the like — are needed. Work then must halt while this is being obtained. We have earlier called this activity "background research," and pointed out that it constitutes a not inconsiderable addition to knowledge. Both scientists and practising engineers, whether working in a university or an industrial laboratory, make continued use of the information prepared by industry for its own purposes, but thus made available to the entire body of scientists.

Although the greater proportion of industrial research is in the applied field, some fundamental research is carried on in industrial laboratories. Two winners of the coveted Nobel Prize have been employed by industry: Irving Langmuir of General Electric, and C. J. Davisson of the Bell Telephone Laboratories. We shall discuss in Chapter 8 the fundamental research done by Wallace Carothers, while working for Du Pont.

Whether carried on in an industrial laboratory or a university, the distinction between fundamental and applied research must be based "principally upon the scope of the work and the extent to which it is limited by certain recognized practical objectives."[10] A general program of study of broad scope on such topics as the structure of cellulose, the nature of organic chemical compounds of high molecular weight, the relation between the bloods of different human beings, the nature of the sun, or the electrical properties of materials at very low temperatures, would be included in the category of fundamental research. Since the goal of the experimenter is to increase our knowledge, he follows his own bent and orients his studies in whatever direction his own curiosity may lead him. He follows up clues that seem promising because they appear related to fundamental problems.[11]

By contrast, let us consider a company producing textiles coated with cellulose derivatives or making photographic film or any other product utilizing derivatives from cellulose. This company might undertake research on cellulose solely in the hope of developing new derivatives with useful properties, especially adapted for application in the manufactured products of the industry. As each new cellulose derivative is discovered, its useful properties are evaluated, and the best ones are then made and used.[12] Our advancing technology depends upon such activity.

Because it contributes only a mite to knowledge, such obviously applied research is far from the category of fundamental investigation. We shall encounter an example of a similar kind in Chapter 11. Fundamental studies had shown that a special kind of hybrid corn is superior to common field corn. Then seed companies studied many different types of corn, not to increase knowledge, but simply to discover the best corns for given localities.

By and large one can readily tell whether a given research project belongs to the "fundamental" or the "applied" category. The test is a simple one: is the goal to add to truth or only to produce something practical? That is, will the investigators study any or all aspects of the problem, or will they limit themselves only to those of apparent economic value? Yet we must keep in mind President Conant's simile of the continuous spectrum. Just as one color shades off gradually into another so that an observer can not be sure where one leaves off and the next begins, so there are many projects on the dividing line between fundamental and applied research. These partake somewhat of the nature of both, just as the twilight partakes both of day and night.

Applied research pays obvious dividends to the stockholders, which is the reason why it is so generously supported by industry (as the table on page 58 makes plain). But this book is a plea for a generous and sympathetic support by every American citizen of the free and unrestricted fundamental research whose only purpose is to add to knowledge. In the following pages we shall see that, even so, the unrestricted search for truth pays practical dividends and makes possible the innovations of the applied scientist.

In the nineteenth century, many academic scientists scorned the practical man in much the same way that we of the twentieth century have scorned the absent-minded and long-haired professor (that is, until he produced the atom bomb and proved that he was not playing with idle toys but rather with grim, serious reality!).

The nineteenth-century point of view was exemplified in an interesting way by the reaction of Clerk Maxwell, one of the greatest mathematicians and theoretical physicists of the nineteenth century, to the discovery of the telephone. He was asked to give a special lecture on the workings of the extraordinary new instrument soon after its invention. The lecture began with a declaration of how wonderful the new invention was and how difficult it had been to believe that the report coming to England from the other side of the Atlantic had some foundation in fact. "When at last this little instrument appeared, consisting, as it does, of parts, every one of which is familiar to us, and capable of being put together by an amateur," Maxwell was forced to admit, "the disappointment arising from its humble appearance was only partially relieved on finding that it was really able to talk."

Well, then, perhaps the telephone, although simple in its construction, and using common elements such as wires, batteries, coils, and little magnets, found in every scientific laboratory, might "involve recondite physical principles, the study of which might worthily occupy an hour's time of an academic audience." Alas! Maxwell declared that he had not met a single person acquainted with the very simplest elements of electricity who had experienced "the slightest difficulty in understanding the physical processes involved in the action of the telephone." Furthermore, he had not seen a single "printed article on the subject, even in the columns of a newspaper," which showed a sufficient amount of misunderstanding "to make it worth preserving" — a proof that the new instrument was all too disappointingly easy to understand.[13]

This example illustrates clearly the point that we have just been discussing. Maxwell, like many other men of science, was at first very much excited by the prospect of a device that was "really able to talk." To his chagrin and disappointment, however, there was nothing to it; no new principle, no new apparatus, but just a combination of common things put together in a way that anyone could understand — a testimony surely to the mechanical genius of Alexander Graham Bell, but not of very much interest to anyone who, like himself, was pursuing the advance of science and pushing forward the frontiers of knowledge!

So blinded was Maxwell by the attitude of his era that he failed to recognize that in the operation of the important instrument he was describing there lay imbedded a host of scientific problems. The operation of the telephone depends on the use of short and somewhat irregular flows of current, related to the speech in-put. These small currents are known as "transients," and the theory of their operation has occupied some of our best scientific minds for a considerable period of time. Indeed, the scientists working at the Bell Telephone Laboratories who have built up the theory necessary to understanding in full the operation of the telephone have made a first-rank contribution and developed a new subject of which *Maxwell was not even aware!*

Maxwell's attitude, like that of other English scientists, was characteristic not of one country but of the age. At about the same time, in 1883, Henry A. Rowland, one of the few important American physicists of the nineteenth century, gave an address before the American Association for the Advancement of Science. He declared, "American science is a thing of the future, and not of the present or past; and the proper course of one in my position is to consider what must be done to create a science of physics in the country, rather than to call telegrams, electric lights, and such conveniences by the name of science." Then he went on, "I do not wish to underrate the value of all these things; the progress of the world depends on them and he is to be honored who cultivates them successfully. So also the cook who invents a new and palatable dish for the table benefits the world to a certain degree; yet we do not dignify him by the name of chemist."

Rowland was annoyed because "some obscure American" could steal the ideas of "some great mind of the past" and enrich himself by the application of it "to domestic uses." Such a man, according to Rowland, would be "often rated above the great originator of the idea, who might have worked out hundreds of such applications, did his mind but possess the necessary element of vulgarity." [14]

Up to at least the middle of the nineteenth century, scientists, whether connected with universities or not, did not draw the sharp line of cleavage between "pure" and "applied" science, characterized by Maxwell and Rowland. As the century drew to a close, however, academic scientists tended to scorn more and more the applications of their discoveries. Today, in the twentieth century, many of the leading scientists connected with universities still assume a snobbish attitude toward their industrial colleagues, although there are signs that a return to the earlier attitude is on its way. Clearly, a recognition of the close relations between discoveries and their applications, between "pure" and "applied" science, in no way demeans the position of the academic investigator.

No one has yet made a serious study of the changing attitude which caused the "pure" scientist to look down with scorn and contempt on the "applied." We know that the change in attitude was coeval with a great development in all the "applied" fields: telephone, telegraph, railroad, electric power, synthetic dye industry, and mass-production methods. What the relation is between the two movements, however, has not yet been fully disclosed, but perhaps the apparent snobbishness of a Henry Rowland was a kind of "defense reaction" in a world that was becoming increasingly materialistic and that was beginning to place too high a value on practical achievement, asking of every new discovery: "What good is it"?

ભ   ભ   ભ

Books on science for the layman usually describe the products of applied research, because science touches our lives most apparently in the new gadgets, insecticides, pharmaceuticals, and other products that we use from day to day. The lay administrator of science needs to learn how applied research brings these innovations from the laboratory test tube to his home. But, even more, he must understand how these practical developments derive from fundamental research, from the continued search and re-search for the foundational principles of the universe, the scientific knowledge of the basic phenomena of the external world.

It is not enough to make a bow to the scientist who discovers principles which others will apply. We must share his experience, go along with him in time, shoulder to shoulder, feeling with him his doubts and perplexities, following with him the light of inspiration when it shines, and joining with him in the final triumph — the discovery of a new and fundamental truth which *may* lead shortly to the solution of a practical problem, but which will *certainly* increase our understanding of the world we live in.

That is the reason why this book has been written in the form of case histories. The reader will become, vicariously and in turn, plant physiologist, physicist, chemist, doctor, geneticist, paleontologist, astronomer. By following the scientist as he makes his discovery, and by seeing how that discovery was put to use, he will see the connection between "thought" and "action," how the incessant search for truth provides him with the useful things he wants and needs. But he will also see that the only way to obtain these practical end-products is to encourage fundamental research — *the free investigation of all and any of nature's secrets* — not merely for our practical advantage, but for the truth that shall make us free.

PART TWO
Practical Applications of Fundamental Research

In former times when philosophy, still rude and uncultured, was involved in the murkiness of errors and ignorances, a few of the virtues and properties of things were, it is true, known and understood; in the world of plants and herbs all was confusion, mining was undeveloped, and mineralogy neglected. But when, by the genius and labors of many workers, certain things needful for man's use and welfare were brought to light and made known to others (reason and experience meanwhile adding a larger hope), then did mankind begin to search the forests, the plains, the mountains and precipices, the seas and the depths of the waters, and the inmost bowels of the earth, and to investigate all things.

— WILLIAM GILBERT (1600)

CHAPTER 5

Practical Applications of Fundamental Research

> The value and even the mark of true science consists, in my opinion, in the useful inventions which can be derived from it.
>
> —G. W. LEIBNIZ (1679)

ONE INESCAPABLE result of studying the history of science is the conclusion that many practical innovations such as our electric power system, the new weed-killers, radio and radar, nylon, and even advances in the practical art of medicine, have come about primarily as the *by-products of the search for truth in the scientific laboratory*. Indeed, it is hardly an exaggeration to say that the most profound and significant changes in our way of living and our control of our physical and biological environment have, in modern times, been wrought by the application of new truths, discovered by scientists whose interest was far removed from the so-called practical sphere.

This is not simply due to a factor of chance: that a scientist who was interested only in finding abstract (or "useless") new truths happened to hit upon something of practical value while looking for something else. Quite the contrary! As a matter of fact, the whole body of research scientists, in their relentless search for new and fundamental truths, are bound by the very nature of their studies to turn up constantly, and sometimes to their own surprise, innovations in the various arts of so great and revolutionary a value that they defy any estimate in terms of dollars and cents. We saw in the opening chapter of this book that the very nature of the scientific enterprise — dealing with aspects of the real, material, external world, and studying them by means of actual experiments and observations, rather than ideal speculation — implies that the results of scientific investigation must have significance in the same real, material, external world. This was also the sense of our likening the various activities of scientists to a continuous spectrum, with fundamental research at one end and applied research and development at the other.

During the last three hundred years or so, since the advent of modern science, the role of the inventor or practical innovator has undergone a radical change. Before the advent of the modern scientific era, beginning some time about the middle of the seventeenth century, the inventor was a man endowed with a superior mechanical ingenuity; he was a better or more accomplished gadgeteer than his fellow men. Today, by contrast, he is usually a man who is himself a scientist or, at least, someone with sufficient scientific training to be able to comprehend and to put to use the latest results of the search for truth obtained in the scientific laboratory. But, even a purely mechanical invention, as it goes through various stages of development, may require the discovery of new scientific truths for its final perfection.

In this chapter we will look briefly at one or two examples of the constant interplay that exists between the technics, on the one hand, and the search for fundamental truth, on the other.

As an example of the way in which the use of a mechanical invention presents problems for the scientist, let us consider the development of pumping machinery.

The common lift or suction pump, such as may still be found in many country homes, has a very long history going back in time to at least the great period of Roman civilization. During the sixteenth and seventeenth centuries, such pumps were in abundant use for a variety of purposes, of which one of the most important was the elimination of water from mine shafts. A great many technologists were aware that the suction pumps they used were limited to a useful working height of about 34 feet. For example, a famous book on mining, Agricola's *De Re Metallica,* published in 1556, showed how a series of pumps should be placed one over the other at different levels. Each of them pumped the water into a small tank, and the pump next above sucked or pumped the water from that tank into the next one. In this way a combination of many pumps in tandem was able to do what a single pump could not, namely suck or lift water up more than thirty-four feet.

But a little less than one hundred years later, the great Galileo himself reported in his *Dialogues Concerning Two New Sciences,* published in 1638, that a pump which apparently failed to work had once been brought to his attention. It would pump the water out of a cistern only when the level of water was higher than a certain minimum. Galileo tells us that at first he "thought the machine was out of order; but the workman whom I called in to repair it told me that the difficulty was not in the pump but in the water, which had fallen too low to be raised to such a height." [1]

Here was a problem. Could the apparently limiting distance of 34 feet be overcome by mechanical ingenuity, by designing a new or better type of pump, or was it due to some principle of nature as yet unknown? Galileo decided (mistakenly) that the limiting height for pumping was a result of the "fact" that in a pipe, a column of water greater than 34 feet would break under its own weight. But one of his pupils, Torricelli, apparently aided by Viviani, concluded that the phenomenon had nothing whatever to do with either the design of a particular pump, nor with Galileo's suspicion. He felt that the effect in question was to be explained in terms of the very cause of the pump's operation.

"We live," he wrote, "immersed at the bottom of a sea of elemental air, which by experiment undoubtedly has weight." The pump works, according to his explanation, roughly as follows. If we move a piston in a cylinder that is connected to a pipe going down into a well, that action tends to reduce the pressure. The weight of the air pushing down on the water in the well then causes the water to rise in the cylinder. A pump can suck up water to a height of 34 feet and no more, because the weight of the atmosphere pushing down can balance just the weight of a 34-foot column of water.

From the time of Aristotle until the time Torricelli made his analysis in the middle of the seventeenth century, many men had believed that the air in the atmosphere might have weight. But no one had thought of applying this idea to the explanation of the action of pumps. Torricelli, however, not only found the correct explanation of a fact which had puzzled even his master Galileo; he also devised a brilliant experiment in order to test his hypothesis.

He reasoned as follows: if the weight of the atmosphere will support a 34-foot column of water, it will support only a 30-inch column of mercury. The reason: since the density of mercury is 13½ times that of water, a 30-inch column of mercury weighs about the same as a column of water of the same cross-section that is 13½ times as high, namely 34 feet.

Torricelli's experiment is repeated today in all elementary science courses. We take a glass tube, sealed at one end and open at the

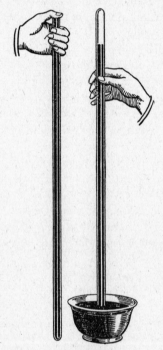

TORRICELLI'S EXPERIMENT

other, and fill it with mercury. Then we place our thumb tightly over the open end of the tube, invert it and place the tube carefully into a dish of mercury, securing it so that it will remain upright. The open end, sealed off by our thumb, is now submerged in the dish of mercury; and we have merely to remove our thumb from the tube to complete the experiment. The mercury in the tube will fall until it stands at a height of somewhere in the neighborhood of 30 inches above the level of the mercury in the dish. Like Torricelli, we have successfully completed the experiment. (See the adjacent figure.)

Torricelli's important discovery uncovered the principle behind the operation of suction or lift pumps, even if it did not provide a means of solving the problem of pump designs. From that day to this, no sensible pump designer has ever tried to make a lift pump that had its "sucker" or piston more than 34 feet above the surface of the water to be pumped up. But Torricelli's place in the history of thought is independent of any relation to his discoveries of the problems of pumping machinery. He had demonstrated that the air has weight, and thereby added a new truth to our store of fundamental knowledge.[2]

Here is an example, then, of the way in which the study of an apparently mechanical problem in technology, the design of better pumps, leads to the unveiling of a law of the cosmos, another milestone passed in the search for truth.

∾   ∾   ∾

Torricelli not only found a new principle of nature, and applied it to explain how lift pumps work and why they have a limitation, but his experiments led to an important new tool for scientific investigation — one which made possible a whole new science which, itself, had practical applications.

It was inevitable that Torricelli should have performed his experiment with mercury more than once, and thus he could hardly help noticing that the height of the mercury column was not always the same. Was the variation an experimental error, or did it arise from an unsuspected cause in nature? Torricelli followed his ideas to their logical conclusion. If the height of the mercury column in his instrument was determined by the pressure exerted by the weight of the atmosphere; then, since the height varies from day to day, the atmospheric pressure too must vary.

Torricelli's brilliant deduction was confirmed by the Frenchman, Pascal, whom most of us know as a philosopher rather than a scientist. Pascal concluded that if the height of the mercury in Torricelli's experiment depended on the pressure exerted by the atmosphere, one should notice a marked effect when performing Torricelli's experiment at various heights. For example, as you climb a mountain, the higher you go, the less air there will be above you pushing down. This decrease in atmospheric pressure on going up a mountain should be sufficiently marked to be observable. Pascal caused his brother-in-law, Perier, to climb a mountain in the neighborhood in which they lived, carrying with him the instruments necessary to perform Torricelli's experiment. As he made observations at various heights, he noted the continuous drop in the mercury level, while Pascal himself conducted an experiment down below to make sure that the pressure that day did not fall at the rate observed by the climber.[3]

After this confirmation by Pascal few people doubted any longer that the atmosphere has weight and that the pressure exerted by it could be measured by Torricelli's instrument, the mercury barometer which is still in use for measuring atmospheric pressure. Its name was suggested by Robert Boyle as a combination of two Greek words: *báros,* weight, and *métron,* measurer.

As man the world over began to make systematic barometric readings, the same kind of logic which had led to the invention of the barometer led also to a new important discovery, namely that the changes in atmospheric pressure could be correlated with changes in the weather: for example a falling barometer means an approaching storm. From the invention of this instrument we may date the birth of the modern science of meteorology or weather prediction. Within fifty years after Torricelli's experiments, the mercury barometer was already renamed the "weather glass."[4]

The science of meteorology itself has provided a vast field of endeavor, not only for supplying useful information about the weather, but also for uncovering further fundamental truths about the atmosphere. Some of these latter have thus far been of interest only to the pure scientist. Others have been of practical value, not only in weather prediction, but also, as we shall see in a later chapter (Chapter 16), in solving vital problems in short-wave radio communication.

Thus it goes, in a never-ending cycle. A problem arises and is solved or explained by the scientist, who discovers a new truth. The discovery leads in turn to other important applications and to the opening-up of a whole new field of scientific research. The new truths uncovered in that field are in turn of value to other scientists, and are themselves sources of still further practical applications.

∾   ∾   ∾

Let us next consider a useful invention based on science from the eighteenth century, as a means of obtaining still further insight into the way the progress of science makes important innovations possible. The story this time is that of Benjamin Franklin's *invention* of the lightning rod, based on his *fundamental scientific discoveries,* of which it was merely a by-product.

Although we think of Franklin today as an apostle of liberty, as the inventor of such useful gadgets as the "Franklin stove" and bifocal glasses, as a civic innovator (public library, fire department, and so on), and as a printer and newspaperman, his world-wide reputation was begun with his electrical experiments. The book in which he describes them, *Experiments and Observations on Electricity, Made at Philadelphia in America,* was so popular that it was printed in ten editions before the American Revolution — five in English, three in French, one in German, and one in Italian. His scientific colleagues knew him as a proponent of a unitary theory of electricity, discoverer of many electrical phenomena and their explanation, and also as the first man to explain the action of the "Leyden jar." The latter was an instrument made of a glass bottle, coated on the outside with metal foil, and filled with metal shot or water. It had the property of being able to store up an enormous "quantity" of electric charge and its modern form, called a "condenser," is an essential ingredient of radios and other electronic equipment.

Franklin's contribution to electrical theory will be forever marked by the words he introduced in an electrical sense for the first time: plus or positive; minus or negative; electrical battery, and many others.[5]

If Franklin seems to us today to be the very incarnation of the hard-headed practical man, his work in electricity was certainly far removed from the economic or practical sphere. When he began his researches in the 1740's, he would hardly have chosen electricity as the subject of his investigations had his interest been limited to discoveries with possible immediate utilitarian consequences. At that time the only "practical application" of electricity was a medical one; and, although Franklin on occasion participated in giving shocks for therapeutic purposes, he never fully believed in their vaunted efficacy. Like many of the other scientists we will discuss throughout this book, Franklin was attracted to a particular branch of science because its phenomena seemed "curious" and he wanted to understand how they occur.[6]

In order to see in what way Franklin's *discoveries* made the *invention* of the lighting rod possible, let us examine a few of them. If we rub a bit of amber with cat's fur it becomes electrified or charged. We can place a piece of charged amber in contact with a conductor, such as a metal sphere, and then some of the charge will transfer itself. If the metal sphere is insulated, for example by a glass mount, the charge will remain on it for a considerable period of time. But Franklin found that if we bring up close to it a pointed metallic object, such as a needle held in our hand, we can "draw off" the charge. Likewise, if we charge not a metal sphere but a metallic object which has pointed or jagged edges, then no matter how good our insulating stand may be, the charge will quickly leak off into the air from each pointed part of the surface. In this same way the residual electric charge of the earth continually leaks off into the air from every blade of grass, branch, tree, and rock.

Franklin not only proved that an insulated conductor will lose its charge if a pointed metallic object is placed near it, but he further found that it will do so only if it is grounded — by either being held in our hand or attached by a wire to moist earth. If we wrap the end of a needle with an insulating material such as cloth, then no matter how close we hold it to a charged metal sphere, it will no longer "draw off" the charge.

Franklin was led to believe that lightning is an electrical phenomenon arising from the discharge of electrified clouds, either from one to the other, or from one to the earth. He was not the first man to think that the lightning discharge might be an electrical phenomenon. We have an almost continuous record of speculation along that line — going back at least a century in time to Otto von Guericke, Burgomeister of Magdeburg, inventor of the first air pump. But Franklin did more than his predecessors who, like himself, had noted the resemblance between the lightning discharge and the sparks obtained in electrical experiments. He devised a means of testing the hypothesis and concluded *his* list of similarities between lightning and electric sparks with the significant sentence: "Let the experiment be made."

The reason why Franklin added this sentence, whereas his contemporaries and predecessors did not, was only in part his superior scientific genius. Whereas his contemporaries had noted that lightning resembles electric discharges, they had been unable to devise an experiment to test the supposed electric nature of the lightning discharge. That Franklin was able to do so was the result of the logical sequence of the discoveries we have just been describing.

If we have a pointed conductor which is grounded (such as an iron rod, one end buried in the ground and the other end pointed and rising thirty or forty feet in the air), it should be able to draw off the charge of an electrified body (such as a charged overhead cloud) at greater than its striking distance. During an "electric" storm, said Franklin, such a rod should be able to "draw off" the electric charge from the overhead clouds, if clouds are in fact electrically charged. This was the form of experiment that Franklin devised to prove that the lightning discharge is electrical; the electrical kite, so dear to generations of schoolboys, was only an unnecessary afterthought. Clearly, the primary experiment depended on knowledge of the action of grounded and pointed conductors.

But, even before the experiment was made, Franklin was so sure of its success that he thought of an immediate application. If we erect a well-grounded, pointed metal rod alongside of a house, surely, he said, we can rob the clouds of their dangerous electrical charge *before* they are able to do any damage, just as in the laboratory experiment we "draw off" the charge from the metal sphere by a needle held in our hand.

It is curious that, although the lightning rod did help to prevent houses from being destroyed by a lightning stroke, it did so in a way quite other than Franklin had originally conceived. He and his colleagues discovered that lightning rods would not act by "stealing thunder" from the clouds; but rather by attracting the actual lightning discharge itself, and conducting it safely into the ground.

This story is an interesting one, not only because it shows how a useful device for preventing our homes from being destroyed derives from scientific discoveries about the shape of conductors and the like, but also because it shows how a useful invention based on science may be founded *upon a misconception!*

ᕀᕀ   ᕀᕀ   ᕀᕀ

It is not an uncommon event in the development either of science or its applications to find an important innovation based on an idea that may be essentially incorrect. One such is provided from the history of medicine in the doctrine of homeopathy, propounded by Samuel Christian Friedrich Hahnemann (1755-1843). Hahnemann had many strange ideas, the chief one of which was the principle of *similii similibus:* that many diseases are to be cured by the administration of drugs which produce in a normal patient a condition similar to the disease. According to Hahnemann, hot compresses would be prescribed for burns, opium to cure somnolence, and so on.[7] The name "homeopathy," from the Greek word *homeion,* meaning similar (as in *homo*geneous), indicated the principle of "like treating like." Opposed to it is so-called "alleopathy," the principle of which is *contraria contrariis,* according to which stimulants are prescribed for depressed states, and sedatives for excited states. Hahnemann's principles of treatment thus were directed not against the disease itself, or its cause, but entirely against the symptoms of the disease. At the time that he was writing, no one knew the true cause of disease, but our present knowledge clearly vitiates his principles.

According to Hahnemann, the action of drugs on the human body produces a modification of the so-called "vital force"; the disappearance of symptoms is owing to an increase in the "energy" of this vital force. He believed, as a fundamental doctrine, that *the effects of a drug would become more powerful as the doses in which it was given became smaller and smaller.* This was the "theory of potencies," which Hahnemann believed was an essential part of his theory. In the use of drugs in liquid form, Hahnemann recommended a procedure as follows: "An original tincture is prepared of which two drops are diluted with 98 drops of alcohol; then one drop of this solution is further diluted in 99 drops of alcohol, and so on for thirty times."[8] Such an extreme dilution, recommended universally, reduces the effective potency of the drug to such an extent that in most cases we know now that the patient might just as well be given a few drops of pure alcohol. Yet *the results of applying such absurd principles had a most beneficial influence on medical treatment.* The minute homeopathic doses had the merit at least of doing no harm to the patient, at a time when the simultaneous use of a large number of powerful drugs, prescribed in truly heroic proportions, had dangerous and unpredictable effects. Before modern science had uncovered the true cause of disease, and enabled the physician to know just how much of any given drug to administer, the homeopathic idea of prescribing drugs in only minute quantities, as introduced by Hahnemann, however much of a delusion it was founded upon, had the useful effect of counteracting a dangerous and pernicious trend in medical practice.

∽   ∽   ∽

The examples that we have been considering in this chapter, the barometer and weather prediction, and the lightning rod, are examples of the way in which practical applications stem from the scientist's relentless search for truth. As we shall see further in discussing the case histories which make up this section of the book, those who apply new discoveries tend to be men trained in science, rather than mechanics or rude technicians. In contrast, let us next consider some examples of mechanical innovations *in which science played no part.* Two such come from the Middle Ages, which most of us have been taught in school is a "dark" period in the history of the human species. Yet it was a time when great advances were made in all of the technical arts, particularly in the innovation of laborsaving devices.[9]

One of the most significant medieval innovations was the horse collar.

To many people the very idea that a man would devote a good bit of his life to the history of the horse collar must seem to be but an example of the pedantry and narrow isolation of academic minds. Yet such an investigation by the late Commandant Lefèvre des Noettes revealed very interesting information. Among other things, it showed that during the period of early classical times — Egyptian, Greek, and Roman — when society was based on slave labor, there was no effective method of harnessing rapidly-moving animals such as horses. Only the heavy cumbersome ox yoke was known, and the draft animal that could be used most effectively was the human being. The invention of the horse collar, occurring during the late Middle Ages at the same time as the invention of iron horseshoes, was a simple one; but it had a vast effect on changing the forms of society; it freed men from the need of enslaving their fellows as draft animals!

Another significant mechanical invention of the Middle Ages was the wheelbarrow, replacing the early handbarrow that had to be carried by two men, one in front and one in the rear. This invention reduced the number of laborers by half, since the man in front was replaced by a wheel; it may be considered typical and one which set a pattern from which we have not deviated in all the succeeding centuries. As Lynn White remarked, "We have been replacing men by wheels ever since." Turning wheels suggest clocks — and the first mechanical clock was another product of mediaeval inventive fertility.

However, in the advance of technology, as we remarked earlier, the solution of one problem always introduces another. Thus, if we have wheels, whether the large wooden affair of a country wagon or the delicate toothed wheel inside a watch, we must lubricate them in order to keep the vehicle or instrument running. The more complex the arrangement of wheels upon which our civilization runs, the better must be the oils needed to keep them turning smoothly freely. The highest standards of lubrication in modern times are to be found in our watches, although most of us, driving automobiles, are more familiar with the oil required to keep the motor turning.

A satisfactory watch oil must always remain liquid and slippery even at very low temperatures; and, furthermore, must not evaporate rapidly at relatively high temperatures. Also, it must not corrode on metal and must never become gummy. Only one type of oil has ever been found that will satisfy to a tolerable degree all of these rigid requirements. This oil is obtained from fishes, and the very best is taken from one species of porpoise, the blackfish. So good a lubricant is this oil that one single drop of it can lubricate all the moving parts of a watch and keep them running smoothly for as much as a dozen years! [10] By contrast, the oils which we obtain from petroleum, such as those with which we lubricate our automobile motors or sewing machine motors, are far inferior. The best grade of petroleum oil is not good enough for the precision gasoline engines used in racing cars, which require some natural oil, usually castor oil. Those who will claim that modern science has *in every case* produced superior products to those of a century ago may be interested in the fact that no synthetic lubricant, nor derivative from coal or petroleum, is as good as the oil which for many, many years has been obtained from certain fishes and used on our watches.

But the complete story of lubrication illustrates once again the principle that we saw exhibited by the story of the pump. The introduction of moving machinery raised the problem of lubrication. In order to advance our basic knowledge of this subject we needed some device to help us investigate what actually happens when metals are covered with thin films of oil, graphite, or grease. These layers, we must remember, may be of the order of but a few molecules in thickness. An analogous problem arises in another use of oil in an age of metals, namely, to prevent the formation of rusts, which are simply chemical compounds formed by the combination of the metal with the oxygen of the air, or the oxygen which is dissolved in water. The study of rusts or oxidation was limited by exactly the same problem as in lubrication. *How was one to study the formation of thin layers?*

Clearly, the solution of this problem was not in the mechanical domain. More was required than an ingenious instrument; one had to be devised that would operate on wholly new principles — fundamental truths that had still to be discovered.

We are today making a great step forward in the study of surfaces of all sorts thanks to the instrument known as an "electron diffraction camera." The sentence just above would have sounded completely absurd to a physicist of thirty years ago, because the combination of *electron* and *diffraction* would then have represented a concatenation of two of the most opposite aspects of nature. An electron was thought to be a particle of definite size and mass, whereas diffraction was considered to be the characteristic phenomenon of vibratory media, such as occurs in pulsating air, whose vibrations give rise to sound.

One of the great achievements of twentieth-century physics, as fundamental to our understanding of the nature of matter itself as nuclear physics, has been the demonstration that the electron exhibits dual properties — those of the wave or vibration, as well as those of the particle.[11] This important idea was presented first as an abstraction by the French physicist, Louis de Broglie, and was verified experimentally in 1927 by G. P. Thomson in England, and by C. J. Davisson assisted by L. H. Germer, the latter pair working in New York in the Bell Telephone Laboratories.

Obviously, nothing was further from the minds of de Broglie, Thomson, Davisson, or Germer, than the problems of lubrication or the formation of oxides. But it soon became apparent that the diffraction pattern obtained was produced by the *surface layer* of the material. An electron beam used to obtain a diffraction pattern does not usually penetrate into a metal target to distances greater than 20 A units, whereas similar patterns obtained by the use of x-rays correspond to a depth of 100,000 A units! [12] The reader need not concern himself with the exact definition of the unit, which the physicist uses to measure very, very small distances, but he should see immediately that the minimum penetration of x-rays is to a distance at least 5000 times greater than that of electrons. Thus the technique of electron diffraction, as Dr. Clark tells us, "performs the same thing for the surface layer . . . that x-rays do for metals in bulk form." [13]

The General Electric Company now manufactures an electron diffraction camera for the use of engineers, and the electron microscope produced by RCA can be adapted to the same purpose. With the aid of this tool, we are now beginning to learn what happens to surfaces that are lubricated as well as those that are polished, how rusts are formed, just how in electroplating one metal is deposited on top of another. Application of the new technique has also solved several riddles important to the use of ball bearings and the construction of cylinders in automobile engines.

And again we see the way in which the search for abstract truth and its experimental verification finds the answers to pressing questions and problems whose solution is essential to our advancing technology.

There is many an important problem faced by engineers and

doctors whose solution awaits some new fundamental truth; but, alas, no one knows in what special field of scientific activity each will be found.

❧   ❧   ❧

We have referred several times to the important fact that the examples which are used for illustrative purposes in this book are not unique. To varying degrees the same pattern may repeat itself on many occasions.

We have already described the significant invention made in the Middle Ages, by means of which the man who carried the front of a handbarrow was replaced by a wheel. A somewhat similar innovation is the replacement of the horse in front of a buggy or wagon by an internal combustion engine.

[It is an interesting social datum that, although everybody knows Edison as the inventor of the electric light (and some know Swann as an independent inventor of the same thing in England), Elias Howe as the inventor of the sewing machine, and Marconi as the inventor of the radio, few, if any of us, know the name of the man who invented the gasoline engine which powers our automobiles, nor even the name of the man who first thought of applying such a device in this way. Yet, as Maurice Holland tells us, "It is quite safe to venture the assertion that no basic patent, granted by the United States, has so profoundly influenced the social and economic life of so many people in so short a time as the Selden patent of 1895 which covered the principle of using an explosion engine in a road vehicle." [14]] We must not lose sight of the fact that the difference between those early horseless carriages and the streamlined automobile of 1948 is not merely one of successive mechanical inventions, such as make possible the location of the gear-shift lever on the steering-wheel post; but — this development also reflects the application of scientific discoveries, many made with no such practical end in view.

This introductory survey would not be complete, however, if we neglected to point out the reverse side of the coin. We have been discussing the way in which the discovery of new scientific truths makes possible new inventions. We have contrasted inventions based on science with the purely mechanical inventions that could be made by any skilled technician with sufficient mechanical ingenuity. Yet the progress of science itself frequently depends on mechanical inventions, just as much as on the work done in science by one's predecessors and contemporaries.

As an example, let us consider the telescope which was invented in the seventeenth century; there are several claimants to the honor of having been the first to put together two lenses in order to make an instrument which would enable one to see objects clearly at a great distance. Not one of those whose claim to this important invention has been put forth was a skilled scientist in any sense of the word!

Lenses, in the modern form of a lenticular-shaped piece of glass, were unknown in classical antiquity, and were first made during the Middle Ages.[15] Spectacles apparently came into use some time in the twelfth century, but not for some five hundred years did anyone think of, or come across accidentally, the principle of using two lenses, separated by a certain distance, as an optical instrument. Interestingly enough, one of the first patents to be applied for in Holland was one covering this principle.[16]

As soon as he had heard of the new invention, Galileo constructed a telescope, and immediately thought of using it to study the heavenly bodies. He soon made a host of important scientific discoveries, such as the existence of many stars invisible to the naked eye, the fact that the planet Venus has phases just like the moon, the existence of three moons circling about the planet Jupiter, the fact that the moon's surface appears to contain mountains and valleys just as are found on the earth, and many more. Indeed, it may be stated unequivocably that the invention of the telescope and its use for astronomical purposes by Galileo marked the beginning of the modern science of astronomy, because all the important work in astronomical science since that time has been done with telescopes.[17]

By combining two lenses in a slightly different way, one produces a compound microscope. By its aid, biologists have studied plant and animal structures otherwise invisible, as well as various microorganisms. The work of such a man as Pasteur would have been absolutely impossible without a good compound microscope.

Professor Percy W. Bridgman, who was awarded the Nobel Prize for his studies on the properties of materials at very high pressures, was able to achieve a greater pressure in the laboratory than any of his predecessors largely because of a special kind of packing or seal which he invented. Yet, when he tried to obtain a patent for the method, he discovered to his astonishment that a patent for a very similar type of device had been granted some years earlier to a manufacturer of sausage machines.[18] In the case of Bridgman, as in that of Galileo, the success of the investigations depended not only on the instrument available, but also and to a marked degree upon the genius which saw so clearly *the way to use the new instrument in studying nature.*

The list of important new instruments responsible to a high degree for the rapid progress of modern science can easily be extended. Two of the most important that come to mind are the spectroscope (the tool of the chemist and the physicist, and second in importance only to the telescope for the astronomer) and the photographic camera. Improvements in the art of making photographic plates have vastly extended the range of spectroscopy, and it is hard to think of any branch of science today working without photography.

The late Professor L. J. Henderson used to remark that prior to 1850 the steam engine did more for science than science did for the steam engine.[19] The experimenter of today is in a vastly superior position to that of his predecessors of one hundred and fifty years ago, thanks to the fruits of modern technology. He can obtain glassware of any size and description, and wire of all sorts. Joseph Henry, only a century ago, had to insulate the wires in his great electromagnets by winding about them strips torn from his wife's petticoats. A scientist working today has merely to turn to the catalogue of any one of a number of suppliers. He can get wire of almost pure copper because the industrialists have found that such wire is a better conductor of electricity than wire made of impure copper, with traces of arsenic or other impurities. Instead of having to make his own galvanic batteries, he has merely to turn on a switch. He may obtain "rare" gases and other chemicals in a pure state, and a host of materials of all sorts prepared for industrial uses.

President J. B. Conant remarks on this score that "the connection is a two-way street. The practical arts at first run ahead of the sciences: only in very recent years have scientific discoveries affected practice to a greater degree than practice has affected science." [20] Today, no large industry is without its research laboratories. But, some three hundred years ago, Robert Boyle wrote a hopeful treatise which he called *That the Goods of Mankind may be increased by the Naturalist's Insight into Trades.* "I shall conclude this," he wrote, "by observing to you, that as you are, I hope, satisfied, that experimental philosophy [i.e., science] itself may not only be advanced by an inspection into trades, but may advance them too; so the happy influence it may have on them is none of the least ways, by which the naturalist may make it useful to promote the empire of man."

⁓   ⁓   ⁓

The purpose of this preliminary survey has been to illuminate the relation between mechanical inventions and technical progress, and fundamental research for new truths of nature. It should be clear that the advance of science affected technics, in wholly unpredictable ways; that the development of technics raised many problems, which the scientists could solve only by the discovery of new and unsuspected principles; and reciprocally — the scientist was provided with tools and materials for his own investigations by the same development of technics.

Now that we have had a cursory glimpse of the interchange between practical applications and the search for truth, let us turn to three case histories developed at full length: the weed-killing chemical compounds; the use of electric power, radio, and radar; and nylon; let us study in detail how these extraordinary practical achievements grew out of what was purely fundamental research. These chapters have been written to give the uninitiated reader the experience of the scientist himself, so that his judgment may be informed by a true understanding. In each example, we will trace the history of the ideas under discussion, how they were discovered, what effect they had on the state of science, and how they were put to use in the service of mankind. Then we shall be able to see in just what way these three examples are typical of all applications of fundamental knowledge, and in what way they form a category distinct from others.

CHAPTER 6

Auxins and Agriculture

Bowed by the weight of centuries he leans
Upon his hoe and gazes on the ground,
The emptiness of ages in his face,
And on his back the burden of the world.
— EDWIN MARKHAM
(Reprinted by permission.)

THE PROSPECT of a world without weeds, of gardening without tears
and agriculture without pain, marks the beginning of one of the
great revolutions produced by science in the twentieth century. We
are rapidly approaching a time when, as the result of the splendid
research work of a relatively small number of plant scientists, the
world's table will be supplied by the labors of a comparatively small
number of people. Agricultural machinery of various sorts, a better
knowledge of soil and fertilizers, and new and improved types of
plants (some of which we shall discuss in later chapters), have already resulted in a rapid decrease in the number of people employed
in the production of food. Only a hundred years ago, 8 out of every
10 Americans were engaged in food production; today, this number
has been reduced to 2 out of every 10! If we can successfully eliminate weeds without using cultivators or hand labor, this figure can
be made even smaller.

The weed has been defined as an undesirable plant, or "a plant
out of place."[1] A weed may be either an unwanted wild plant, or
an equally undesirable plant left over from a previous crop, such as
last year's wheat growing in the midst of this year's patch of tomatoes. Weeds occupy space and compete with the harvest crop for
a "place in the sun." They also compete with the farm crop for
nutrients in the soil. Their presence thus reduces not only the yield
of farm crops, but also their quality. Weeds may be either woody or
herbaceous plants.

The action of weeds has been described as "an unseen tax on the crop harvested."[2] In California, the losses from weeds amount to sixty million dollars annually, and, according to F. J. Taylor, the total annual loss to farmers in the United States from weeds alone is in the vicinity of three billion dollars a year.[3]

Still another way of seeing the economic importance of weeds is in terms of the cost of production of crops. Where vegetables such as carrots and onions are grown, the weeding operation may comprise 30 per cent of the production cost. The hand labor involved in the first weeding of carrots and onions is very tedious, and the cost of this careful initial weeding is about thirty dollars an acre.[4] Quite obviously then, any rapid, inexpensive method of killing weeds is a boon to farmers, and constitutes a discovery of the utmost practical importance.

One of the most recent applications of fundamental scientific research has been the development of a type of selective "weed killer" which may in time eliminate once and for all the labor of the man with the hoe. Actually, the day may not be far distant when hand weeding will be referred to as a curious, backbreaking activity of our forefathers.

The new weed killers, already being advertised in garden journals and the garden pages of Sunday newspapers, operate on an entirely fresh principle. Most of the weed killers known in the past have been chemicals which attacked the plant itself, or mechanical devices like flame throwers, or methods of treating the soil. The new weed killer is an "auxin," or "synthetic plant hormone," and the very knowledge of the existence of hormones in plants is but twenty-five years old. Not only may our fields be freed from common weeds by the use of the new auxins, but already the auxins are being applied on a large scale to a host of other important practical problems in agriculture, horticulture, and silviculture, which we shall describe at the end of the chapter.

As far as the practical world is concerned, then, there is no question but that the investigators in the field of plant hormones have really hit pay dirt. Let us go back in time, and briefly trace the history of this subject in order to discover how this most practical field of endeavor started and grew. We will see that not one of the early investigators had the slightest idea that his results might, in so short a time, be of interest and importance to anyone outside the laboratory.

∽   ∽   ∽

No scientific story ever has a true beginning. If we investigate the history of most scientific ideas, it usually turns out that as we go further and further back in time, we end up with some concept of the Greeks. The ancient Greek thinkers are considered to have been the first scientists because in classical Greece, some five or six centuries before Christ, men first had the idea that the observable phenomena in the external world permitted of a complete rational explanation. Thus, the idea of atoms goes back to the Greek, Demokritos; and the idea that the laws of nature should take the form of numerical relations goes back to the Greek, Plato, and to his predecessor, Pythagoras, whose theorem in geometry is still one of the requirements of the high school study of that subject. But the notion of plant hormones, or, more particularly, of growth hormones in plants, is of recent vintage and was entirely unknown not only to the Greeks, but also to the plant scientists of the last century.

∽   ∽   ∽

The significant work marking the beginning of our knowledge of this important new subject begins about the year 1880, when Charles Darwin asked himself the question: Why do plants bend toward the light? The experiments Darwin made in order to find the answer to this question were embodied in his last work, published two years before his death, entitled *The Power of Movement in Plants*.

Darwin's experiments, carried out in collaboration with his son Francis, were as simple as they were illuminating. He grew oat seedlings in total darkness save for a few seconds during which he held a lighted match near them. The seedlings responded by subsequently curving in their growth so as to point toward the place where the light had been. Furthermore, if he cut off the tip of the oat seedling before exposing it to the light, or if he covered the tip with a small black cap, no curvature took place. In other words, even though most of the curvature occurs in the lower part of the seedling, the portion essential for a response to light is the tip. "We must therefore conclude," Darwin wrote, "that when seedlings are freely exposed to a lateral light, some influence is transmitted from the upper to the lower parts causing the latter to bend." [5]

So radical were Darwin's findings that they met with considerable opposition until other workers, chiefly W. Rothert (1894) and H. Fitting (1907), established beyond any doubt Darwin's observation of "the separation between the zones which perceive and the zones which react" to the light. [6]

The next step was to determine how this influence might be transmitted from the tip of a plant in order to affect other parts of the plant itself. At that time similar influences in animals were thought to be transmitted by a nervous system, and quite clearly an analogy to plants would have offered a simple explanation.

No one was able to give a satisfactory explanation of Darwin's experiments until the decisive investigations made during the years 1910–1911 by P. Boysen-Jensen in his laboratory in Copenhagen. Like Darwin's experiments, Boysen-Jensen's were very simple. He cut off the tip of an oat seedling and "glued" it back on with gelatin; the tip was not grafted onto the stem, to become again a part of the seedling's living structure, but was merely held in place by the gelatin. He then repeated Darwin's experiment of growing the seedling in total darkness, save for a few minutes when it was exposed to a source of light. The result? This seedling responded to light in exactly the same way as did all the others, and grew curved, pointing to the spot where the light had been.

Whatever the "influence" might be that caused the seedling to respond to the light, it was certainly not a nerve impulse; no nerve impulse ever passes through jelly. But a soluble chemical substance would do just that; every college student of biology knows that salt and sugar pass easily through a thin layer of gelatin. Boysen-Jensen correctly concluded "that the transmission . . . is of a material nature."

Because of the importance of Boysen-Jensen's experiment, it was repeated and extended by the Hungarian botanist, A. Páal, in the years during and just after the First World War. Páal showed that although the influence or stimulus of light could cross a layer of gelatin from the tip to the rest of the plant, it was effectively blocked by mica, as well as by platinum foil. His next experiment was even more decisive. He showed that even *without the influence of light,* curvature could be induced in the base of the seedling by the simple process of cutting off the tip and replacing it off to one side of

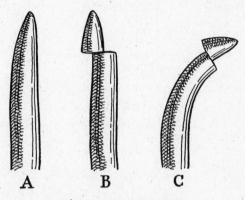

PÁAL'S EXPERIMENT

A. *A normal seedling*
B. *A seedling that has been decapitated and the tip placed back, off to one side of the stump*
C. *Subsequent growth: the left side of the seedling receives most of the growth substance, grows more rapidly, and causes the seedling to curve and point to the right*

the stump, as in the figure. The curvature was caused by the fact that the side of the plant below the tip *grew* at a more rapid rate than the opposite side, which had no tip above it. From this experiment he correctly deduced that the "growth substance," secreted from the tip even without the light stimulus, promotes the growth of the tissues in the lower part of the plant.[7]

The curving of the plant thus obtained by Páal was not only similar in appearance to that which occurred in Darwin's experiment of exposing the young shoot to a momentary sensation of light, but evidently was caused *in the same way.* In Páal's experiment the displacement of the tip made one side of the shoot grow more rapidly than the other *because it had received a greater quantity of the growth substance.* The action of light had not *produced* the sub-

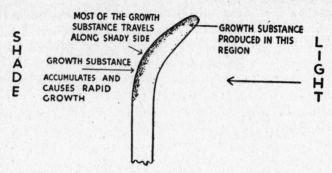

SCHEMATIC DIAGRAM OF DARWIN'S ORIGINAL
EXPERIMENT

(From F. S. Taylor, Science Front *1939, Copyright 1940 by
The Macmillan Company.)*

stance, but merely made it migrate to the dark, or shady side, and
the shoot curved so that the tip appeared to point towards the light.

ᵔᵔ   ᵔᵔ   ᵔᵔ

Since the rate of growth of plants was apparently affected by a
chemical substance, produced in the tip and acting upon the lower
part of the plant, physiologists came to think of it as being similar
to the hormones found in animals, which were already being extensively investigated.

The concept of hormones had been developed by zoologists to account for the many phenomena in which a secretion of one organ of
an animal influences tissues in other parts of its body. It is eloquently
described by Thimann: "The heroine of the dime novel, who is suddenly confronted by the villain, or by the family ghost, turns as white
as a sheet, her hair stands on end, and her eyes widen with horror.
These effects result from her having received a dose of hormone
(adrenalin) which is secreted in a special gland and travels about
in the blood stream, causing the capillaries to contract all over the
skin and scalp." [8] Many similar hormones are known and have been
studied by physiologists. One such is the secretion of the pituitary
gland, a subject investigated by the late Harvey Cushing, and brought
to fruition by the labors of Herbert Evans and his associates in Cali-

fornia. The secretion of this gland determines whether animals and human beings will be giants, dwarfs, or of normal stature.

The peculiarity of hormones, according to the authoritative definition given in 1904 by Bayliss and Starling, is "that they are produced in one organ and carried by the blood stream to another organ on which their effect is manifested." [9] Furthermore, hormones are characterized by the property of serving as the chemical messengers which co-ordinate all the activity of certain organs with that of others.

Páal's experiments seemed to indicate that a similar type of substance controls the growth of plants, although it must be noted that there is no blood stream in plants. Nevertheless, the ideas are similar, for a substance produced in one part of the plant apparently affected the growth in another. These substances are now known as "phyto-hormones" (from the Greek word *phyton,* meaning plant), or growth substances, growth regulators, or growth hormones. Substances which belong to the type of growth hormone whose reaction may be measured by the curvature of seedlings are usually called "auxins," a nomenclature first suggested in 1931 from the Greek word *auxein,* denoting increase, which is also the root of such words as *aug*ment and *auc*tion.

～   ～   ～

The step following Páal's in the development of our knowledge concerning plant hormones should be obvious to all readers: If plant growth is in fact promoted by a substance produced in the tips and distributed from them to the rest of the plant, one must isolate this substance, and study its properties in detail. This important task was begun by the Dutch plant physiologist, F. W. Went, now of the California Institute of Technology, but who in 1928 was still in Holland. Went discovered that if the tips of seedlings were cut off and placed on a jelly of agar, the jelly itself then acquired the property of hastening the curvature of a shoot, when the jelly was applied to one side of it. The auxin evidently diffused from the tip into the agar, and from the agar back again into the plant. The curvatures which resulted were so regular that Went found the reaction could be used as a test for the existence and quantity of the auxin.

Went's brilliant researches indicated a means of obtaining auxin from the plant. But soon other and more plentiful sources were uncovered. During the years 1930–1934, two other Dutch scientists, F. Kögl and A. J. Haagen-Smit, found that certain cultures of bacteria and the urine of animals and human beings were rich sources of the growth-promoting auxin.

In all, the two Dutch scientists found three plant hormones: auxin A, auxin B, and indole-acetic acid. Meanwhile, cultures of fungi, another source of auxin, were being investigated; in 1935 K. V. Thimann, working with Went in California, isolated the substance produced by fungi and showed it to be identical with one of the three substances found by Kögl and Haagen-Smit.

An animal which eats a large quantity of plant material has no use for the growth substances in the plants, so it gets rid of them again in its urine. Since urine is easy to obtain in large quantities, and since it is well adapted to chemical treatment, it proved an ideal source for such material. Kögl and Haagen-Smit started with about forty gallons of urine, from which they were able to abstract several hundred milligrams of pure growth substance, an amount compared by F. S. Taylor to about one eighth of an aspirin tablet.[10] Small as this quantity may be, ten girls would have had to work ten hours a day for about twenty-five years to abstract the same quantity of growth substance from the tips of seedlings. Improvements in the method of chemical analysis of small quantities (discussed in a later chapter) made possible a chemical study of the auxins.

        ∾   ∾   ∾

A great step forward took place just as the auxins were being isolated. This was the understanding of the distribution of auxin in the whole plant. Investigation showed that auxin is formed mainly in growing buds and young leaves; the sequel to this was very important. Plants usually have a "leader" or terminal bud. If it is cut off, one of the other buds on the stem begins to grow, and takes its place, becoming the leader. In other words, this other bud was equally capable of growth all the time, but it did not grow so long as the terminal bud was present. Its growth seemed to be inhibited by the terminal bud, which produces relatively large quantities of auxin. Skoog and Thimann made the ingenious experiment of removing the leader bud, and putting in its place a supply of auxin.[11] They found that the lower buds were then inhibited to the very same extent that they had been by the terminal bud itself. Thus it was revealed that the auxin which is produced by the terminal bud has two separate and distinct functions. First, it causes the stern below it to grow, and second, it prevents the buds below it from growing. This phenomenon proved to be but the first example of what was later recognized as a general principle: that auxin elicits different responses from different parts of the plant. Normally it causes the stems to grow while the buds are inhibited, but the reverse is not necessarily true; that is, that if the buds grow, the stem does not. By using the right conditions, Skoog and Thimann found that the growth of the buds could be prevented without causing the stem to increase appreciably in length.

At the same time another problem was being investigated: the formation of roots. Most readers know that under certain conditions, isolated parts of stems, called cuttings, form roots. In general the cuttings root better if there are young buds or leaves on them. Therefore Went and Thimann thought that perhaps the formation of roots is controlled by an auxin. They undertook a series of investigations of this problem and discovered that certain preparations could be applied to cuttings which were not in condition to root, having been kept in the dark. These preparations not only caused roots to be formed, but the number of roots so formed was roughly proportionate to the concentration of the material used.[12]

Work was undertaken on the purification and isolation of the root-forming substance. Soon it was clear that the richest sources of this root-forming substance were the very same materials which had already proved to be the richest sources of auxin — namely, urine and cultures of fungi. Went and Thimann became convinced, as they obtained the root-forming substance in a more and more purified form, that it must be identical with one of the auxins. This was proved when these two workers synthesized an auxin called indole-acetic acid, and found it to be highly active in producing roots. Indole-acetic acid, synthesized by Went and Thimann, had just been isolated by Kögl and Haagen-Smit from urine.

This substance, known also as hetero-auxin, seems to be derived from protein and may be produced when tryptophane is exposed to ultraviolet light. The important feature of the discovery of indole-acetic acid is that, as organic compounds go, it is a fairly simple chemical substance and can be synthesized from well-known and easily available chemicals in the laboratory or factory, and need not be obtained from gallons of urine, or from literally bushels of plant material. Indole is a material contained in coal tar and has been used for many years in making perfumes. The crude material has, according to F. S. Taylor, "a most unpleasant odor of the lavatory, but when highly purified has a delightful and persistent odor of flowers." [13] One curious aspect of its synthesis is that it had been synthesized by two Japanese scientists (Majima and Hoshino) in 1925, some eight years or so before it was found to be a growth substance.

At first it was generally thought that the knowledge about, and availability of, growth hormones would enable us to obtain larger plants. "Had," asks F. S. Taylor, "the food of the gods really been found?" But the vision of wheat plants as large as bamboos, and cabbages beneath whose shade a regiment might shelter, proved illusory. "Experiments showed that growth substances did not make the plants larger, but directed the point at which growth was to take place. The capital of the plant is made by the labor of leaf and root, the growth substances are the board of directors who give orders that the capital shall be expended in building an addition to the factory at some particular point." [14]

Normally, a root cannot grow of itself, independent of the food provided it by the part of the plant above ground. But how independent are the parts of the plant above and below the ground? For example, can we cause roots to grow all by themselves in a medium containing water, salts, and sugar? Although early experiments showed that this was not possible, William J. Robbins reported in 1922 that isolated root growths might be obtained in some cases if one added yeast extract to the nutrient solution. Many years later, Dr. Robbins and another independent investigator discovered that vitamin B_1 was the most important constituent of the yeast extract. [15] It is now possible to grow flax roots indefinitely in a medium that contains salts, sugar, and vitamin B_1. Pea roots, however, require nicotinic acid as well as vitamin B_1, while tomato roots do not need nicotinic acid, but do need vitamin B_6. Thus, vitamin B_1 is a general root-forming hormone in plants and is supplied to the root from the leaves, which produce it in the presence of sunlight. As

Went tells us,[16] growth hormones in plants may be vitamins for animals. "This means that the animal organism has completely lost the ability to form these substances and therefore has to derive them from its food. In plants this process has not progressed so far, and certain cells (in the leaves) are still able to produce them. This shows how closely vitamins and hormones are connected and it also indicates the essential unity between plants and animals." Plants produce vitamins, not in order to supply them to animals, but rather because they are "essential factors in their own lives."

～　　　～　　　～

The investigations begun by Went, and carried out by Went and Thimann, on the root-forming hormone indicated that one possible use of the growth substances would be to promote the rooting of cuttings. If a little indole-acetic acid and a given quantity of lanolin are made into an ointment and rubbed anywhere on the stem of a tomato plant, within a few weeks a bristling array of roots grows out from the stem at that point. Almost any kind of plant can be made to put forth roots in abnormal positions by the application of the growth hormones.

Rooting from cuttings is of great importance in horticulture. The important flowers are not races or species, but rather hybrids, or single individuals, with particularly desirable characteristics. Flowers such as chrysanthemums are hybrids; new plants obtained from seeds will not, in general, be identical to the parent chrysanthemums. The result of sowing a seed from such hybrids would be a miscellaneous batch of flowers, somewhat similar to the original perhaps, but far from being identical to it. On the other hand, if a small part of the stem (that is, a cutting) is taken and made to grow roots, the plant which results will be an exact replica of the "parent." Thus, most of the fine varieties of plants cannot be raised from seed, but *only* from cuttings.

Furthermore, many species of trees and shrubs, which, unlike the hybrid flowers, could be raised from seed, are raised from cuttings instead; because in this way a more rapid growth is obtained, with a saving of anywhere from two to four years. Hence, since most of the stock of the fancy gardener and nurseryman is raised from cuttings, he must make sure that the cuttings which he obtains will actually take root and grow. In the past, when the art of rooting cuttings was still enshrouded in mystery, a person skilled in this profession could command an enormous salary, since the success or failure of a nursery might depend upon his skill. His knowledge was based on "experience" and on certain tricks which he had acquired from his father, or perhaps from other gardeners. Today the ready availability of commercial solutions of auxin enables anyone with a reasonable amount of skill to use a prepared solution of plant hormone, which will almost guarantee that cuttings soaked in it will take immediate root.

Curiously enough, gardeners do not purchase pure hormone in bulk to make up their own solutions, but prefer to buy ready-made solutions. The reason is that the concentration of the hormone is extremely important. If the solution is too weak, it has little or no effect. If it is too strong, it will actually retard growth, causing the base of the plant to spread and the top to be retarded, so that even if the plant survives the strong solution, it will be stunted. (If the gardener thinks a double dose will be twice as efficacious, he is sadly mistaken.) The concentration is very small, being about one part of growth hormone to ten or twenty thousand parts of water — no more than a teaspoonful of salt would be to five gallons of water!

It must not be thought, however, that the taking and planting of cuttings has now become an entirely mechanical job. To take cuttings from some herbaceous plants, such as delphinium, is still very difficult, whereas others, such as dahlias or chrysanthemums, may be rooted as easily as seeds may be planted.

While the use of auxin will generally cause the rapid appearance of a bristling array of roots wherever it is applied, there is one major exception. In some plants, including notably pine, spruce, oak, and apple trees, one finds what is known as the "age effect." Cuttings taken from such varieties as the northern red oak or bright pine will root with the application of auxin if they are taken from a tree three years old or less. But if the cutting is taken from a tree that is much older, say twenty years old, it will not root at all, no matter how much auxin is applied. Why this should be so, nobody yet has any clear idea. Here is a problem for the future.[17]

The transformation of the gardener's art which we have just described was the first practical application of the new knowledge. Another, now receiving wide use in horticulture, depends on a fact we have referred to earlier, namely, that auxins may inhibit, as well as promote, growth. In apples and many other fruits, the long shoots are purely vegetative, while the flowers are born on short shoots or spurs.[18] Mature leaves or fruits fall from the main part of the plant itself, because of the development of a special layer of cells at the base of the leaf or fruit stalk. The walls of the cells forming this special layer fall apart readily, so that the whole stalk is severed.

The formation of this special layer is inhibited so long as the leaves or fruit actively produce auxin. An external application of auxin to the fruit stalk or petiole prevents the falling of the fruit, just as does the presence of the auxin normally produced in the plant itself. Many acres of apple trees are now annually sprayed with auxin during the early fall, in order to keep the apples on the trees a few weeks longer, enabling them to reach fullest maturity, and reducing the losses which orchardists used to suffer because of windfall and pre-harvest drop.

Another interesting and useful application of the auxins stems from the research made many years ago in Germany by Fitting (whose work we have discussed earlier), in which he discovered that when certain varieties of orchids are fertilized by the application of pollen to the stigma, the petals soon fall off and the ovary begins to swell. Further experimentation by Fitting showed that the pollen itself is not needed to produce this effect, but that an extract from the pollen will produce the same effect. The swelling of the ovary is not due to the fertilization of the ovules, but results from some substance in the pollen grains. This substance is also an auxin, which is present in the pollen in very considerable amounts.

The phenomenon is a general one. By simply applying auxin to the ovary or stigma without pollen, that organ can be made to swell up into a fruit which has not been fertilized and which therefore does not contain seeds. Seedless tomatoes, seedless squash, seedless peppers, and even seedless watermelons have been produced in this way by Dr. Gustafson and his co-workers in the University of Michigan. This interesting application of auxin to produce seedless fruit

and vegetables has not as yet received the very wide use in horticulture which is certain to come about in the future.

But the most dramatic use of auxin is that one which eventually
will straighten the back of the man with the hoe, by killing the weeds
against whose encroachment he eternally struggles.

Theologians have always held that man would not return to the
Garden of Eden until he had achieved the state of grace befitting
God's paradise. But today the chemist holds forth the prospect of a
return to a possible state of Eden — at the same time that the physicist, his brother scientist, has uncovered the formulas by which the
earth itself may perhaps be totally destroyed by an atomic blast, an
event that would necessitate a new Creation and a new Eden if life
were to continue. So it is that Science sharpens the inner meaning of
the ancient prophecies.

It is recorded in the majestic cadences of the English Old Testa-
ment how, after the fall of man, God said, "Cursed is the ground
for thy sake: in sorrow shalt thou eat of it all the days of thy life."
The descendents of Adam, laboring in the fields, were to be plagued
by insects and weeds. "Thorns also and thistles shall it bring forth
to thee."

During the last few years two developments achieved by the chemist give promise to lift, in some measure, the curse put upon Adam.
DDT provides an effective means of combating insects, while an
auxin with a somewhat similar name, *2,4-D,* will eliminate many of
the weeds, including the thistles.

This new weed-killing chemical, applied in a spray, or dust, or
aerosol, and in such a small quantity that it may be measured in *parts
per million* rather than in pounds or gallons, will kill most of the
broad-leaved annuals in fields, a category that includes almost all
important or common noxious weeds. Yet at the same time 2,4-D
produces no deleterious effect on the most valuable of all plants to
man — the principal fodder for his animals, and his own most important food plants — the grasses, grains, and cereals: including
corn, wheat, rice, barley, millet, and many others, as well as sugar
cane.

2,4-D has proved successful in destroying such common weeds as lamb's quarters and pigweed. Fields of young oats and wheat containing a variety of weeds, such as mustard and wild radish, have been treated with 2,4-D and the weeds successfully eliminated without adversely affecting the wheat or oats. Rice fields have been weeded by an application of 2,4-D in a dust disseminated from an airplane. Of particular interest to home owners is the ease with which an application of 2,4-D frees grass lawns of dandelions and narrow-leaf plantains, without injury to the grass. 2,4-D will also destroy poison ivy plants.

2,4-D is effective against noxious weeds — that is, weeds that are so efficient as competitors of useful crops that they have thus far thwarted the efforts of man to control them by any other means. These include, among many others, wild thistle, knapweed, English plantain, wild oats, quack grass, and so on.

In one of the first tests, a dilution of only several hundred parts of 2,4-D per million killed perennial bindweed on nursery fruit trees: a notable achievement, as it was pointed out in a report in *Science,* because bindweed "is considered the number one enemy of crops (herbaceous and woody)."[19]

As test after test indicated the effectiveness and the cheapness of this easily applied weed killer, new areas in which control was needed were investigated. Power companies and railroads learned that 2,4-D would help them eliminate climbers and woody plants from their rights of way. Sewage engineers discovered that 2,4-D would, for one year at any rate, clear the sewers and streams of the southern part of the United States, which are annually clogged with water hyacinth. It was found that common sources of pollen allergy (hay fever), notably ragweed, could be easily eradicated from parks, vacant lots, and back yards, by spraying with 2,4-D; while, at the same time, the vicious marihuana plant would also be destroyed. In the summer of 1946 the Health Commissioner of New York City embarked on a large-scale program to rid New York of irritating and dangerous weeds by spraying 2,4-D, using the regular equipment on the trucks used for other purposes by the Department of Sanitation. The success of that campaign convinced the Commissioner of the advisability of repeating it in 1947, and of enlisting the co-operation of neighboring cities and towns.

So remarkable were the first tests of the new weed killer that a large number of public and private agencies in America and in England undertook extensive experiments. Within a single year, interest on the part of commercial companies had been aroused to such an extent that large-scale manufacture of 2,4–D was undertaken and the price per pound dropped from $125 to $3. The fact that this reduction in price was possible reflects not only the increase in demand, but also the more important fact that 2,4–D is relatively easy to manufacture, as compared to many organic chemical compounds.[20] Last summer the average cost of the new weed killer was well under $5 an acre, and more than thirty different preparations containing 2,4–D were on the market. This summer, an even greater number of preparations are available to the farmer, gardener, and home owner.

Barely out of the first stages of experimentation, 2,4–D seems to offer almost everything we ask of a weed killer. It is cheap. It is not difficult to use. It is noncorrosive, nonexplosive, and generally non-irritating to the skin. 2,4–D may be handled without undue precautions, stored without danger, and disseminated from existing equipment. In the minute quantities necessary to kill weeds, it apparently produces no harmful effects on fish, animals, or human beings, who eat it. Fish have continued to live unharmed in water treated with 2,4–D for the elimination of water hyacinth. Cows have grazed in pastures sprayed with 2,4–D without showing any ill effects. Applied in small amounts — in a quantity, remember, measured in parts per million — no traces of 2,4–D have been found in the milk of such cows, although a very small quantity has been detected in the blood-stream. However, if animals imbibe an enormous quantity of 2,4–D, a marked physiological disorder will ensue, with symptoms very like certain well-known muscle diseases.[21]

        ᕫᕫ   ᕫᕫ   ᕫᕫ

The full name of 2,4–D is "2,4-Dichlorophenoxy-acetic acid." Its discovery was made known a few years ago when it was included in a list of chemicals having "growth-regulative properties," in a patent assigned by Lontz to E. I. du Pont de Nemours and Company.[22] In other words, 2,4–D is an auxin, but, strange to relate, it is never found in nature.

The latest aspect of the subject of auxins has been the production in the laboratory of chemical substances which affect growth in much the same way as the three naturally occurring auxins: auxin A, auxin B, and indole-acetic acid. The best current practice reserves the expression "plant hormone" for these three auxins found in growing plants, and uses the more general word "auxin" to denote the whole class of substances that affect plant growth — irrespective of whether they are produced by nature in the plants, or by the chemist in his laboratory.

It had long been known that whereas small doses of auxin would promote growth, larger doses were toxic and killed the plant. Some of the auxins affected some types of plants more than others, thus giving the key to possible weed-killing. "Naphthalene-acetic acid" was first used in England with good results, but proved to be too expensive for any large-scale application. "2,4,5-T" also has been used. But no substance has yet been found to compete with 2,4-D, which, in addition to its many other superiorities, is stable against soil bacteria.

Knowing that 2,4-D is an auxin, many people have had the mistaken idea that it acts by producing such rapid growth that the plants, so to speak, "grow to death." We have not yet discovered all the secrets of growth, in either plants or animals. No one knows exactly by what mechanism the auxins affect growth in just the way they do, any more than anyone fully understands why certain cells in cancer grow suddenly and at an unprecedented rate. We do know, however, that when a seedling is killed by 2,4-D, this action may occur in so short a time that very little growth takes place at all.

It is still a mystery why 2,4-D should produce a toxic effect on some plants and not on others. The plants it destroys, the common weeds, are broad-leaved annuals; they are also of the class known as dicotyledons, whereas those it leaves unaffected are monocotyledons. 2,4-D is not the only synthetic auxin having herbicidal properties; its cheapness, effectiveness, and stability against soil bacteria are the factors that have caused it to be adopted, rather than other known weed killers.

Considering the large number of research workers in this field, we shall probably know soon just why an auxin such as 2,4-D acts in the selective way it does. When that time comes, we may be in a position to manufacture in the laboratories weed-killing auxins of an even greater selectivity, by applying the newly discovered knowledge to this problem. The important point is that 2,4–D is not only a new and better chemical for weed killing; it represents a whole new approach to the problem — that of using auxins to control weed growth.*

This account by no means exhausts the present applications of auxins. Some others are: to stiffen the stalks of plants that would otherwise bend over owing to a heavy load of seeds, or the action of rain and wind; and to prevent bud formation in stored plants.

The development of the auxins exhibits a pattern common to many advances in the fields of both plant and animal physiology. First, a naturally occurring substance is isolated. Then, the chemist produces one or more of these substances synthetically in the laboratory. Finally, the chemist synthesizes new compounds, never found in nature at all, but which act in much the same way as the naturally occurring ones; they may be easier to manufacture or to use, cheaper, or more effective for certain purposes.

The first scientists investigating this field certainly had no idea that the results of their research would yield so soon a practical result of great importance in agriculture. Part of the original work, as we have seen, was concerned with photo-tropism, or the effect upon plant movement of the action of light. Initiated by Charles Darwin and his son, such research was extended primarily because plant scientists were curious as to the cause of this strange phenomenon, whereby so little light, as that from a match burning for only two or three minutes, could cause such a marked effect on plant growth. As it turned out, the work of later investigators showed conclusively that the light itself did not produce this effect, but simply caused a non-symmetrical distribution of a growth substance in the plant. That this substance and others like it might eventually be used for the practical ends we have described was an astonishing result, even to those plant physiologists who had investigated the plant hormones, isolated them, and gradually uncovered their properties. After all,

---

* The relation of the weed-killing properties of 2,4–D to its auxin properties is as yet unknown. Some weed killers, such as "bromo-nitro-benzoic acid," have no auxin properties at all. It has been suggested that "weed stopper" is a better name than "weed killer." [23]

the only obvious end product of such research was to find the answer to the nursery rhyme, appropriately placed at the beginning of the standard treatise on *Phytohormones* by Went and Thimann:

> *Oats, peas, beans, and barley grow,*
> *Oats, peas, beans, and barley grow,*
> *Can you, or I, or anyone know*
> *How oats, peas, beans, and barley grow?*

Had anyone in the early 'twenties gone to the laboratory of Boysen-Jensen, Páal, Kögl and Haagen-Smit, or Went and Thimann, to enlist their aid in the practical problem of finding weed killers, and had these same plant physiologists agreed to devote their energies to this problem, the fundamental research in which they were engaged would have been stopped; they would have pursued the more conventional methods of approach to the problem, such as the use of poisonous chemicals, oils, mechanical devices, or flame throwers. Only because these investigators were *not* interested in the practical problem of killing weeds, and because they *were* interested in investigating a series of plant phenomena, with the aim of increasing knowledge and adding to the scope of fundamental research, did mankind gain the simple solution to the problem of killing weeds, as well as all the other benefits accruing from the application of the auxins.

CHAPTER 7

The Electric Current and Radio

> If there is no other use discovered of electricity, this, however, is something considerable, that it may *help to make a vain man humble.*
> — BENJAMIN FRANKLIN (1747)

UNTIL ABOUT a hundred years ago, power could not be transmitted more than a few feet from the point at which it was developed. The use of electric power, by contrast, enables the source to be hundreds, and even thousands, of miles from the point at which the power is applied.

The steam engine operates by converting the potential heat energy of coal or wood into mechanical energy,* or the energy of motion; harnessing the forces of expansion and contraction as water vaporizes into steam and steam condenses into water. A plant or factory run by steam must have transported to it the coal which is the source of power. A plant run by electricity, on the other hand, has transported to it not the source of power, but the actual power itself. The source, whether a hydroelectric system located at a dam, or a dynamo or generator operated by steam, may be, and usually is, situated far from the plant where the power is delivered and used. As those eminent historians of technology, Hugh and Margaret Vowles, tell us, "The coming of steam was revolutionary enough, changing the whole face of industry and creating an altogether unprecedented type of civilization. But without electricity, steam power was like a friendly giant tethered to a stake." [1]

The conversion of energy from one form to another is a fairly common phenomenon in our industrial civilization. We use the mechanical energy developed by a steam engine to run a generator, send the electrical energy along wires to the point where it is needed,

---

* By "energy," the engineer or scientist means simply a measure of the ability to perform work.

and there use it to run a motor — that is, convert it back again into mechanical energy.

The technical age in which we live, drawing heavily on the resources of electrical power, owes a great debt to the electric generator and motor. But, although the generator run by steam or water power provides an economical means of producing electrical energy as compared to the chemical action in a battery, we must be able to transmit that energy cheaply and efficiently.

When we send electrical energy from one place to another, a certain amount of it is always used up "in heating the wires." In any electrical circuit, the energy used in this way in a given amount of time depends on the square of the current, rather than on the voltage at which the current is supplied. Thus, if we send 10 amperes of current over a certain system for a period of 20 minutes, the energy used up in the transmission is 100 (that is, 10 $\times$ 10) times as much as if we sent only 1 ampere of current. But, the reader may ask, can we get as much work done with 1 ampere as we can with 10? The answer depends on the voltage at which the current is supplied. The electric energy available to do work (unlike the energy losses in transmission, which we saw depend on the square of the current) is a function of the voltage *multiplied* by the current. For example, an appliance that is rated at 100 watts requires 1 ampere of current supplied at 100 volts, or 2 amperes of current at 50 volts, or 20 amperes of current at 5 volts, or ½ ampere at 200 volts, or even 1/100 ampere at 10,000 volts. In our homes and business establishments in most of the United States, we use a maximum voltage of 110 or 115 volts because it is dangerous to use the higher voltages, which also aggravate the problem of proper insulation. But we need not adhere to such a limit when transmitting the electrical energy from the power station to our homes.

Suppose we wish to provide electrical energy to a small residential village, consisting of 100 homes. If, during the evening, each home owner uses 10 amperes of current, then the village must be supplied with 1000 amperes at 110 volts. During each second, the village uses up 1000 $\times$ 110 units of electrical energy, 110,000 units per second, called "watts," that is, the village consumes energy at the rate of 110,000 watts. But we can send that same amount of energy to the village at a voltage of 110,000 volts and a current of only 1 ampere;

and then the losses in getting the energy from the power station to the village would be reduced, not by a factor of 1000, but, as we have just seen, by 1000 × 1000 or 1,000,000!

The efficient way to use electrical power generated at a source some distance from the place where it is to be used is to have a device for transforming energy delivered at low current and high voltage to energy available at a relatively higher current and lower voltage. Such a device is aptly named a "transformer." By its use, we can take advantage of inexpensive sources of power to run our generators, such as natural waterfalls (Niagara Falls) or man-made dams (TVA), even though they are located at a great distance from our cities, where most of the electrical energy is to be used.

Anyone who travels in the country has seen the high-voltage or "high-tension" lines — 3 or 6 copper cables of about ¾ of an inch in diameter, suspended about 75 feet above the ground on giant steel pylons, transmitting electrical energy, sometimes at as high as 220,000 volts. From the hydroelectric power plants at Niagara, electrical energy is sent to the great industrial cities of Rochester and Syracuse at 60,000 volts. Outside the city limits, the transformers in the substations reduce the voltage to about 2000 volts and the electrical energy is then distributed throughout the city to factories, homes, and the city lighting and traction systems. Before entering the buildings, additional transformers step the voltage down still further to 110 or 220 volts.

Since a transformer works only on alternating current (A.C.) and not direct (D.C.), we may understand why it is that whenever we send electrical energy over long distances, we use A.C. and never D.C.

      ∽   ∽   ∽

The realization of our modern electrified world depended, to an extraordinary degree, upon the discoveries of Michael Faraday. His brilliant researches uncovered the principles of the generator and the electric motor, making it possible to produce electrical energy by inexpensive mechanical action rather than by expensive chemical action, and at the same time making it possible to use the electrical energy to do mechanical work, such as propelling an elevator or trolley car, running a lathe, and so on. But Faraday's experiments not only showed how to generate and use electrical energy, they also uncovered the principle of the transformer, which has enabled us to send A.C. efficiently over long distances.

Before delineating Faraday's career, let me reassert that I have no interest whatever in pitting in contest, one against the other, the genius of the scientist, like Faraday, who makes fundamental discoveries, and that of the inventor or engineer who, like Edison, works out ways in which such discoveries may be used. Yet it must be pointed out that a fundamental discovery in science may be mother to a multitude of different inventions. The principles discovered by Faraday have been used in a thousand different ways and form the basic knowledge on which hundreds of thousands of patents have been issued. Nevertheless, Faraday's work, like that of other contributors to electrical knowledge — Maxwell, Hertz, Volta, Galvani, and Franklin — while vastly productive of innovations which have greatly affected our daily lives, was carried out simply in the desire to increase fundamental knowledge.

Let us set the stage upon which Faraday played his part. At the end of the eighteenth century, electrical knowledge consisted largely of what we denote as "static electricity" or "electrostatics," the subject of electricity at rest, as on charged bodies, and in motion only in large sudden discharges as in the case of a stroke of lightning or the rapid discharge of a "Leyden jar" or condenser. This is the part of electricity with which, as we saw in Chapter 5, Franklin's name will always be connected.

Soon after Franklin had finished his work, Galvani, the Italian doctor and anatomist, made the chance observation which his compatriot Volta extended so as to complete the "discovery" of the electric current. Volta's research showed how to make an electric battery and provided experimenters with a means of obtaining a continuous or steady electric current. Sir Humphry Davy used it to isolate in a pure state, for the first time, such chemical elements as sodium and potassium.

Many scientists wondered whether there were some relation between the forces of electrical and magnetic action; whether, for example, by the use of an electric current it might be possible to produce magnetic effects. The way in which an electric current affects a magnet was discovered in 1819 or 1820, as the result of a

"happy accident," just as Galvani's original observation of the frog
was made by chance.

Like many other experimenters, Hans Christian Oersted had tried
to produce an effect upon a magnetic compass needle by placing a
wire carrying an electric current at right angles to it, but to no avail.
One day at the end of a lecture on electricity, "as he had used a
strong Galvanic battery for other experiments he said, 'Let us now
once, if the battery is in activity, try to place the wire parallel with
the needle.' As this was made he was struck with perplexity by seeing the needle make a great oscillation, almost at right angles with
the magnetic meridian. Then he said 'Let us now invert the direction of the current.' "

The above description, in its original quaintness, comes from a
letter written to Michael Faraday by Professor Chr. Hansteen, who
frequently assisted Oersted in his experiments. He continues: "Thus
the great detection was made, and it has been said, not without
reason, that 'he tumbled over it by accident.' He had not before any
more idea than any other person that the force should be transversal.
But as La Grange has said of Newton in similar occasion, 'Such accidents only meet persons who deserve them.' " [2] This great discovery
of Oersted's probably has the unique distinction of being the only
important scientific discovery ever made before students in the lecture room.

Oersted's experience demonstrates why an apparently simple phenomenon may not be observed for a long time. Most of the experimenters had supposed that the current in a wire would act on
a magnetic needle in such a way as to make the needle turn until
it was parallel to the wire. This was a logical enough conclusion,
because if you placed a magnet that was in the shape of a long bar
over a magnetic needle, the latter would orient itself parallel to
the bar. Following the analogy, and thinking that a wire carrying a
current might behave like a long wire-shaped magnet, the experimenters had placed their wire at right angles to the needle, expect-
ing to see the magnetic needle swing about. Oersted, happily, not
only placed his wire parallel to the needle to begin with, but also
had a sufficiently powerful battery to deliver the extremely large
electric current necessary to show that an electric current can affect a
magnetic needle.

Once magnetism had been produced from electricity, or rather a magnetic effect had been produced by an electric current, the next problem was to discover whether or not an electric current could be produced from magnets. This step was taken by Michael Faraday.

ↄ∾   ↄ∾   ↄ∾

Faraday's biography reads like a Horatio Alger story and might well be entitled "From Newsboy and Bookbinder's Apprentice to the Greatest Scientist of His Time." Completely self-educated, he rose by dint of his innate ability, perseverance, and integrity, to become the director of the Royal Institution in London, where his experiments over a considerable period of years set the seal to his eternal fame.

One of the interesting aspects of greatness in science is that the truly heroic figures are celebrated for many discoveries, never just one. Isaac Newton's greatness would survive had he made but one of the four important contributions with which his name is associated: the calculus, the law of universal gravitation, the laws of motion, and the nature of white and colored light. Likewise Albert Einstein's name would be great in the annals of twentieth-century science even if he had never expounded the general theory of relativity and had only discovered the equations of the Brownian movement, the Einstein-De Haas effect, the corpuscular theory of light in the explanation of the photoelectric effect, or the equations governing the relations between mass and energy which resulted from the restricted theory of relativity.

The case is the same with Michael Faraday. Had he done nothing except in the field of chemistry, where he discovered the fundamental laws of electrolysis, the liquefaction of gases, and isolated benzene for the first time, he would still be remembered as one of the great men of the nineteenth century, if not of all time. His motto in scientific inquiry was, "Let the imagination go, guarding it by judgment and principle, but holding it in and directing it by *experiment*." [3] Thus he wrote, "Nature is our kind friend and best critic in experimental science if we only allow her intimations to fall unbiased on our minds. Nothing is so good as an experiment which, while it sets an error right, gives as a reward for our humility an absolute advance in knowledge." [4]

Faraday's electrical researches were motivated by a conviction "that the various forms under which the forces of nature are made manifest have one common origin, or in other words are so directly related and mutually dependent that they are convertible, as it were, one into the other, and possess equivalence of power in their action." [5] He sought relationships between electricity, magnetism, heat, light, and gravitation. The phenomenon whereby the plane of polarization of light in a crystal of heavy lead glass is related to a magnetic field, in honor of its finder, is called the "Faraday effect." The principle of induced currents will likewise always be associated with his name although some independent observations of the same effect were made contemporaneously by Joseph Henry in the United States. These discoveries form the bedrock on which contemporary science, technology, and civilization are reared.

Stripped to its barest essentials, Faraday's great experiment may be reduced to the following terms. Faraday wound two separate coils of wire around an iron ring. One he attached to a battery through a switch, and the other to a sensitive galvanometer, an instrument which records the flow of small currents. When he closed or opened the switch, he noticed that the current flowed through the secondary coil (the one attached to the galvanometer) — but only at the instant of closing or opening the switch in the circuit of the primary coil (the one attached to the battery). Thus in one experiment Faraday discovered the principle of induced currents and the instrument we call today the "transformer." He was quick to recognize that the reason why current flowed only at the instant of opening and closing the switch in the primary coil circuit was the fact that, as the current built up or decayed, the magnetic field threading through the secondary coil was in a state of flux or change. To prove this point, he took a coil connected to a galvanometer and inserted into it an ordinary bar magnet, which he then withdrew. He found, as he had expected he would, that while the magnet was in motion a current flowed, but if the magnet were held still, the flow of current would stop. Furthermore, he was able to show that moving the coil instead of the magnet produced the same effect.

In another experiment, Faraday placed a metal disk between the

poles of a horseshoe motor. Two wires were pressed against the disk
— one at the center, where the disk was mounted on an axle, and the
other at the outermost edge — and the wires were connected to a
galvanometer. As the disk turned, a small current was generated.

Faraday's experiments uncovered the principles of induced currents, and also the theoretical basis of the generator and the transformer — that is, the basic knowledge which made possible the
production of electrical energy and the satisfactory transmission of
A.C. Every generator that has ever been built makes use of Faraday's
"induced" currents and is, in some form or other, merely an adaptation of the fact that an electric current is induced in a wire whenever
it is waved in front of a magnet (whether a steel magnet or an
electromagnet) or a magnet is waved in front of a wire. An electric
motor, furthermore, is simply a generator run in reverse. In an
ordinary generator * we apply mechanical energy — steam or water
power — to make the motor turn, thereby releasing electrical energy.
But if we apply electrical energy to the same instrument, we can
thereby cause the motor to turn and harness that motion in the form
of mechanical energy; in other words, our generator is now an
electric motor.

Faraday made his great and wonderful discoveries because of his
quasi-religious conviction that the forces of nature, such as electricity and magnetism, must be convertible one into the other.[6] His
belief in the essential unity of apparently diverse natural phenomena
was vindicated by other discoveries of his. For example the successful
liquefaction of chlorine, which is a gas at ordinary temperatures and
pressures, showed that the distinction between common liquids and
gases was not one of kind, but merely of environmental conditions.
And he opened up a whole new field of scientific research by showing that magnetism is not an isolated phenomenon confined to iron,
and perhaps also cobalt and nickel, but that magnetic effects of various sorts could be demonstrated in all solids (and even in gases!), in
a smaller degree.

∽   ∽   ∽

While Faraday took but little interest in applying his discoveries,
he was willing to sponsor the work of others, in particular those

* Certain types of A.C. motors and generators are exceptions — for example, the
3-phase synchronous motor.

who wished to apply the new discoveries not for commercial use, but for the so-called "magneto-electric light" to be used in lighthouses.

Faraday himself wrote in 1831, "I have rather been desirous of discovering new facts and new relations dependent on magnetic electrical induction than of exalting the force of those already obtained." If his own interest was primarily to advance the outermost fringes of knowledge rather than to put his own discoveries to use, he nevertheless declared that he was assured that practical applications "would find their full development hereafter." [7]

We know that Faraday did not spurn the world of practical affairs. One would hardly expect that he would, he who had begun life as a manual laborer in a bookbinding establishment. He was, for example, primarily responsible for the adoption of gutta-percha, so-called India rubber, as an insulator for conducting wires in preference to the commonly used cloth windings.[8] He also served on many practical commissions, such as those to investigate the cause of mine explosions and the ways of improving the manufacture of optical glass.

Faraday was once consulted by Cyrus Field in connection with the proposed Atlantic cable. Faraday told the American entrepreneur that he doubted the possibility of getting a message all the way across the Atlantic. Intensely disturbed by his doubt and knowing that the principle of the telegraph was closely associated with Faraday's own work, Field pressed him to investigate the problem thoroughly, offering to pay him any fee he desired. Faraday declined remuneration but worked on the problem and finally replied, "It can be done, but you will not get an instantaneous message." Field, somewhat but not entirely encouraged, inquired, "How long will it take?" "Oh, perhaps a second." "Well," replied Field, "that's quick enough for me," and proceeded with his heroic project.[9]

Although Faraday had discovered the principles by the 1830's, not until the 1870's did the cumulative efforts of a vast number of inventors, of which the most notable innovation was that of the Belgian Gramme, produce a truly successful dynamo and motor and make the use of electricity commercially feasible.[10]

What a long step it was from the principles to the practice! The world can hardly be said to have become electrified until the beginning of the twentieth century. The electrification of Russia did not begin until after the Bolshevik revolution. And today, despite our vaunted progress, most of Asia and great areas of continental Europe as well as our own United States do not yet have electric power available for either commercial or household use.

Considering how many years of first-class thinking were necessary before the development of the modern electric motor, dynamo, and generator, one may well wonder whether even the genius of Faraday would have been sufficiently great to have allowed him to solve the problem had he turned his mind to it. The development of practical electricity, especially the use of alternating currents, demanded not simply the devising of new gadgets, but the discovery of new physical laws and effects; also the introduction, into practical electrical science and practice, of mathematics so complicated that a man of the time of Faraday, with Faraday's background and training, if present at a power engineering conference of today would understand as little of the talk as a man from Mars.

Yet the record is clear that the discovery of the electric current, with its many practical aspects in our society, derived entirely from the work of scientists like Faraday, who, like those who investigated the reaction of plants to light, had no other aim in view than the increase of knowledge. In the same way the discovery of x-rays by Roentgen derived from an interest in a new effect which seemed so strange that his natural curiosity was sufficiently aroused. It is highly to be doubted whether x-ray analysis could ever have been discovered by any group of men, however well-trained and however brilliant their genius might have been, who decided at the turn of the century to seek a method for examining the interior organs and structure of the human body, or for testing metal castings.

∾   ∾   ∾

A most startling example of a practical development arising from fundamental research in a wholly unexpected way is afforded by the development of the electromagnetic theory by Clerk-Maxwell, who extended Faraday's ideas about the way in which electrical "action" occurs.

One body may affect another in two different ways. One is by contact, as in the case of a stick pushing a box which it touches or a horse pulling a wagon with which it is connected by traces. The other is called "action at a distance," in which one body draws another to it or pushes it away, even though separated from it and with no apparent physical contact. An example of the latter may be found in the universal gravitation discovered by Isaac Newton, according to which every body in the universe attracts to itself every other body in the universe, whether it be an apple attracted by the earth or the earth attracted by the sun.

In the seventeenth century many scientists found the idea of "action at a distance" repugnant because it smacked of an occultism or mystery, very much like astrological influences which planets and other heavenly bodies supposedly exerted upon the lives of human beings. So abhorrent did this idea seem to Galileo that he rejected completely the possibility of the moon's influencing the tides, even though there seemed to be a close correlation between tidal phenomena and the position of the moon. Newton himself, considering the whole problem in a famous series of letters to Bentley, came to the conclusion that the "action at a distance" of one heavenly body upon another must arise somehow from an alteration of, or strain in, the medium which separates two bodies gravitationally attracting each other. Faraday believed that electrical attraction and repulsion could be explained in the same way.

In order to explain this abstraction let us consider a simple example. If we run a comb through our hair on a dry wintry day the comb will become electrically charged, usually negatively. This charged comb then has the property of attracting to itself small bits of paper, dust, hair, or straw. If we take two such charged combs and suspend them by silk threads close to each other, they will repel each other with considerable force. We say that each of these two charged bodies "acts" on the other. But this does not explain how the action is produced.

We know also that such a charged comb will attract to itself a piece of glass which has been rubbed with silk. We explain this phenomenon by saying, following the terminology introduced by Franklin, that the comb is charged negatively and the glass positively, and that two positively charged bodies will repel each other, as will two negatively charged bodies; but a positively and negatively charged pair of bodies will always attract each other. By experiment Coulomb determined a quantitative law, by means of which we can compute the value of the force which two charged bodies will exert on each other. But, exact as this knowledge is, it does not explain *how* one charged body affects another at a considerable distance. We likewise can compute the force with which one magnet will attract another, but this law of attraction likewise does not explain *how* the action takes place. The two are certainly related, because the experiments of Oersted and Faraday showed how electricity can give rise to magnetic effects and magnetism to electrical ones. And the work of the great French scientist, Ampère, whose name is celebrated in the unit of current, showed how even the natural magnetism of a lodestone could be reduced to electrical terms.

Faraday conceived that bodies affecting each other electrically or magnetically were separated by an elastic medium; and that there were "lines of force," very much like stretched rubber bands, which originated in north poles of magnets or positive charges and ended respectively in south poles of magnets or negative charges. Extending through space, these lines of force, being under tension like a stretched rubber band, drew the bodies together; but, since these lines of force were mutually repellent, they pushed bodies apart in cases of repulsion.

These lines of force came to be understood as strains in the "ether," an all-pervading medium whose chief property was to transmit waves or vibrations or light. Almost all nineteenth-century physicists believed in such a medium, but many did not accept Faraday's ideas because they doubted whether the medium necessary to the transmission of light waves could also adequately account for electrical and magnetic action.[11]

Maxwell was a great admirer of Michael Faraday, and was firmly convinced that Faraday's genius had provided new and lofty standpoints from which to consider electrical and, therefore, magnetic phenomena. He asked himself what properties a medium such as the ether would have to have to account for the transmission of electromagnetic effects. He discovered, amongst other things, that such a medium would transmit a variety of electromagnetic waves with a velocity exactly equal to that of light. His careful measurements showed that a system of electrical units based on electricity at rest (electrostatic) was related to a system based on electricity in motion (as in a current, electromagnetic) by exactly the factor of the speed of light. Maxwell built an imposing mathematical structure based on these observations and pointed out that any medium which could truly explain electrical action could also explain the transmission of light. Thus, his famous electromagnetic theory provided a unity between theories of electricity (including magnetism) and theories of optics. One interesting conclusion to which his theory led was the statement that electromagnetic effects are transmitted with a finite velocity.

Everyone knows that the position of a delicately suspended needle in a compass is affected by a magnet placed near it. If the magnet is shifted, the needle will turn to one side or the other. So far as our senses can judge, the action happens instantaneously; the needle turns at the very instant that the magnet is displaced. But Maxwell said, "No! Not at the same instant, but only after a certain definite interval of time." If this seems to contradict the experience of our senses, he explained that if the distance between the magnet and the compass needle were one foot, the time of transmission of the effect would be only one billionth part of a second.[12]

But if Maxwell's theory were true, then certainly we should expect to obtain an experimental verification of the time of transmission. Such an experiment was not made in England. The reason for that may well be, as suggested by Sir Arthur Schuster, that Maxwell was surrounded by a number of young physicists who so firmly believed in his electromagnetic theory that it did not seem necessary to furnish an experimental proof of their master's theoretical deductions.[13] But on the Continent, others had a different mind. The great Helmholtz, pioneer in many different branches of science, suggested to one of his most brilliant pupils, Heinrich Hertz, that he take up the experimental investigation of the problem.

Hertz was faced with formidable experimental difficulties. A whole book could be written about the way in which he accepted the task and succeeded in convincing the scientific world at large of the truth of Maxwell's theory. Hertz not only showed that the time of transmission required by Maxwell's theory was correct, but he also demonstrated the existence of electromagnetic waves in space, which we now call Hertzian Waves.[14]

Today we know that this category includes a great number of phenomena: light, radio waves, radiant heat, cosmic rays, x-rays, and certain types of radiation from radioactive substances. These are all examples of one fundamental type of electromagnetic radiation. Although they differ in the frequency or wave length, the speed with which all move is the same.

This speed, 186,000 miles per second, has proved to be one of the fundamental constants of the universe. It is the limiting velocity that no motion can exceed. It is, furthermore, the constant that tells us the relation between the mass of any object and the energy which can be obtained from it, a relation which is the very basis of any considerations of atomic energy.

༄ ༄ ༄

The Hertzian Waves, their discoverer found, had very interesting properties. They could be transmitted through the walls of a building, and they could also be reflected from metal surfaces. Soon after their discovery, a great many investigators conceived the idea that they might be applied to problems of communication, and the success of Marconi in devising the first wireless or radio communication on a practical scale needs no recounting here.

Yet it is interesting to see that the radio, which has so profoundly affected the world in a variety of ways, derived from the experiments of Hertz, whose primary concern was to discover whether or not an experimental proof could be had of Maxwell's conclusion that a medium which would account for electrical action would also account for the transmission of light.

Clearly, it is not entirely correct to state that the radio begins with "the experiments of a German professor." Hertz was bringing to experimental fruition the theoretical conclusions of Maxwell, which were a sophisticated mathematical improvement of Faraday's more primitive ideas. Hertz's great experiments of 1887 were made possible by the knowledge that a spark obtained from the discharge of a Leyden jar is oscillatory, a fact derived by calculation from the principle of the conservation of energy by Helmholtz just forty years earlier, but suspected by Franklin more than a century before. But the *invention* of the radio was made by Marconi, who first success-fully applied Hertz's experimental findings, and its improvement from that time until today was made possible by the contributions of countless physicists, engineers, and inventors.

∽   ∽   ∽

The development of radar, one of the great innovations of the recent war, goes back also to Hertz's experiments, those in which he showed that radio waves (Hertzian Waves) are reflected from metallic objects. The results of these experiments, however, were applied for the first time not during the years of the recent war, but in 1904 when a German engineer was granted a patent in England as well as in Germany on a proposed method for using the principle discovered by Hertz in an obstacle detector and navigational aid for ships.[15] One important difference between the radar developed during the war and the proposal of the German patent of 1904 is the fact that wartime radar used very short wave lengths, whereas the German patent used the very much longer wave lengths of the sort produced by Hertz. Yet as early as June, 1922, the great inventor of radio himself, Marconi, strongly urged at a meeting of the Institute of Radio Engineers held in New York that short waves be used in the future for detecting purposes.[16]

Although the entire history of radio and radar illustrates to a high degree the great truth that important practical innovations frequently derive from research whose avowed aim was simply the increase of knowledge, let us not forget that the applications are usually not made by the original research workers, in this case Maxwell and Hertz, but by the practical men who are keen enough and sufficiently well educated to appreciate the possibilities latent in a new truth.

CHAPTER 8

Synthetic Rubber and Nylon

> The greatest invention of the nineteenth century was
> the invention of the method of invention.
> — ALFRED NORTH WHITEHEAD (1925)

THE TRANSFORMATION of industrial processes and products which scientific research hath wrought is at once both profound and far-reaching. The Du Pont Company, for example, in 1942 did a business in gross sales of which nearly half (actually, 46 per cent) consisted of products that either did not exist in 1928 or were not then manufactured in large commercial quantities.[1] A manufacturing concern such as the Du Pont Company has an extensive research program, the history of which begins with the founder of the company.

Eleuthère Irénée du Pont de Nemours, founder of the Du Pont Company, was a pupil of the founder of modern chemistry, Antoine Lavoisier, who lost his head on the guillotine during the French Revolution. From his teacher, Du Pont learned not only the art and science of making gunpowder, which was long a staple of the Du Pont Company, but he also learned the importance of research as an instrument for improving old products and the methods of producing them. Throughout the nineteenth century most of the research done by the Du Pont Company was undertaken in the actual works plants; one of the achievements was the production of a cheaper blasting powder which was used extensively throughout American iron and coal fields.

The first formal research laboratory erected by the Du Pont Company, in 1902, was for research on explosives, and a great deal of attention was devoted to the development of nitroglycerine and forms of dynamite to be used with safety in coal mines.[2]

Today this company operates thirty-eight distinct research laboratories. These are devoted to reducing costs in manufacturing processes, to the improvement of existing processes and products, and to the development of new products. In addition, considerable fundamental research is undertaken — the object of which is to discover new scientific facts without necessary regard to immediate commercial uses.

All industrial organizations which maintain research laboratories have programs more or less similar to that of the Du Pont Company. Although much of the work classified as "applied research" adds nothing fundamentally new to scientific knowledge, nevertheless, even in this type of investigation, valuable information accrues to the body of knowledge.

The contributions to scientific knowledge from such organizations as the Bell Telephone Laboratories and the laboratories of RCA, Du Pont, Eastman Kodak, General Electric, and Westinghouse can be compared, with honor to industry, to the contributions of many of our universities.

Charles M. A. Stine, who started a program of fundamental research in the Du Pont Company in 1927, tells us that industry conducts fundamental research today in order that it may be prepared for tomorrow. Such research, according to Dr. Stine, is carried out not merely for the purpose of contributing something of value to science, but "is conceived to be sound business policy, because fundamental research has proved to be indispensable in assuring continued earning power."[3] The leaders of industrial research know that a program devoted to the increase of knowledge pays cash dividends to the stockholders. Some of the ways in which this occurs are simple. For example, the very presence of top-flight scientists in an industrial research organization insures a high intellectual or scientific level, and attracts to the particular laboratory some of the best young men produced by the universities. The comprehensive knowledge and healthy attitude of curiosity of such research workers are valuable assets: occasions arise in which knowledge must be quickly obtainable, and the easiest way to obtain it is to have immediate access to an authority in the field.

Or again: if one were to survey the state of fundamental knowledge in any one field, one would soon find certain gaps, perhaps small ones or perhaps whole vast areas, in which fundamental work was needed, not to advance any particular art, but simply to fill in that portion of scientific knowledge. A chemist working for an industrial corporation never knows what knowledge will be needed on the morrow. He hopes that when he needs it, it will be available. If it is not available, he may have to find someone, either in his own research organization or in some university, who will obtain it for him. Such a procedure would be satisfactory if the information desired were of a limited character. But if a whole branch of science remains a great unknown terrain, and if very few scientists throughout the country or the world are working in that particular area, it may then be very sensible for the industrial concern to embark on a research program of broad scope, with no immediate or predictable economic aim or practical result in view — simply to be prepared.

Soon after Dr. Stine had established Du Pont's program of fundamental research, he looked around to find a suitable man to head the section of organic chemistry. After much deliberation and investigation, Dr. Wallace Hume Carothers, then an instructor at Harvard University, was chosen.[4] Carothers found the decision to leave his academic post was a difficult one. But the freedom of university life was overbalanced by the temptation which the industrial appointment offered to do nothing but research, as well as by the opportunity to have as assistants and co-workers a number of trained research scientists, and resources in equipment and materials on a scale such as no university could provide.

Although there were to be but nine years of work before his death, Carothers made major contributions to the theory of organic chemistry, and his discoveries led to the production of materials of extraordinary commercial importance. Yet, as President J. B. Conant tells us, "Those of us in academic life always cherished the hope that some day he would return to university work. In his death, academic chemistry quite as much as industrial chemistry suffered a severe loss."[5]

Wallace Carothers was born in 1896. His early death in 1937 was a tragedy. He was brought up in Iowa, and most of his education was obtained at the cost of earning his own way.[6] He completed his studies for the degree of Doctor of Philosophy in Chemistry at the

University of Illinois under Dr. Roger Adams in 1924. By that time
Carothers had already published several independent contributions
to the science of chemistry, an unusual achievement for a pre-
doctoral graduate student. He came to Harvard in 1926. His achievements were recognized, one year before his death, by his election to
the National Academy of Sciences. He was the first organic chemist
working in industry to be so honored.

∾   ∾   ∾

One of the first tasks which Carothers undertook for the Du Pont
Company was in connection with the development of a synthetic
rubber.

The problem of making synthetic rubber depends upon our
knowledge of the composition and structure of the molecules of
natural rubber. As far back as 1860, an English consulting and industrial chemist named Charles Greville Williams [7] had subjected
rubber to destructive distillation and had obtained a substance which
he named "isoprene." Each isoprene molecule is made up of 5 atoms
of Carbon and 8 atoms of Hydrogen, and the chemist indicates this
fact by writing the formula for this molecule as: C_5H_8. Williams
found that if he allowed this isoprene to remain in contact with the
oxygen of the air, a viscous liquid would be formed, from which he
could obtain "a pure white spongy elastic mass." When he burned
the "elastic mass," it gave off the characteristic odor of burning
rubber.[8]

The next important step was taken some twenty years later by
William Tilden, in 1882. Tilden began with common turpentine,
whose vapor he passed through a red-hot tube. In this way, beginning
with *turpentine,* he was able to produce isoprene; and by subjecting
the latter to the action of concentrated hydrochloric acid, and of
nitrosyl chloride, he was able to convert it into a rubberlike mass.[9]
He stored some of the "limpid, colorless isoprene" for some years,
and, as he reported in 1892, he found that it had changed into "a
dense syrup, of a yellowish colour. Upon examination this turned out
to be india-rubber." [10] Thus, beginning with turpentine, the first
man-made rubber was produced.

Not only had Tilden produced synthetic isoprene from turpentine, but he had shown how the isoprene molecules might be caused

to join together, in the process that the chemist calls "polymerization," to form a rubberlike material. This process is one in which small molecules join together to form a larger molecule, but without changing the proportion of the component atoms. For example, let us suppose that in polymerization, 10 isoprene molecules "link" themselves together to form a "polymer." We may denote the polymer by the formula $C_{50}H_{80}$, indicating that there are present 50 atoms of carbon and 80 of hydrogen. But note that the ratio of carbon to hydrogen atoms is still 50 to 80, or 5 to 8, just as it was in the original isoprene molecules C_5H_8 which had polymerized.

Another example of polymerization is the change of acetaldehyde, a white, aromatic liquid, into paraldehyde, a much heavier, colorless liquid with a contrastingly different, pungent odor. Each molecule of acetaldehyde is composed of 2 atoms of carbon, 4 atoms of hydrogen, and 1 atom of oxygen; its formula, therefore, is written C_2H_4O. But the formula for paraldehyde is $C_6H_{12}O_3$, indicating that the polymer is formed by the union of 3 molecules of acetaldehyde. The chemical compound resulting from polymerization has quite distinct properties, as contrasted to those of the original molecules. Acetaldehyde and paraldehyde are both used medically, the former as an inhalant for catarrh, the latter as a soporific in sleeping potions.[11]

∾   ∾   ∾

Today we produce many types of synthetic rubber. The type of rubber depends, in addition to other factors, on the number of separate molecules that have linked up end to end. The springiness of natural rubber derives from the fact that there are present chains of anywhere from 200 to 2000 isoprene molecules. When Tilden allowed his isoprene to stand in the bottle, the isoprene molecules polymerized and linked up end to end to form the type of long chain we associate with rubber. This process has been well described by Williams Haynes, one of the best writers on the subject of chemistry for nonchemists, as follows: "What had happened was that great numbers of C_5H_8 molecules had linked themselves together for all the world like a chain of paper clips hooked together end to end."[12]

∾   ∾   ∾

Organic chemists have a method of writing chemical formulas "structurally" which explains a great deal about organic chemical compounds and their reactions. The formula for the isoprene molecule is:

Isoprene

In this structural formula and the ones on the following pages, four of the carbon atoms have been made a little larger than the other atoms, so that the reader's attention may more easily be drawn to the central structure. Yet it must not be thought that these atoms are in any way different from the others; the chemist always draws them all the same size.

in which each carbon atom is again represented by the letter C, and each hydrogen atom by the letter H. Let us compare this structural formula with our previous formula for the isoprene molecule, which was C_5H_8. In the structural formula, the letter C occurs five times, and H eight times, so that the two agree as to the atomic constitution of the molecule. The "links" or "valence bonds" that hold the atoms together are indicated in the structural formula by the short straight lines emanating from each letter (or atom), C or H. It will be observed that one such bond emanates from each of the hydrogen atoms, and that four of them emanate from each of the carbon atoms, and that each such bond represented by a short straight line emanates from one atom and terminates at another. The carbon atoms at the extreme left and right are joined to the adjacent carbon by *two* straight lines, which we call a "double bond."

We can see what happens during polymerization by examining the structural formula of the central portion of an isoprene polymer:

The individual isoprene molecules that have joined together in polymerization are indicated by a brace (‿‿‿⌄‿‿‿). The reader should check the following points: (1) in each unit marked off by a brace, there are still five atoms of carbon and eight atoms of hydrogen, just as in the original isoprene molecule C_5H_8; (2) from each carbon atom (represented by the letter C) there emanate four valence bonds (indicated by the lines), while from each hydrogen atom, there emanates but a single valence bond; (3) bonds emanating from any atom always terminate in another atom.

An early form of synthetic rubber, made in Germany as a rubber substitute during the First World War, was based on butadiene, a hydrocarbon very much like isoprene in structure, but somewhat simpler, and easier to polymerize. The similarity between the two molecules (and therefore the fact that butadiene, like isoprene, can be polymerized into long chains) may be seen from a comparison of the two structural formulae:

$$
\underset{\text{Butadiene}}{
\begin{array}{cccc}
H & H & & H \\
| & | & & | \\
C & = C & - C & = C \\
| & & | & | \\
H & & H & H \\
\end{array}}
\qquad
\underset{\text{Isoprene}}{
\begin{array}{cccc}
& & H & \\
& & | & \\
H & H-C-H & & H \\
| & | & & | \\
C & = C & - C & = C \\
| & & | & | \\
H & & H & H \\
\end{array}}
$$

The German rubber was inadequate and expensive, and since no one knew very much about how and why polymerization took place, progress in making synthetic rubber seemed to have reached a dead end.

The individual isoprene molecules

We take up the story again in December of 1925, when Dr. E. K. Bolton, director of the chemical section of Du Pont's Dyestuffs Department, attended a symposium on organic chemistry which was part of the meeting of the American Chemical Society at Rochester, New York. There he heard a paper, read by a Catholic priest, Father Julius Arthur Nieuwland, professor of organic chemistry at Notre Dame, which dealt with some of the reactions of acetylene. Dr. Bolton was extremely interested in the possibility of applying Father Nieuwland's results to the problem of synthesizing rubberlike polymers.

Father Nieuwland was an extraordinary man "whose graduation essay had been a paper on Keats' poetry, whose hobby was botany, and whose avocation was mounting and selling biological microscope slides to raise funds for Notre Dame's chemical research." [13] Father Nieuwland spent a lifetime of research on the chemical reactions of acetylene gas, his hobby since undergraduate days. He was in no way interested in the search for a satisfactory synthetic rubber. His only aim was to advance knowledge.

In his paper, Father Nieuwland showed how, by using a catalyst, he had produced from acetylene a polymer made by the union of *three* molecules of acetylene gas: a colorless liquid called divinyl-acetylene. The presence of a strange odor led him to believe that he had also produced monovinyl-acetylene, a polymer made by the union of *two* molecules of acetylene gas. It was not at all apparent that Father Nieuwland's investigations might contribute to the solution of the synthetic rubber problem. However, Dr. Bolton was interested in this possibility, for only that year he had initiated in the Du Pont laboratories a study of the possibility of making rubber from acetylene. It could be that "Dr. Nieuwland's divinyl-acetylene might serve as a starting point for making a satisfactory synthetic rubber." [14]

The results of attempting to use divinyl-acetylene as a starting material for synthetic rubber were negative, although this material did prove useful for another purpose: the preparation of a valuable type of corrosion-resistant finish.

Dr. Carothers and his group of co-workers, to whom the problem had been assigned, had better luck with monovinyl-acetylene. They sealed this substance in test tubes with many different chemical reagents, in order to study the effects of each. One of them was hydrochloric acid, which produced a substance called "chloroprene." The similarity of chloroprene to isoprene and butadiene may again be seen from the structural formulae:

Butadiene   *Chloroprene*   *Isoprene*

The chief difference between the chloroprene molecule and the other two is that an atom of chlorine (Cl) replaces the atom of

hydrogen (H) in butadiene and the $H-\overset{\overset{\displaystyle H}{|}}{\underset{|}{C}}-H$ group in isoprene.

But what a difference that single atom makes!

Chloroprene could be polymerized much more quickly and more easily than either isoprene or butadiene, and it led to a product vastly superior to all previously known synthetic rubbers. Known widely as "neoprene," the chloroprene polymer had one of the most important characteristics of rubber, namely, that of developing "fibrous orientation when stretched and instantly reverting to the amorphous condition when released from stress." [15] As Dr. James K. Hunt of Du Pont writes, "What the chemists had actually done was not to synthesize rubber, but to synthesize a material having rubber's desirable qualities and, in addition, superior qualities of its own." [16] Neoprene resists the action of most chemical reagents; it has a greater resistance than ordinary rubber to sunlight; it can be milled like rubber, mixed in any proportions with natural gum, molded and colored; it has great resistance to heat, gasoline, and lubricating oils.

The new synthetic rubber, neoprene, was introduced formally at the annual dinner of the rubber section of the American Chemical Society at Akron in 1931. Dr. Carothers and three of his associates presented a paper describing it; they showed samples of it, and announced that the Du Pont Company was building a plant at Deepwater, New Jersey, for commercial production.

The reader should be warned that, in the words of the Rubber Survey Committee, composed of James B. Conant, Karl T. Compton, and Bernard M. Baruch:

Strictly speaking, no material has yet been produced which warrants the name of synthetic rubber — at least in the sense in which we speak of many other synthetic substances. Synthetic indigo, for example, is identical in every way with the dyestuff prepared from the indigo plant. Likewise synthetic camphor may be manufactured which is identical in every way with the substance obtained from the camphor tree. On the other hand no one of the synthetic rubbers so far developed — and at least a thousand more or less rubberlike substances have been produced — is exactly the same as natural rubber either in its chemical make-up or its physical properties. [17]

The original clue came, as we saw, from the years of patient research carried out by Father Nieuwland, who was not interested in practical applications but simply in discovering the properties of a group of chemical substances and the nature of their reactions. In the course of his work, Father Nieuwland had shown how to obtain the acetylene polymers, and this was the clue that enabled the Du Pont chemists to solve the problem of synthetic rubber.

In addition to producing the practical end product, neoprene, Carothers's part of the investigation brought forth theoretical knowledge of great importance. Although this is of too technical an aspect to be discussed here, we may at least indicate its importance by quoting Dr. Carothers's teacher, Dr. Roger Adams: "Fundamental information concerning the character and formation of the various polymers . . . was revealed and their structures clarified. The real activity of vinyl acetylene and the mechanism by which products formed was studied in detail." [18] This experience set the stage for the most outstanding scientific accomplishment of Carothers, one which not only established a new field of chemical research but also laid the foundation for a new industry which has vastly affected many aspects of our daily lives.

᎙   ᎙   ᎙

Carothers was interested in the general problem of polymerization and polymeric molecules. His part in the rubber program may be thought of as a sort of preparation for his later work, which not only constituted an important advance in the chemistry of large molecules, but also led to the development of the new family of synthetic compounds known as nylon.

Most people know that purely mechanical inventions, such as the "spinning jenny," had revolutionized the textile industry at the end of the eighteenth century. This change removed both spinning and weaving from the home to the highly mechanized plants today so familiar a part of the contemporary industrial landscape. But in order to appreciate the significance of the invention of nylon, we must first consider that there have been only five major scientific discoveries in the history of textiles that have affected our knowledge and practice. [19]

The first was the process of bleaching. Until the end of the eighteenth century, bleaching required many months of the action of sunlight, and the application of naturally occurring substances, chiefly urine. The development and use of chlorine bleaching powders has been discussed in an earlier chapter,* and constitutes the first chemical innovation in textile history. The second was the development of synthetic dyes derived from coal tar. In the middle of the nineteenth century, these largely replaced the dyes hitherto obtained from roots, barks, berries, and insects. The third was mercerization: a process discovered by an English dyer, John Mercer, who was born in Lancashire in 1791 and died in 1866. A self-educated chemist, he has been called the "father of textile chemistry" and the "self-taught chemical philosopher."

The process discovered by Mercer consists of altering the natural fibers of cotton fabrics in order to give them qualities more closely approaching those of the more expensive linen. Mercerization is the immersing of woven fabrics in a solution of caustic soda where they are held under tension while the caustic solution softens and swells the individual fibers. The caustic soda is later washed out in water, and the fabric retains the power of absorbing moisture, has a glossier finish, and will not shrink as much as unmercerized cloth.[20]

The fourth great innovation was the production of rayon yarn, using cellulose, the skeletal or fundamental structural material of all plants, as the basic raw material. The largest volume of rayon is commonly obtained by the "viscose process," in which caustic soda and carbon bisulfide act on purified cellulose, obtained largely from wood pulp or cotton linters. The result is a syrupy material which is then squirted through tiny holes in a platinum plate into a precipitating solution, usually dilute sulfuric acid, making it form long fibers which, after chemical and physical processing, are then used to make cloth. This method of forming a fiber filament may be described as a man-made adaptation of nature's own method. The silkworm forms its filaments of silk in somewhat the same way, by squirting a thick viscid fluid through tiny holes in its head.[21]

Another type of rayon is made by the "acetate process," in which cellulose is treated with the anhydride of acetic acid (the same acid used by photographers as a short-stop solution, and familiar to most of us as the most important constituent of common vinegar). This

* See page 49.

produces a compound called cellulose acetate, which is then dissolved in acetone, forced into filaments like ordinary rayon, and dried in hot air where the acetone evaporates, leaving the fine threads. In contrast to viscose rayon, which is simply regenerated cellulose, cellulose acetate is a new compound, and one not found naturally occurring in nature. Because acetate rayon requires a different type of dyestuffs from those used on viscose process rayon, beautiful "cross-dyed" effects can be obtained from fabrics comprising both types of yarn. Still another type is cuprammonium rayon.

Nylon, unlike rayon, is formed by taking such products as coal, air, and water, and combining their constituent elements to make a wholly new material. Viscose process rayon is naturally occurring cellulose which has been chemically modified and then regenerated as pure cellulose; only the physical form of the starting material has been changed. Acetate rayon, although a new compound, is a simple derivative of natural cellulose. Nylon, on the other hand, is a completely new creation, having no counterpart in nature, and made by putting together atoms of carbon, nitrogen, hydrogen, and oxygen, to form the desired molecules and then causing these molecules to polymerize. Nylon is, therefore, the first textile material of which we can truly say that it has been *wholly created by man*.

સ્જ   સ્જ   સ્જ

The actual development of nylon can best be understood by dividing it into three distinct periods. During the first of these, fundamental research activity, under the direction of Wallace Carothers, provided the foundation for its development. During the second, attention was concentrated on polyamides, which led to the synthesis of a polymer whose properties were suitable for use as a new fiber. The third period was marked by the development of practical processes for making intermediate materials as well as polymers, and perfecting methods for spinning fibers.[22]

Carothers set out to explore the general subject of polymerization (by methods of condensation) and the general problems connected with the structure of substances of high molecular weight. He had no idea, nor could he possibly have known in advance, that his research would lead him to a wholly new product, nylon. He was conducting an exploration into the unknown, and in a field whose literature was very meager. In fact, so little was known about this whole general area of chemistry that it looked very promising to a man of Carothers's talents, backed up by the resources made available to him by Du Pont.

His program of work was stated clearly in a letter of 14 February, 1928, to Dr. John R. Johnson of Cornell University. He wrote: "One of the problems which I am going to start work on has to do with substances of high molecular weight. I want to attack this problem from the synthetic side. One part would be to synthesize compounds of high molecular weight and known constitution. It would seem quite possible to beat Fischer's record of forty-two hundred, and it would be a satisfaction to do this. Facilities will soon be available here for studying such substances with the newest and most powerful tools." [23] The rest of the letter (of which a portion too technical for the general reader is printed below as a footnote *) further emphasizes the fact that what attracted Carothers to the field of polymerization and the synthetic production of large molecules by polymerization was simply the fact that so little was known.

Carothers referred in his letter to the fact that the highest known molecular weight of a substance that had been synthesized was 4200. To see what this means, it may be in order to indicate some molecular weights.

TABLE OF MOLECULAR WEIGHTS

Substances	Formula	(Approximate) Molecular Weight
Water	H_2O	18
Hydrochloric Acid	HCl	36.5
Carbon Dioxide	CO_2	44
Bicarbonate of Soda	$NaHCO_3$	84
Sulphuric Acid	H_2SO_4	98
Auxin A	$C_{18}H_{32}O_5$	328
Salvarsan ("606")	$C_{12}H_{14}O_2N_2Cl_2As_2:2H_2O$	457

* "Another phase of the problem will be to study the action of substances xAx on yBy where A and B are divalent radicals and x and y are functional groups capable of reacting with each other. Where A and B are quite short, such reactions lead to simple rings of which many have been synthesized by this method. Where they are long, formation of small rings is not possible. Hence reaction must result either in large rings or endless chains. It may be possible to find out which reaction occurs. In any event the reactions will lead to the formation of substances of high molecular weight and containing known linkages. For starting materials will be needed as many dibasic fatty acids as can be got, glycols, diamines, etc. If you know of any new sources of compounds of these types I should be glad to hear about them." [24]

Our knowledge of substances of high molecular weight has increased vastly since Emil Fischer's death in 1919. The highest molecular weights known today are found in the proteins; here are a few of them: [25]

Hemoglobin	68,000
Phycocyan	272,000
Edestin	309,000
Hemocyanin	6,700,000

On the theoretical side, Carothers's ideas bore fruit in thirty-one papers in the field of polymerization, in which he proposed "a general theory of condensation polymerization and a logical and systematic terminology suitable for use in this previously disorganized field." [26] He illustrated the implications of his theory with a series of experimental studies on different substances, and these provided the material for correlating chemical structure and physical properties of substances of high molecular weight, and they furnished evidence of a view now generally accepted for the structure of such naturally occurring high polymers as cellulose.

Carothers's results were of great importance in increasing chemical knowledge. He was successful in producing molecules having higher and higher molecular weights. Eventually he applied the term "super-polymer" to materials whose molecular weights were enormously high.

The success of Carothers's work depended on the vision of such men as Dr. Bolton, who allowed him to continue his investigations in this relatively unexplored field of chemistry without any insistance on the production of immediate practical results. Of course, the Du Pont Company's industry was based on chemistry, and both Stine and Bolton knew that any increase in fundamental chemical knowledge might well provide the basis for new products and new industries.

Carothers obtained some super-polymers (called "super-polyesters") which were tough opaque solids and which at high temperature became transparent viscous fluids. The observation was made that filaments could be obtained from these materials if threads were pulled from the molten polymer with a rod. Even more important was the later observation that after these filaments had cooled, they could be drawn still further, to several times their original length. Such cold-drawn fibers had physical properties quite different from the initial mass of polymer, and even from the fibers pulled from the molten polymer. This cold-drawing developed transparency and a high degree of luster.[27] Furthermore, the cold-drawn filaments were more elastic and had a much greater tensile strength than the undrawn filaments. Whereas the latter were inelastic and fragile, the cold-drawn filaments could be tied into hard knots and then untied again.

It was later found that filaments could be formed not only by pulling threads out of the molten polymer with a rod, but also by dissolving the polymer in chloroform and then dry-spinning it like cellulose acetate rayon. This type of fiber, like the ones pulled from the molten polymer, had a marked orientation of the crystals, but these too could be drawn further when cold, so that the crystals would be oriented in a straight line along the fiber axis. Hence the name "linear super-polymers."

Dr. Bolton tells us: "Up to the time that the above superpolymers were made, this study was wholly fundamental in character and was designed to throw further light on certain aspects of polymerization. The rather striking properties of fibers obtained from the super-polyesters aroused the hope that it might be possible to make a fiber of commercial utility from some type of synthetic linear super-polymer. Research was accordingly directed to this practical end. Continued investigation showed, however, that fibers from the polyesters were of only theoretical interest, as their melting points were too low for general textile purposes and their solubilities were too great." [28]

Carothers had been able to form linear super-polyesters having molecular weights above 10,000 and from which fibers could be formed. Nevertheless, hope was aroused that further research might develop a more useful synthetic fiber. Effort was therefore concentrated on synthesizing a new type of polymer which might form the basis for a commercial textile fiber.

Thus far the work of Carothers had been of greater interest to chemists than to industrialists. Dr. Bolton says that a large amount of time and money had been spent on the work, but the only results to date were of purely "theoretical" interest. To determine what practical use could be made of the scientific information that had been acquired was therefore of considerable concern. Dr. Bolton's statement affords proof that the researches of Carothers had not been thought of in any such simple terms as laying the foundations for a fiber industry.

Carothers's motives had been quite other than providing the basis for a simple practical development. His reports, presented in papers delivered to the American Chemical Society, were well received as contributions to knowledge. The members were interested in the additions to chemical knowledge contained in these papers, even if they appeared to be of no practical use to the Du Pont Company, which had supported him.

Now, however, Carothers was encouraged by Dr. Bolton to direct his future work on super-polymers as specifically as possible toward the development of a product which could be spun into practical fibers. The synthetic rubber development was already in the production stage, and the directors of the Du Pont research were interested in fibers as a new field of conquest. Carothers therefore surveyed his scientific work and decided to center attention on super-polyamides.

After some time there were clear indications that by building on Carothers's fundamental work on linear polymers, it might be possible to synthesize a material for producing fibers of commercial utility.

The first useful polyamide was called "No. 66." Like the earlier polyesters, "66" fibers could be drawn when cold to produce material of great elasticity and high tensile strength. Furthermore, these fibers were insoluble in common solvents; there was no danger of cloth made from them being dissolved during processing or even washing. They melted at 260° Centigrade, which gave a margin of safety well above the temperature commonly employed in ironing.

Carothers continued to explore other polymers to see if polymer

"66" was the best suited for the production of fibers. This later work simply confirmed the wisdom of the original selection, which had been made at a time when only a small number of the many possible super-polymers had been examined.

The period of research we have just described constitutes the second period, in which, with a practical end in sight, the work was directed toward the actual production of a synthetic fiber. In contrast to the first period, which culminated in Carothers's presentation of his findings to the American Chemical Society in Buffalo, New York, and in which the research effort was directed to increasing knowledge, the second period was specifically directed to using the new knowledge for a practical purpose.

∽   ∽   ∽

The third period included the development of manufacturing processes for the intermediate materials; and the gathering, on a semi-works scale, of the chemical and engineering data necessary for the erection and operation of a large-scale plant for production of the intermediate materials, the polymers, and the nylon yarn itself. The Du Pont Company's Executive Committee wanted these processes worked out as quickly as possible to reduce to a minimum "the time between the test tube and the counter," [29] to quote W. S. Carpenter, Jr., President of the Du Pont Company.

A large number of chemists and chemical engineers were transferred to the "66" project in order to speed up the development, and a great many important contributions were introduced by chemists and engineers who until now had no connection with "66." The new material was given a coined name, nylon, selected from several hundred suggested names, because it had a pleasing sound and was not likely to be mispronounced. Also, because of cotton and rayon, the ending "on" suggested a textile fiber, and it was anticipated that a major outlet for nylon would be in the form of textile-fibers. On 27 October 1938, nylon was formally announced to the world by Dr. Stine at the *New York Herald Tribune* eighth annual forum on current problems, as the climax of his address on "What laboratories of industry are doing for the world of tomorrow — Chemicals and Textiles." [30]

Nylon is a generic term much like glass or leather, and is applied not to one particular product, but rather to a large family of related polyamides. The term "nylon" is thus used not only for the yarn of which stockings and ladies' undergarments are made, but also for the bristles used in toothbrushes, surgical sutures, fishing lines, and a host of other products.*

Nylon yarn was produced at the beginning of 1942 at the rate of 8,000,000 pounds a year, and by the summer of that year the annual output was increased to 16,000,000 pounds. The fortunate development of nylon at this particular time was of great importance to the war effort, since it made us independent of lightweight, tough-fibered silk which had hitherto come almost entirely from Japan and was essential for such vital military products as parachutes.

The development of nylon affords a clear picture of the way in which advances in pure knowledge lead to unexpectedly great practical results. When Carothers came to the Du Pont Company he was interested in producing substances of high molecular weight and in investigating their structure and properties. Since no one knew very much about linear super-polymers — in fact, they had never before been produced systematically in the laboratory — no one could have predicted their properties. Certainly at that time no one could have foretold that a super-polymer, or giant molecule, would be produced having a long threadlike structure — a chain, so to speak, whose physical properties of great elasticity and tensile strength would enable it to be used in the manufacture of textiles.

Dr. Stine and Dr. Bolton were of course convinced of the fact that in time all scientific research yields results likely to be of inestimable practical value, and that it was sound business policy to encourage fundamental research with no immediate practical end in view, *especially* in those chemical fields where there was little existing knowledge. Since the Du Pont Company is founded on chemistry, and since there existed in 1927 vast gaps in chemical knowledge, Dr. Stine was fully convinced, when he inaugurated a

* For the technically minded: the official Du Pont definition of nylon is, "A generic term for any long-chain synthetic polymeric amide which has recurring amide groups as an integral part of the main polymer chain, and which is capable of being formed into a filament in which the structural elements are oriented in the direction of the axis." [31]

program of fundamental research, that any program of sufficiently broad scope would add greatly to the store of chemical knowledge on which the industry was based. He was also certain that in the long run such a program would turn up processes and products of a commercial value at least sufficient to cover the costs involved in obtaining that fundamental knowledge.

The Du Pont Company did not sponsor its fundamental research program because of any vague idealistic motive, such as repaying a debt owed to fundamental science because of its commercial successes in the application of such knowledge, nor was there any reason why it should. Whatever the motive, the fact remains that Du Pont's program of fundamental research yielded results which not only contributed to a better understanding of polymerization, but also gave the world a wholly new and useful family of materials. The Du Pont Company embarked on its fundamental research program fully convinced that knowledge acquired in the relatively unexplored field of polymerization would, over the years, yield practical results measurable in dollars and cents.*

The development of nylon may be likened to the discovery of selective weed killers and other auxins, to the development of radio and radar, and our system of electric power. In each of these examples, fundamental research directed towards increasing knowledge produced, as by-products, results of economic importance to a practical world. The only surprising aspect of the story of nylon may be that, in this case, the fundamental work was done in an industrial laboratory rather than in a university or a privately endowed institute of research. Most of us do not expect the fundamental advances in knowledge to come out of industrial establishments. Therein we betray an attitude which is a vestigial remain from the Victorian period, in which too great a distinction was made between

* Dr. James K. Hunt of the Du Pont Company, speaking for the industry with which he is connected, asks leave to add: "This point of view, which, in the case of nylon, was fully justified by the results, is of course predicated on the protection afforded an inventor by our patent system. Modern industrial research is a costly undertaking, and large expenditures such as were involved in developing neoprene and nylon are justified only if there is assurance that a fair return on the research expenditure will be realized. Such assurance is to be had through a patent, which gives the inventor a right to exclude others from the practice of his invention for a period of 17 years."

"pure knowledge" and "practical knowledge." The contributions of so-called "industrial" scientists loom large in the body of fundamental knowledge acquired by science in the twentieth century. We may confidently expect that further contributions to fundamental knowledge will be made by the laboratories of enlightened industry, just as by those of the universities. Nevertheless, there is good reason to suppose that in the future, as in the past, the greater part of industrial research will be carried on in the "applied" end of the spectrum; and that the burden of advancing basic knowledge will still rest on the shoulders of university scientists.

PART THREE
Fundamental Research in Which a Practical Application Seems Likely

The underlying problems of science, from the solution of which all great industrial advances spring, must be attacked no less vigorously than the more obvious practical questions.
— GEORGE ELLERY HALE (1919)

CHAPTER 9

Fundamental Research in Which a Practical Application Seems Likely

> Our civilization is essentially different from earlier
> ones, because our knowledge of the world and of
> ourselves is deeper, more precise, and more certain,
> because we have gradually learned to disentangle the
> forces of nature, and because we have contrived, by
> strict obedience to their laws, to capture them and
> to divert them to the gratification of our own needs.
> — GEORGE SARTON (1927)

THE CASE HISTORIES to which the last three chapters were devoted show how the search for fundamental truth constantly yields practical innovations of the greatest importance in our daily lives. It should be manifest to the reader that, in each of these instances, the particular use to which the new knowledge was put could not have been predicted in the early days of the research. Those who studied the way in which plants bend to the light could have had no idea that their studies would lead to a practical weed killer; Maxwell, when he propounded his electromagnetic theory of light, could have had no idea that he was laying the foundation for a new mode of communication and a method for detecting distant aircraft; Wallace Carothers, when he began his studies on compounds with high molecular weight, could have had no idea that he was laying the foundation for the manufacture of a new artificial fiber. I was tempted to write that each practical innovation came about as a *complete* surprise, but this would not be quite true. For example, the executives of the Du Pont Company, who encouraged Carothers and supported the research which led to nylon, were firmly convinced that this type of fundamental research would eventually produce *something* of economic value, even though they had no idea as to what the innovation might be.

From a viewpoint fully informed by the history of science during the last several centuries, it is patently obvious that in the long run, all kinds of fundamental research yield practical dividends. Nevertheless, there are some fields of scientific research which seem more certain of yielding their dividend in a shorter time than others. For example, a fundamental study on the basic nutritional requirements of plants or animals would appear to be in this category.

Anyone who undertakes research on such a nutritional problem, and who uncovers important new facts about just which conditions must obtain in the soil for healthy plants to grow in it, may have *in advance* the satisfaction of knowing that his findings will be used in a practical way. If he discovers that certain conditions must prevail for plants to be healthy, then quite obviously agriculturalists will put his discovery to use, and will see to it that those very conditions will be met on their farms.

At the beginning of the twentieth century, a considerable amount of research had established the fact that the higher green plants appear to require ten essential chemical elements; seven of these they obtain from the soil and are absorbed by the roots, constituting the so-called "minerals" — iron, calcium, nitrogen, phosphorus, sulphur, potassium, and magnesium. An eighth element, carbon, is obtained by green plants from the carbon dioxide in the air; and the ninth and tenth, oxygen and hydrogen, from water.

Today, however, as a result of the fundamental research of the last twenty or thirty years, we know that at least four other chemical elements are necessary, namely, the metals — boron, copper, manganese, and zinc. "Well," the reader may say, "if these four additional elements are absolutely essential to a green plant, why were they not discovered earlier?" This is a very interesting question, and one whose answer reveals the way in which a fact is established in science.

These four chemical elements are required by the plants in such infinitesimal amounts that a few hundredths of a milligram will produce considerable growth, and as little as a thousandth of a milligram will cause an obvious response in a single plant. To illustrate how small these quantities are, we may point out that a milligram is a thousandth part of a gram; and an aspirin tablet weighs approximately one third of a gram.

Even before the First World War, it was on record that a bare trace of these four metals, and of some others, was very frequently present in plants. It was even known that such a trace might prove "beneficial to the plant." Thus, the elements in this category were often considered to be plant "stimulants" in low concentration, but "toxins" in high concentration, producing a deleterious effect. But this is far indeed from indispensability. To satisfy this canon, we must grow a plant to all intents and purposes absolutely free from even a trace of, say, zinc, and show that such a plant either shows symptoms characteristic of a deficiency disease or dies.

The method used to study plant nutrition is known as "water culture." It consists of growing a plant without soil in a vessel containing distilled water, to which the experimenter adds definite and measurable quantities of chemical compounds and then determines the effect of each. A few years ago, when the successful growth of plants without soil, so-called "hydroponics," seemed to have possibilities for the commercial growth of plants on a large scale, the public press waxed eloquent on the latest "miracle." But like many other "most recent" advances, the water culture of plants has a history that goes back considerably in time — in this case about 250 years.

෴   ෴   ෴

The first instance of the water culture of plants occurred during the last years of the seventeenth century, when a physician named John Woodward, an amateur geologist as well as a botanist, performed a series of experiments which he published in the *Philosophical Transactions,* the journal published by the Royal Society of London, in 1699.

Woodward was anxious to discover the so-called "principle of vegetation." He therefore grew several species of plants in different kinds of water — rain water, river water, spring water, conduit water, and distilled water. These experiments convinced him that water carries "terrestrial matter" from which all vegetation is formed, and that earth material in the water, rather than the water itself, is what nourishes plants.[1]

The history of this subject has been investigated by Dr. John W.

Shive, professor of plant physiology at Rutgers University. He tells us that although others performed similar experiments during the next fifty years, "so little was known about the fundamentals of plant nutrition that there was small chance for any profitable issue from such experiments."[2]

By the middle of the nineteenth century, owing to the great strides made in the sciences of both chemistry and biology, the continued use of the water-culture method and the refined procedures of chemical analysis had made it possible for plant scientists to discover which chemical elements were absolutely necessary for a plant to grow and be healthy. On the basis of this knowledge a standard solution was established, in the latter part of the nineteenth century, and was used by anyone who wanted to grow plants in a solution without soil.

∽   ∽   ∽

In the opening years of the twentieth century, plant scientists were still puzzled by the traces of other elements than the ten so-called essential ones. Were they absolutely necessary? In order to answer this question, the investigators had to develop techniques far surpassing in delicacy any that had been employed hitherto.

For example, if there is a slight amount of zinc in a given plant, then there will be a trace of zinc in the seeds it produces. As a result, the plants grown from those seeds will also contain a trace of zinc, even if they are grown in a culture *absolutely free* of zinc.[3] The salts used in preparing the solution must be absolutely pure. Dr. D. R. Hoagland of California, whose important work in this field will be referred to presently, tells us that so-called "ordinary 'chemically pure' reagents are generally not pure enough."[4] They may contain a minute quantity of some impurity — a compound of zinc, copper, manganese, or boron — and would thus spoil the experiment by introducing into the culture solution a trace of the very element it was hoped to avoid. Lastly, the material of which the containing vessels themselves are made may contain a small amount of these elements, which might dissolve into the culture solutions.

In the historical introduction to the most recent treatise on this subject, Walter Stiles, the distinguished plant physiologist and Mason Professor of Botany in the University of Birmingham, points out that we have been able to acquire knowledge of these so-called trace elements largely owing to the possibility of obtaining a high degree of purification "of the water and nutrient salts used," and also by "the choice of suitable culture vessels." [5]

We shall not trouble the reader with the details of how such purification was obtained, nor with a description of the delicate instruments used to detect the very barest trace of copper, zinc, boron, and manganese, in a single plant. Suffice it to say that the techniques developed and used came from physics and chemistry proper.

Here again we see how the use of new instruments and techniques makes possible the advance of science. And once again we may observe the fructifying effect of advance in one area of science upon another.

During the last twenty years or so, thousands of investigations have been made on a very large number of plants, in order to determine which of these trace elements are needed by each plant, and in what quantities. Because plants need boron, copper, manganese, and zinc in such minute quantities, they have been referred to variously as "minor," "rare," "micro-nutrient," or "trace" elements. The very lack of standardization of name indicates the newness of this knowledge, just as in the case of the auxins, which are called "plant growth regulators," "plant hormones," and "growth hormones," as well as auxins. Molybdenum, aluminum, and silicon may, in some cases, have to be added to the list.

It was finally established by means of careful, controlled experiments that plants need tiny quantities of these trace elements in order to grow in a healthy manner. But since these chemical elements are almost always found in plants, and since they are usually present in the soil, it may seem to the reader that this research really did little more than reaffirm with scientific accuracy the fact that the trace of these elements usually found in the plants was actually essential to their health. Such was not at all the case. The experience of the last ten or fifteen years leaves no doubt whatsoever upon this point. Reports have come in from all parts of the world giving ample testimony to the fact that economic crops may suffer badly from diseases arising from what is now recognized as a deficiency of boron, manganese, copper, or zinc, as the case may be. Even though most soils have an adequate supply of these elements, yet "a sufficiently large number of areas of deficiency have already been observed to warrant the assertion that the results of research on the micro-nutrient elements," as Dr. D. R. Hoagland tells us, "constitute a major advance in application of knowledge of plant nutrition." [6]

We shall describe one such result which is highly typical, and which derived from the work of Dr. Hoagland and his associates in California. In that state, a common pathological condition of great practical importance was the "little-leaf," or "rosette," disease which affects deciduous fruit trees and was particularly marked in pears. The most characteristic symptom is the development, during the spring, of rosettes of very small leaves which, according to Dr. Hoagland and his associates, F. B. Chandler and P. L. Hibbard, usually have less than 5 per cent of the area of normal leaves.[7] The affected leaves are mottled in appearance, and the fruit generally fails to set on branches which are badly affected; any fruit which does set tends to be small and malformed. In addition to pear, plants likely to be affected by the disease are apple, plum, cherry, peach, apricot, almond, and grape.

For many years, plant scientists had experimented on the cause of this pathological condition. Some had even thought that the disease was due to a virus, or other micro-organism, which attacked the plant. Drs. Chandler, Hoagland, and Hibbard found, however, that rather than being caused by a micro-organism, the disease arose from a deficiency of zinc.

It had been discovered that a certain fertilizer containing iron sulphate seemed to cure the disease. But the purest iron sulphate available had no such beneficial effect. The investigators found that the cure was in no way related to the iron sulphate, but rather to the trace of zinc contained in it as an impurity. Once it was known that the disease arose from a deficiency of zinc, and could be cured by getting zinc into the plant, growers put the discovery to work. Today, this disease may be cured speedily by either spraying affected trees with zinc sulphate or by injecting solid zinc sulphate into the trunks of the trees.

Another disease of economic importance in California is the "mottle-leaf" disease which affects citrus trees. This disease, whose name is derived from the fact that yellowish areas appear between the veins of the leaves, giving them a mottled appearance, was investigated by Dr. J. C. Johnston. Since mottle-leaf of citrus and little-leaf of deciduous trees may often appear in the same orchard, it occurred to Johnston that the two might be related. Since Chandler, Hoagland, and Hibbard had found that the application of zinc sulphate would cure little-leaf, Johnston applied the same treatment to mottle-leaf of citrus trees. He obtained favorable results in all cases.[8]

In spite of the evidence of experiments, the very minuteness of these quantities — the bare trace of them is said to be necessary for the growth of healthy green plants — makes it hard for us to believe that so little can indeed produce so large an effect. But the experience in the laboratory has been confirmed in the field, and to such a marked degree that today both plant physiologists and practical agriculturalists not only accept this startling new discovery, but apply it in their everyday work.

We cannot conclude this discussion without pointing out that the development of knowledge concerning the trace elements follows two related paths, dictated by the primary interests of two groups. As Walter Stiles points out, the new knowledge of the trace elements presents the biologist with two sets of problems — one we may designate the pathological, the other, the physiological.[9] The pathologist has as his problem the abnormal conditions which result from a deficiency of these trace elements in plants, and that of providing the means by which this deficiency can be removed. The physiologist, on the other hand, has a much more subtle problem, for he must discover what the actual function of these various elements may be in the actual life process of the organism. The two problems are very closely related. The physiologist will continue to be provided with important knowledge by the work of the pathologist who discovers the effects of deficiency. The pathologist is likely to be helped immeasurably in determining methods for the diagnosis and treatment of deficiency diseases, by any knowledge which the physiologist obtains of the part played by these trace elements in the life process of the organism.

Surveying the state of knowledge in this field today, one finds that the knowledge of the pathology of trace elements in plants apparently is considerably more advanced than our knowledge of the physiological function of these same elements. We can recognize a considerable number of trace-element deficiency diseases and we know how to cure them. This number will certainly increase. But when fundamental research will explain adequately what these trace elements actually do in the plant, not only will our knowledge then be on a more solid foundation, but our application of that knowledge in diagnosing and treating plant diseases will thereby become more secure.

Because the pathology and physiology of the trace elements in plants have been so closely related, the plant scientists who studied the nutritional effects of these elements during the last twenty years have known that any fundamental results they might obtain would be of great practical value. They have known, for example, that as they discovered that certain types of healthy plants need a trace of this or that element, the agriculturists would immediately see to it that their plants were supplied with the quantity needed.

But, clearly, no one studying the role of zinc in plants, no matter how sure he was that his findings would be of economic value, could have known that he would find the cure for the little-leaf or the mottle-leaf disease! Because, prior to that research, no one had the slightest idea that these pathological conditions were manifestations of zinc deficiency in the plants.

How far justified are we, on the basis of the examples we have considered thus far, in believing that fundamental research may be divided into two categories? In one, the scientists, although hoping to increase knowledge, can have no idea that an immediate practical application may result; in the other, it seems reasonably certain that, if any result will be obtained, and if it be truly fundamental, it will have an application.

From the long-range point of view all science is useful. As J. B. S. Haldane tells us, what is commonly called "pure science" might better be called "long-range science," that is, "science which will not find a practical application for some years to come." If some fields of research seem to us to be more certain of speedily yielding a useful end product than others, may not such a distinction merely represent our myopia, and demonstrate that even the most informed amongst us may not have as secure and adequate an understanding of the scientific process as may some day be possible?

The point is well worth making, however, because our very near-sightedness may actually affect our conduct. In considering programs for future research, for example, we must take special pains to make sure that we do not limit ourselves to those fields of activity which, like studies of plant nutrients, seem more certain of yielding quick dividends than do others. That scientific research whose practical effect may not be marked for many years may, nevertheless, eventually produce a greater and more far-reaching effect than the research whose applications may appear more immediate. In any case, the important problem of why some scientific discoveries are applied immediately and others lie fallow for many years is a complex question, and we reserve a discussion of it until the final chapter of the book.

Furthermore, even if scientific research supported by us may not seem to yield any tangible result of immediate measurable value in dollars and cents, it nevertheless may provide an important new basis for our understanding of the physical universe. Even if our support of science derives from our anticipation of useful end products, we must not try to limit the scientific enterprise only to such practical ends, in the false hope that we are thereby spending our scientific resources more wisely.

Above all, we must keep in mind that nature yields knowledge through science by strange and unpredictable routes. For example, as Dr. Harlow Shapley tells us, "It was the fossil bones that led us to knowledge of the atom-splitting in the stars." [10]

Over the course of years, the geologists found fossil remains of extinct animals and plants in rocks all over the world, and every evidence seemed to point to their great age. Yet exactly how old they were could not be accurately determined until the discovery of radioactivity. Uranium, as everyone knows today, is a naturally radioactive substance, and undergoes a continuous process of disintegration. In the end, nothing is left but lead and helium gas, which are the final disintegration products. Since this disintegration goes on continuously from the time a rock is first formed, one can use this knowledge of radioactivity to obtain a measure of the age of any particular rock. The older it is, the longer the uranium will have been disintegrating, and the more lead and helium will have been formed. Since we know the rate of disintegration, the lead-uranium ratio tells us the age of many rocks.

Once such determinations had been made, the evidence showed that the earth itself was considerably older than the geologists had previously estimated it to be.

The effect of these discoveries on astronomy was most marked.[11] So far as air, light, and heat are concerned, conditions on the earth must have been very much the same as they are today *three hundred million years ago,* and maybe even *five hundred million years ago,* because the remains of plants and animals from that distant Paleozoic era indicate that they were much the same as those which are living today. And we know how long ago those plants and animals lived, because we can determine the age of the rocks in which their remains are imbedded by analyzing the lead-uranium ratio.

Thus the astronomers knew from the evidence of fossils that the sun has been giving out approximately the same quantity of sunlight for at least the past three hundred million years. The sun is a star and differs from those stars that we see at night only in degree, not in kind; that is, it differs only in size, temperature, and so on. All theories held previous to the radioactive determination of the age of rocks at the beginning of the twentieth century could not possibly account for a source of energy in a star like our sun which would enable it to give off light and heat continuously for so many millions of years.

Almost in desperation, the astronomers turned to the idea suggested by J. H. Jeans in 1904, "that if in their frenzied agitation the electrons and protons of high-temperature matter could collide and exterminate each other, there would be an effective release of energy."[12] (Today we do not accept the particular form of conversion of matter into energy suggested by Jeans.)

In the following year, Einstein proposed his Special Theory of Relativity, with the equation which the atom bomb has brought into prominence, telling us exactly how much energy one can get from a given quantity of matter. The amount is enormous. To use an example suggested by Hans Bethe, a single ounce of matter is "energetically equivalent" to the output for a whole month of the hydroelectric plant at Boulder Dam.[13]

The new knowledge indicates that, in radiating sunlight and heat, the sun must lose more than four million ounces of its mass in every second. But, large as this may seem to the reader who is unacquainted with astronomical numbers, the sun is so very large, and its total material so great, that even with such a loss it could run steadily for millions on millions of years. The hypothesis of the many millions of years of steady sunlight which the evidence of paleontology and the radioactive analysis of rocks demanded could be amply provided by such an atomic process. To meet all the requirements, the sun and the stars would not even need to completely annihilate matter, but merely to transform 1 per cent of the mass of the atoms into radiation.[14]

This brief glimpse at the cause of solar radiation shows the reader how the sciences are inextricably mixed. Paleontology combines both biology and historical geology. The analysis of radioactive rocks, and an understanding of what goes on in them, involve both chemistry and physics. The application of these findings to the problem of solar and stellar radiation shows how closely bound together are the different branches of modern science. Therefore, not only is the progress of astronomy related to developments in the field of atomic physics but, as we shall shortly see in a chapter on the sun (Chapter 16), the astronomical study of the sun itself has had repercussions on physics, which not only have been important from the point of view of our fundamental knowledge, but are in turn the source of our understanding, and solving, a significant group of practical problems.

፠ ፠ ፠

Keeping in mind therefore that all types of fundamental research turn up by-products of use to humanity in a thousand different ways, let us, in the next chapters, examine two further case histories:

one, the discovery of the blood groups, and the other, the story of hybrid corn.

In the first of these we shall see that Landsteiner's fundamental observations concerning the agglutinization of human blood have yielded results crucial to transfusion therapy, the practice of legal medicine, and our understanding of man himself — the study of physical anthropology. But a fundamental study of the blood, such as Landsteiner made, would, if it were to come to any successful issue, obviously yield important practical results. A study of the blood, like a fundamental study of the heart, or any other organ or aspect of the human body, is bound to have results that not only will affect our understanding of the human frame and its functions, but will also alter the way in which we treat it. Since such an investigation, like any other research of a fundamental character, is an adventure into the unknown, no one can define in advance what the findings will be; nor pronounce on whether they will be immediately useful, and for one particular purpose rather than another. In the case of the blood groups, an application was not made until a decade had passed.

As we must point out repeatedly, many important advances, even in the practice of medicine, do not necessarily come from fundamental investigations in fields such as human physiology, which would seem to be most directly related to the need. X-rays for the diagnosis of human ailments, and radioactive substances for use in treating various disorders, were discovered by physicists, a group no more interested in the problems of medicine than any other laymen. In the same way, the discovery of many organic chemical compounds derived from coal tar, and made by chemists who were not primarily interested in medicine, have provided us with vital therapeutic agents.

In the second case history, that of hybrid corn, we shall see a slightly different picture. Here the research that at first seemed to have interest only at the fundamental level suddenly appeared to have economic value. The motivation behind the fundamental research actually changed, on the part of one of its first investigators, *during the very process of investigation!*

It should thus be clear why we must set no limit or strict boundary to any program of fundamental scientific research which we, as laymen, will pay for, sponsor, and support. There will always be branches of scientific research which will seem, even in the eyes of "omniscient" scientists, to be far removed from any immediate practical application, but which, nevertheless, will uncover, as they progress, innovations of the greatest importance for our security and well-being, and our state.

Let us continue to support and to encourage fundamental research on all levels and in all directions. If we like, we can adopt a superior attitude, and flatter ourselves that we are furthering "pure" scientific research, with no possible immediate, obvious economic, or otherwise useful end product in view; and that we do so because we revere truth and are willing to support the pursuit of knowledge for "its own significance." But we would be far more realistic if we kept before us the lessons taught by the history of science, and realized that whenever we sponsor "pure" science, we are simultaneously sponsoring the "practical" science of the future.

CHAPTER 10

Blood Groups and Blood Transfusion

> The studious and good and true, never suffer their
> minds to be warped by the passions of hatred and
> envy, which unfit men duly to weigh the arguments
> that are advanced in behalf of truth, or to appreciate
> the proposition that is even fairly demonstrated.
> Neither do they think it unworthy of them to change
> their opinion if truth and undoubted demonstra-
> tions require them to do so. They do not esteem it
> discreditable to desert error, though sanctioned by
> the highest antiquity, for they know full well that
> to err, to be deceived, is human; that many things
> are discovered by accident and that many may be
> learned indifferently from any quarter, by an old
> man from a youth, by a person of understanding
> from one of inferior capacity.
>
> — WILLIAM HARVEY (1628)

FROM EARLIEST TIMES man has bestowed upon blood a unique status, and attributed to the vital body fluid properties far removed from the physiological sphere. Many common expressions give evidence of ideas which have become imbedded in the language. A calculating person, unmoved by emotion and human sympathy, is called "cold-blooded." A supposedly well-born person is called a "blueblood"; and the closeness of family ties is referred to in the phrase "Blood is thicker than water," which, in terms of measurable viscosity, may be considered scientifically true.

At least as old as the art and practice of medicine itself is the use of blood as a therapeutic agent. We know the ancient Egyptians took baths of blood for therapeutic purposes, and in Roman times drinking the blood which flowed out of gladiators in the arena (described by Pliny as drinking "out of living cups") was considered a cure for epilepsy. Although a few writers, such as the Roman physician Celsus, deplored the practice, most, including the great Galen, approved this form of treatment. As late as the seventeenth century, many serious writers on medicine prescribed the blood of cats, dogs, turtles, and other animals in the treatment of epilepsy. One medical book, published in 1673 by Thomas Bartholin, described an epileptic girl who, after taking cat's blood, took on all the characteristics of a cat. She climbed up on roofs, jumped, scratched, meowed like a cat, and even sat for hours gazing into a hole in the floor, apparently in the hope of catching a mouse! [1]

In ancient times most people believed that blood carried the vital force of the body and was the seat of the soul. Insanity was thought to occur as a result of sickness of the soul, and the infirmities associated with old age to be due to a using up of this essential force. It was but a simple step, therefore, to the idea which held that a cure for the diseases of old age, and perhaps insanity, was to substitute in the body healthy young blood for used-up or ailing blood. Thus we find in early times many attempts to cure disease by blood infusions.

The origin of "transfusion" is attributed in mythology to the sorceress Medea, consort of Jason. The poet Ovid tells us that when the Argonauts returned from Colchis, their festivities were considerably dampened by the debility and senescence of Jason's father. Jason therefore asked his wife to use her magic powers as a sorceress and restore youth and strength to his old father. She brewed a mixture so powerful that the withered olive branch with which she stirred it at once bore leaves and fruit. Then she unsheathed her knife, cut the old man's throat, let the old blood run out, and filled his veins with her brew. Jason's father, it is related, became young again, "his beard and hair lost their hoary grey and quickly became black again; went the pallor and the look of neglect, the deep wrinkles were filled out with new flesh, his limbs had the strength of youth." [2] This mythological story differs in at least one way from later ideas of transfusion: the substance introduced in the old man's veins was a brew of herbs rather than the blood of some other living creature. By "transfusion," the medical man means simply the introduction of any fluid into the blood vessels — a brew of herbs in this case; in others, salt solution, plasma, or whole blood itself.

Prime among the reasons why the ancient writers did not visualize the possibilities of actual transfusions of blood was their limited conception of the nature of circulation. The early writers were unacquainted with the continuous circulation of the blood, the discovery of which was announced by William Harvey in 1616. Previously it had been believed, following Aristotle, that blood was prepared within the heart and from thence flowed to other parts of the body where it was used up and never returned to the heart again. Some considered that the arteries carried only air from the lungs to the tissues. But the prevailing belief from 100 A.D. until Harvey's discovery was that of Galen, who taught that blood is formed in the liver and goes back and forth in the vessels until it is consumed; and that the supply is replenished constantly by the liver. The writings between the time of Galen and Harvey thus cannot be expected to refer to transfusion of blood in the modern sense, but only to various attempts to get new blood into the human body by simpler means, such as drinking it.

Yet an early attempt at blood transfusion supposedly occurred in Rome sometime in the last decade of the fifteenth century, when Pope Innocent VIII was dying from the "disease of old age." A Jewish physician, so the story goes, attempted to rejuvenate the pontiff by giving him the blood from three small boys who were each to receive a ducat as a reward. According to some versions, the blood was actually transfused into his veins; according to others, the blood was simply used in the preparation of a drink. There is no assurance that he received either drink or transfusion, but there does seem to be agreement that the three boys died, that the death of the pope was not prevented, and that the physician fled as quickly and as far as possible.[3]

Once Harvey had demonstrated that in animals and human beings the blood circulates throughout the system, leaving the heart by way of the arteries and returning through the veins, and that the heart merely acts as a pump to keep the blood in circulation, investigators undertook experiments infusing various substances into the blood stream, and on transferring blood from the arteries of one individual to the veins of another. This was the age in which the so-called "new science" had aroused men's curiosity to inquire into all phenomena of nature. In England, where Harvey's lectures first announced his momentous discovery, many scientists began experimenting on this subject. Sir Christopher Wren, more famous today as an architect than as a scientist, in 1656 injected several materials into the veins of dogs — ale, wine, and opium — hoping to develop a new method of administering drugs.[4] The record is not clear concerning work which might be interpreted as transfusion between the time of Harvey's announcement of the circulation of the blood in 1616 and Wren's experiments in 1656. Many vague accounts are to be found, but some modern historians dispute whether a good part of these are to be taken literally or to be considered ironic! [5]

The first authenticated transfusion was probably performed in 1666 by the Cornish physician, Dr. Richard Lower, who was also the first person to prove that venous blood becomes red on passing through the lungs by virtue of being brought into contact with the air, a contribution described by Dr. John F. Fulton as "one of the greatest discoveries in the history of medicine." [6] Lower's transfusion was from one dog to another. In describing it, under the date of 14 November 1666, the famous diarist Samuel Pepys tells us: "This did give occasion to many pretty wishes, as of the blood of a Quaker to be let into an Archbishop, and such like." The description of Lower's experiments, containing diagrams illustrating his instruments, graced the first volume of *Philosophical Transactions* published by the newly founded Royal Society of London. In the fall of 1667, Lower performed a transfusion of lamb's blood into the veins of a "mildly melancholy insane man," a 32-year-old Bachelor of Divinity of Cambridge, named Arthur Coga. He received twenty shillings for his trials. The experiment had a successful issue and the patient gave a short address in Latin to the Royal Society.*

But the first transfusion of animal blood *into a human being* had been executed by the French philosopher and mathematician, Jean Baptiste Denys (or Denis), one year before Lower. The patient on whom Denys's first transfusions were performed recovered, but the third or fourth resulted in death. As a result, Denys was charged with murder. Although he was eventually exonerated, a decree was passed prohibiting further transfusions except by special approbation of the Faculty of Medicine of Paris. Since this body led the opposition to transfusion, the decree in effect prohibited any further ex-

---

* *Sanguis ovis symbolicam quandam facultatem habet cum sanguine Christi, quia Christus est agnus Dei.*[7]

periments. Ten years later, in 1678, attempts at transfusions with human beings were expressly prohibited by an edict, thus ending for the time any further development in France. But in other countries experiments continued.[8]

∾   ∾   ∾

Many of the early transfusions were successful, by which we mean only that the patient did not die. In some cases the blood was introduced a little at a time and if an untoward reaction occurred, no more was given. Yet the effects, when they were bad, were horrendous — accompanied by chills, fever, and violent vomiting. The symptoms arising from reactions of incompatible blood may appear early — that is, after anywhere from 50 to 100 cubic centimeters have been introduced. A modern description indicates the extreme character of the reaction:

The patient complains of tingling pains over the entire body, fullness in the head, precordial oppression, and later excruciating lumbar pain. Gradually the face becomes cyanotic, and breathing is labored. The pulse rate falls sharply, sometimes as much as twenty to thirty beats a minute. Consciousness may be lost momentarily. . . . The most characteristic reaction is a severe chill, which is followed by a rise of temperature of 103–105° F. The urine is distinctly bloody and appropriate tests show the presence therein of a large amount of hemoglobin. . . . Delirium and jaundice are inconstant symptoms.[9]

The reader may compare Dr. Feinblatt's description with the classic account written by Denys himself:

As soon as the blood entered into his Veins, he felt the same heat all along his arm and in his Armpits which he had done before. His Pulse was forthwith raised, and a while after we observed a great Sweat sprinkeled all over his face. His pulse at this moment was very much altered; and he complained of a great Pain and Illness in his Stomach and that he should be presently choaked, unless we would let him go. . . . By and by he was laid in his bed, and after he had for two hours sustained much violence, vomiting up divers liquors which had disturbed his Stomach, he fell into a profound Sleep about ten a clock, and slept all that night without intermission till eight a clock the next day. . . . When he awakened he seemed wonderfully composed and in his right mind, expressing the Pain and universal weariness that he felt

in all his members. He pist a large glass full of such black Urine that you would have said it has been mixed with soot. . . .[10]

In addition to reactions arising from the incompatibility of blood, the great danger of any operation performed before the discovery of asepsis and antiseptics made transfusion a therapeutic measure of doubtful value. Owing to the pressure of both administrative and ecclesiastical disfavor, and the lack of success in many trials, further experiments at human transfusion ceased. The practice apparently fell into almost complete desuetude until revived in the early part of the nineteenth century by the English physician and obstetrician, James Blundell.

Blundell was appalled by his complete helplessness in cases of puerperal hemorrhage, when after delivery of the child the mother frequently bled to death. He thought of returning blood to such women by transfusion. His most difficult problem was to get the blood from the donor to the patient without its coagulating on the way. He was, however, only able to get a small quantity into the veins of his patients, a fact which probably accounts for the relatively small number of fatalities.

He wrote in 1834 that if he had any claim, "however small, to rank among supporters of transfusion, it lies entirely in this; that undeterred by clamor and skepticism, I have made it my endeavor again to bring the operation into notice." [11]

Blundell devised various means for effecting a direct transfusion from one human being to another without having to draw off the blood in a vessel, then allow it to enter the blood stream of the patient. He worked out mechanical devices to enable direct transfusion to take place without performing an operation upon the artery of the donor, in those days a formidable and dangerous procedure.

From our present-day vantage point of knowledge of blood groups and blood incompatibilities, we may well wonder how it was possible for as many successes to occur as actually did. The reason may be that the transfusions were most often given in extreme cases, when the doctor thought that no other remedy could possibly save the patient. Since the patient would have died in any case, a death from transfusion was not so marked. Dr. Geoffrey Keynes remarks, for example, that all the patients transfused by Blundell were "either exceedingly ill, or, judging from his description, already dead." His results, therefore, "considered statistically, were not favorable." [12]

⁊⧜   ⁊⧜   ⁊⧜

The great problem was how to get the blood to flow into the patient's veins without coagulation. One means of overcoming this obstacle was the use of defibrinated blood — that is, blood deprived of its normal fibrin, or coagulable lymph. Even so, the results were not too encouraging. A report in 1863 indicated that of 116 transfusions performed during the previous forty years, only 56 (a little less than half) had been successful.[13] No one at that time could fully explain the fatalities, which were thought to be due to the introduction of air bubbles into the circulation.

Since human donors of blood were in any case difficult to find, and the reactions of the patients were frequently severe, in many cases followed by death, several experimenters used animal blood as well as the transfusion of physiological salt solutions (to replace lost blood fluid) directly into the human blood stream. The use of physiological salt solutions had definite advantages; it eliminated the donor, the technique was simple, the solution did not coagulate during administration, and, above all, it was a safe procedure in which no severe reaction took place in the patient to cause his death.

During the last forty years or so of the nineteenth century, while the development of physiological salt solutions was taking place, tremendous progress was made in all fields of the medical sciences. The advances in bacteriology, associated with the germ theory of disease and the development of aseptic surgical practice, largely eliminated the danger of infection during transfusion. Of equal, if not greater, importance was the growth of the science of immunology to which contributions were made by scientists of many different countries. One field of immunological investigation was concerned with studies on blood coagulation and agglutination. This was to help create a revolution in medical practice, as well as in our knowledge of physiology, that would make possible blood transfusion as a safe and regular procedure, and also lead to the large-scale use of blood plasma and other products of the blood with which we were all familiar during World War II.

⁊⧜   ⁊⧜   ⁊⧜

The momentous discovery was made by the Austrian immunologist, Karl Landsteiner, in 1900. Landsteiner found that human blood contains substances which are capable of agglutinating other red blood corpuscles, and that human bloods can be divided into groups in accordance with their agglutinating reactions.* After having obtained his M.D. degree, Landsteiner studied chemistry under the great Emil Fischer and other famous chemists, and devoted the greater part of his mature lifetime to research in medicine, which he conducted, after his discovery of the blood groups, mostly at the Rockefeller Institute for Medical Research in New York.[14]

Like all first-rank scientists, Landsteiner made many contributions. He introduced the dark field microscope into the identification of syphilis; he first demonstrated that the dread disease of infantile paralysis is transmitted by a virus. Some of his greatest scientific discoveries were in the field of "immunological specificity," to which his only book was devoted.† Nevertheless, the Nobel Prize was awarded to him for discovery of the blood groups in view of its practical importance.

∽   ∽   ∽

If sedimented red corpuscles of blood are shaken up in a fluid, they will generally disperse themselves evenly, none of the corpuscles sticking together. If, on the other hand, the red corpuscles of one individual are mixed with the blood (plasma) or the liquid part of the serum of a second individual, they may disperse evenly and remain separate, but they may also aggregate rapidly to form clumps and clusters. This serological reaction is known as *agglutination*.

Landsteiner's investigations showed that the red blood corpuscles in human beings may possess agglutinable substances which we denote as *A* or *B*. Called *agglutinogens,* because they may be ag-

---

* *Agglutination,* which we shall discuss at length in the following pages, refers to the sticking together of the red cells of a blood; it may be caused by a number of agents, of which the commonest is the serum or plasma of an incompatible blood; thus agglutination might result from mixing two different bloods. *Coagulation* of blood refers to its change from the normal liquid state to a solid or jellylike mass, which occurs sooner or later after it is withdrawn from the circulation, unless special measures to prevent it are taken. Contact with skin, air, glass, metal, etc., generally speeds up coagulation.

† "Immunological specificity" refers to the fact that substances produced in our bodies to act counter to disease-producing micro-organisms or their products show a certain selectivity, usually reacting most strongly with the micro-organisms which caused their production.

glutinated, they may be present singly, double, or not at all. If the red blood cells of an individual contain agglutinogen *A,* we say that he belongs to *group A,* if *B* then *group B,* if both *A* and *B* then *group AB,* while if neither, then *group O.* In this way we can classify all human beings into four fundamental blood groups, *A, B, AB,* and *O.*[15] When Landsteiner announced his discovery in 1900, he knew of only three of these groups; the fourth (*AB*) was added in 1902 by his pupil DeCastello and by Sturli.[16]

Blood not only contains agglutinogens such as we have just described, but also substances which cause these agglutinogens to agglutinate and which are called agglutinins. These occur in the blood serum rather than in the red corpuscles. Landsteiner's great discovery may be expressed therefore in the three-word sentence made of the new words we have just learned: *Agglutinins agglutinate agglutinogens.* The agglutinins are denoted in a fashion that makes their action both easy to understand and easy to remember. That which causes agglutinogen *A* to clump or agglutinate is denoted *anti-A,* while that which agglutinates *B* is denoted *anti-B.* No individual can carry in his blood both *A* and *anti-A,* since in that event agglutination would swiftly occur and cause death. Likewise no single individual can carry both *B* and *anti-B.* But Landsteiner discovered a less obvious law, namely, that if a person's blood cells do *not* contain the agglutinogen *A,* then his blood serum contains the agglutinin *anti-A,* and if not *B,* then always *anti-B.* We may state this information conveniently in a table.[17]

BLOOD GROUP	BLOOD CORPUSCLES		SERUM
International classification	*Contain the agglutinable substance (agglutinogen)*	*Are agglutinated by serum of group*	*Contains agglutinating substance (agglutinin)*
O	*none*	*none*	anti-A *and* anti-B
A	A	O *and* B	anti-B
B	B	O *and* A	anti-A
AB	A *and* B	O, A, *and* B	*none*

Let us examine the table in order to see what occurs when persons of different blood groups undergo transfusions from one to the other. Let us suppose, for example, that a transfusion of blood from a donor of group *A* is given to a patient of group *B*. The red cells of blood transfused contain the agglutinable substance *A*, while the serum of the patient contains the agglutinating substance *anti-A*. As a result, the red cells which have been transfused will be agglutinated and produce a reaction which may cause death. In the same way, if the donor belongs to group *B* and the patient to *A*, then the red cells of the donor's blood will contain the agglutinable substance *B*, while the patient's serum will contain the agglutinating substance *anti-B*. The result, once again, will be that the red cells transfused into the patient will be agglutinated and may cause death.

If a donor who belongs to group *AB* gives his blood to a patient belonging to either group *A* or group *B*, a reaction will always take place. Such a donor has in his blood corpuscles the agglutinable substance *A* and also *B*. In the one case, these will be agglutinated by *anti-A*, in the other by *anti-B*.

A person who belongs to group *AB* can in general receive blood from any group because his serum contains *no* agglutinating substances (neither *anti-A* nor *anti-B*) and will not, therefore, cause the agglutination of any red cells introduced into his blood stream. Such a person, who cannot give blood to anyone not a member of the same group *AB*, but who can receive blood from anyone, is sometimes denoted a "universal recipient."

Those who belong to group *O* have no agglutinable substances (neither *A* nor *B*) in their blood corpuscles. Thus they may give their blood safely to members of any of the four groups and are sometimes known as "universal donors."

∾ ∾ ∾

Today, universal laboratory practice is to reject as a possible donor anyone whose red cells may be agglutinated by the agglutinating substances in the patient's serum. It does not matter quite so much if the serum of the donor may contain agglutinating substances which affect the red cells of the patient. The reason for this curious fact was given in 1911 by Dr. Reuben Ottenberg of New York City. It explains the clinical evidence that when transfusions are made between persons belonging to different blood groups, accidents occur less regularly than superficial thinking might lead one to expect.[18]

Human agglutinins, or agglutinating substances found in the serum or the plasma of the blood such as *anti-A* or *anti-B,* are relatively weak in their action and are seldom active at a dilution of 1/10 or higher. The average volume of blood in an adult human being is 5000 cc. to about 8000 cc., and the average transfusion 500 cc. or less. A total mixture of the two bloods occurs quite rapidly and the dilution of the donor's blood is of the order of 500/5000 or 1/10. Thus no appreciable agglutination of the corpuscles in the patient's blood is produced by the action of the agglutinins in the serum of the blood of the donor. In other words, because of the small amount of agglutinating substance distributed over so large a number of agglutinable cells, each red cell is too feebly sensitized to produce any effect. When, however, a small volume of agglutinable cells from the donor are introduced into the blood stream of a patient whose serum contains an agglutinating substance for those cells, a quite different situation obtains. Each such cell receives at once a large amount of the agglutinating substance from the serum of the blood into which it has been introduced by the transfusion, and a reaction will occur in which the red cells introduced into the patient will be agglutinated.[19]

Peoples who are of European stock have approximately the following blood-group distribution:

Group O	40 per cent
Group A	40 per cent
Group B	15 per cent
Group AB	5 per cent

Assuming that diseases, and the need for transfusion, occur with equal frequency among people of all blood groups, then the great majority of transfusions will normally occur between members of group *O* and group *A,* which together account for 80 per cent of the European population. In the event of a donor belonging to group *O* giving blood to a patient of group *A,* we have a case of what was described in the preceding paragraph; even though the donor's serum contains the agglutinating substance *anti-A* and the patient's red cells contain the agglutinable substance *A,* there is no danger of a serious reaction. Thus 40 per cent of the population (the members of group *A*) can safely receive blood from persons belonging to group *O,* and also, of course, from members of their own group, *A.* In other words, this 40 per cent of the population can receive blood from 80 per cent of the population (groups *O* and *A*), and only the blood of 20 per cent of the population (groups *B* and *AB*) will be sure to cause a serious reaction. This type of analysis shows why it is that a goodly number of transfusions did *not* produce death, nor even violent reactions, despite the fact that they were made before tests had been established for inter-group incompatibility.

We shall not discuss here the manipulative technique of determining blood groups, although it may be pointed out that on the basis of the table which we have printed above, one can determine the blood group of an individual by testing the reaction which occurs between his blood and bloods of other known types.

Since Landsteiner's original discovery, research workers have added greatly to our knowledge. Landsteiner originally, in 1900, had conceived of only three blood groups, and two years later a fourth group was added. Today we have not only these four groups into which we classify all human blood but there are subgroups within these, and also an *M* and *N,* and other classifications which we do not have space to discuss at any length, such as the *Rh* factor.

Landsteiner's work had not been directed at solving the vital problem of transfusions; his interest was largely in the general fields of immunology and biochemistry. Although Landsteiner had pointed out possible applications, it was not until some seven years later that Hektoen (1907) succeeded in calling attention to the significance of agglutinins in human blood transfusions and their relation to the hitherto unexplained fatalities from the infusion of human blood.[20] Two separate classifications of the reactions were worked out, one by Jansky in Europe, and another by Moss in this country. For a considerable period of time, therefore, the situation was confused by the existence of two different and partly contradictory systems of denoting the blood groups. In recent years an international agreement has resulted in a classification using letters.

Nevertheless, in many parts of the world, including the United States, a few hospitals continue to use confusing old notations.

COMPARISON OF GROUP NAMES

International	Jansky	Moss
O	I	IV
A	II	II
B	III	III
AB	IV	I

In 1908, improved chemical methods for typing human bloods with relative rapidity were published by Dr. Ottenberg, who urged that they be applied before attempting transfusion of blood.

ᖇᐤ   ᖇᐤ   ᖇᐤ

Did the surgeons adopt the new fundamental discoveries about blood? Were the principles of blood grouping applied universally and forthwith as a guide to transfusion? Apparently not.

This whole problem has been investigated by Dr. Bertram M. Bernheim, associate professor of surgery in the Johns Hopkins Medical School.[21] As a young surgeon, Dr. Bernheim was personally associated with the development of blood transfusion and himself made a significant contribution to the art.

Dr. Bernheim writes that we must keep in mind "that two things, more than anything else, conspired to retard the consummation of blood transfusion. One was blood incompatibilities, while the other was the phenomenon of blood coagulation." We have seen that Landsteiner's discovery of the blood groups showed the cause of agglutination. Another result of mixing two bloods was "hemolysis," a disintegration of the red blood cells themselves, frequently ending in death. Agglutination is sometimes considered an early stage of hemolysis,[22] and it always is present when hemolysis occurs.* Tests

---

* Within a few years of Landsteiner's discovery of the blood groups, it was shown by Moss that "isohemolysins" (*anti-A* and *anti-B*), antibodies that produce "lysis" or disintegration of the red cells in the blood, occur with regularity in human serum and that "susceptibilities" (or "hemolysinigens" *A* and *B*) occur with perfect regularity in human red cells. These substances exactly parallel the agglutinogens and agglutinins, the only difference being that the hemolysins in the serum are *not always* present when they would be expected. Agglutination tests, therefore, also assure safety in transfusion with regard to hemolysis.[23]

for compatibility of donor and patient prevent not only agglutination, but hemolysis as well.

But, as Dr. Bernheim points out, what practical value would all this knowledge have if one still couldn't *do* a transfusion? Fundamental research on the blood groups, although the chief topic of this chapter in the general context of this book, was far from being the major concern of the surgeon. What good was a mode of ensuring that no serious reaction would follow the transfer of blood, so long as *the blood could not be transferred!* Dr. Bernheim suggests the following analogy: "A similar situation would exist if we had electricity but no wire to transmit it — or, perhaps, only a flimsy, uncertain thing that twisted and broke under pressure and at critical moments." [24]

We have referred earlier to the stages whereby interest in transfusion during the last three centuries repeatedly waxed and waned. This subject was reborn in our own times by the classic experiments of the late Alexis Carrel on arterial anastomosis, the method of uniting together, end to end, the blood vessels of two living creatures. Carrel had perfected his technique on dogs before performing his first human transfusion, one in which an artery of a well-known New York surgeon was united to a vein of his newborn child, whose life thereby was saved.[25]

By using Carrel's method, blood could pass directly from one person to the other without coming into contact with metal or with glass, which would induce coagulation. This remained a difficult procedure requiring a formidable technique, and a transfusion was still a major operation. Various improvements were suggested to make transfusion simple, the most important being that of George Crile in 1907, which brought the intima of the two blood vessels (that is, their innermost coat) close together, without offering any raw surfaces that might promote coagulation. Another was Dr. Bernheim's double tube of 1912, coated with oil or vaseline to prevent coagulation. The disadvantage remained, however, that the donor must sacrifice an artery in the process, and this was not eliminated until the years just before the First World War when oil- or paraffin-coated syringes made indirect transfusions possible.

In addition, however, to the devices for linking together the circulatory systems of patient and donor, a most important discovery was made in 1915 by Dr. Richard Lewisohn of New York City. Lewisohn found a way to prevent human blood from coagulating, by introducing sodium citrate. As a result, blood could thenceforth be transferred from one person to another with a relative ease that would have astonished the workers in this field a century earlier. Curiously enough, this significant innovation was published independently, within a few weeks, by Lewisohn in New York and L. Agote in Buenos Aires, Argentina. Dr. Hustin in Brussels had also been working with sodium citrate, as had Dr. Richard Weil in New York. Lewisohn is generally given most of the credit, which he earned because he "worked out the upper and lower limits of dosage so carefully and his technique was so simple that it has hardly been changed to this day." [26] Here is yet another example of that phenomenon of simultaneous, independent discovery which we discussed in Chapter 3.

It is difficult to overestimate the importance of sodium citrate. As Dr. Bernheim tells us, once and for all the difficulties of performing an operation in order to transfuse blood were gone. To obtain blood from a donor today, one has simply to stick a small hollow needle into a vein and attach a bottle to the needle by means of rubber tubing. The addition of citrate prevents coagulation and the citrated blood can be given to the patient as needed. "Young doctors, old doctors, internes, nurses, technicians, all do citrate transfusions without the slightest difficulty." [27]

There can be no question, then, that it was the discovery of citrate that put blood transfusion on the map, making it a part of everyday procedure. Without citrate, transfusion on the scale of World Wars I and II * would have been impossible. In this chapter, however, we are not so much interested in the history of transfusion as such, but rather in the contribution to transfusion of Landsteiner's fundamental discovery of the agglutinative properties of normal human bloods.

⁕⁓   ⁕⁓   ⁕⁓

In the early years of the twentieth century, while the surgeons were busy at their appointed task of getting the blood to flow easily, with-

---

* In World War II, a combination of citric acid, sodium citrate, and dextrose (rather than sodium citrate alone) was used.

out coagulating, and in measurable quantities, little if any consideration was, in general, given to blood grouping. Furthermore, the
surgeons usually did not even employ the Wassermann test, to make
sure that the blood transfused into the patient was free of syphilis
spirochetes. Cases are on record of a patient not only contracting
syphilis as a result of a transfusion, but also malaria.

A comprehensive review of blood transfusion was published in the
New York Medical Journal of 16 May 1908.[28] This article stressed
the need of aseptic conditions as the most important factor in safe
transfusions and did not once refer to the possibility of intergroup
blood incompatibilities. All cases listed in the article had been transfused without any preliminary tests.

In the following year, a widely read book on the subject of transfusion was published by the surgeon George Crile, whose important
contribution to operative technique has already been described.
Despite the fact that Landsteiner's results had been published *nine
years earlier,* and that further additions to the subject had grown
into a considerable literature, Crile expressed the generally accepted
opinion of the day, that "healthy" bloods are "apparently inter-
changeable." He concluded: "At the present time we are probably
only on the boundary line of knowledge concerning the different
constituents of the blood and their reactions. Moreover, what is apparently true today may be contradicted tomorrow, so that we cannot feel very sure of our ground until more research work has been
undertaken and the results tested by time."[29] Crile was a very great
surgeon even though he advanced some rather wild theories, and,
but for his own contributions, the art of transfusion might have been
delayed considerably in its development. I would not wish to dis-
parage his achievement in any way, yet it is hard to resist the temptation to remark that what Crile said in his widely read book "may be
contradicted tomorrow" had actually been contradicted nine years
earlier. The fundamental knowledge concerning agglutination, if it
was known to this great contemporary clinician at all, was obviously
not highly regarded.

Another interesting story is that of Dr. Roy D. McClure, who,
in collaboration with his chief, Eugene H. Pool, a renowned surgeon
of New York City, reported a series of twelve transfusions performed
on ten patients without making any reference to tests for blood

incompatibilities, beyond the statement, "Haemolytic and agglutination tests with the two bloods may be carried out if circumstances
permit, but the necessity for and the value of these tests is undecided." [30] Seven years later, in 1917, Dr. McClure published a
report on 150 transfusions at the Johns Hopkins Hospital.[31] In this
article he remarks, "Eight or nine years ago, great discredit was
thrown upon these laboratory tests [for matching blood] by most
of the men doing transfusion. It was a common saying that haemoly-
sis or agglutination might occur in vitro [the test tube], but not
in vivo [the body], and vice versa. At first I agreed with this attitude,
and while in New York good fortune was on my side and I had no
serious accidents. Later, however, I became convinced of the great
importance of these tests, and shall never again consent to do a transfusion except under the most extreme emergency without the proper
report from these laboratory tests."

Most revealing of the attitude of the times is an article cited by
Dr. Bernheim which appeared in the *Journal of the American Medical Association* in 1907, a report on a case in which death was caused
by hemolysis following a transfusion, first from the patient's wife
and a few days later from his brother-in-law.[32] The investigators
published an extensive report, including the results of autopsy, pathological findings, and so on. They actually tested the "serum of the
patient's blood against the red cells of a normal individual" (whatever the word "normal" may mean in this connection) "but with
negative results." As Dr. Bernheim comments, we wonder why they
failed to do what seems obvious — namely, to test the blood of the
patient against that of the two donors. Since the patient lingered on
for a week, it was perfectly possible to perform such tests. It is apparent the authors were groping for light but were not sufficiently
informed on the subject, or had failed to search the literature to
find the true cause.

All the examples cited above come from the records of American
clinicians and surgeons. How did they miss the great discovery of
the Austrian, Landsteiner? Was there nothing in the American
literature on this great issue? Were they unfamiliar with the
European literature? And did the Europeans take more speedy
advantage of blood groups?

Moss, who established a method of grouping, and whose names for the four primary blood groups were standard in a large part of the world until recently, was an American. He published his "Studies on Isoagglutinins and Isohaemolysins" in the *Bulletin of the Johns Hopkins Hospital* in 1910 for all to read. Ottenberg, another American, who developed a more speedy and practical test for blood groups, reported in 1911 that these tests should invariably be made, that in cases where time does not permit the tests, "one had to weigh the possible dangers of agglutination or hemolysis against the dangers of letting the patient go without transfusion." In 1911 in an article published in the American *Journal of Experimental Medicine,* he warned surgeons of the possibility of accidents and deaths and pointed out that they could be prevented.* Some Americans, at any rate, were not only aware of the European progress in fundamental knowledge but were also advancing it.

        ∿   ∿   ∿

As to European developments in the art of transfusion — there were practically none. Geoffrey Keynes, the British surgeon and bibliophile, pointed out in 1922 the lack of interest in direct transfusion of blood in England as well as on the Continent prior to World War I. According to Keynes, the decline of interest was due to "the increasing number of fatalities which had followed the more general use of transfusion" at the end of the nineteenth century. But it was also to be accounted for "by the increasing use of normal saline solution for intravenous injection in the treatment of hemorrhage." [34] The situation at the beginning of the century was, of course, much the same in America. But Carrel's work stimulated ingenious American doctors like Crile and Bernheim to perfect the necessary devices to allow direct transfusion; while the Europeans were apparently as indifferent to the practical advances made by the Americans as those same American surgeons, who developed and practiced transfusion, were to the fundamental discovery of Landsteiner!

The education of the European doctors came about through American participation in the First World War. After describing the great advances made in America in the art of blood transfusion, Keynes wrote in 1922 that they "coincided so nearly with the be-

* Dr. Ottenberg was "the first to apply Landsteiner's discovery for determination of compatibility in an actual transfusion." [33]

ginning of the war that it seemed almost as if foreknowledge of the necessity for it in treating war wounds had stimulated research. Yet during the first two years of the war almost nothing was known in the British Army of its possibilities. I have no evidence that the French or German army doctors were any better informed than ourselves. . . . It was not until 1917, when the British Army Medical Corps was being steadily reinforced with officers from the United States of America, that knowledge of blood transfusion began to spread through the Armies." [35]

Dr. Keynes informs me that he learned the "American" technique of blood transfusion from the Harvard Medical Unit of World War I. They showed him and his colleagues how to use citrate and the technique was introduced immediately, together with preliminary tests for compatibility.[36] The method of transfusion as introduced by the Americans to the British "united the four cardinal virtues of simplicity, certainty, safety, and efficiency." [37]

The great European doctors must have either failed to read the American medical journals and books, or, having read them, refused to believe them.* Since only in America was blood transfusion practiced, while in Europe the fluid used was usually a salt solution, Landsteiner's discovery was not as immediately related to practice for European surgeons as for Americans.

ᕤᕗ   ᕤᕗ   ᕤᕗ

Although the application of Landsteiner's discovery to transfusion is unquestionably one of the utmost importance, there have been others as well. One such has resulted from an extensive study of the inheritance of blood groups in offspring whose parents are of known blood groups.

Today in many cases, one can, by knowing the blood group of a child and its mother, determine whether or not a given man may be the father of the child. This test for parenthood is now recognized in many states and is accepted as evidence by the courts. In questions of doubtful parenthood these tests cannot tell us whether a given man *is* the father of a child, but they can always tell us whether the man in question *can possibly be* the child's father.

* L. and M. Hirszfeld, who discovered the racial variation in blood group frequencies, were working on transfusions and grouping on the Macedonian front and are egregious exceptions.[38]

Yet, astonishing as it may seem — and the whole story of blood groups is replete with just such astonishing facts — there is no state of the Union in which evidence from blood groups concerning parenthood must be accepted as conclusive. In other words, the scientific principles that make blood transfusion safe need not be applied in forensic medicine. Thus there are well-known instances of a "father" so named by court decision and ordered to support a child, even though the blood groups indicate without any doubt (to the scientist, if not the jurist!) that he could *not possibly* have fathered it.

෴ ෴ ෴

A vastly important and fascinating application of knowledge of the blood groups has been to the study of man himself — physical anthropology. This work begins with the pioneering efforts of the Hirszfelds, published soon after the end of World War I.

Studies on the blood groups of various persons, and on various groups of individuals in different parts of the world, have been carried out extensively during the last thirty or more years. The results give us, for the first time, definite information on the mechanism of differentiation of peoples and enable us to classify races of mankind according to whether the genes which produce particular blood groups are present or absent. Thus Dr. P. B. Candela maintains that blood group *B* was "almost certainly introduced into Europe between the fifth and 15th century A.D. by the Asiatic armies which invaded Europe during the lapse of those ten centuries." [39] He was able to reach this hypothesis by correlating the data of history, physical anthropology, and the analysis of the blood groups. Dr. William Boyd has combined the details of blood group frequencies in many different parts of the world, and has been able to obtain thereby considerable information on the early history of man and theories concerning the early migrations of peoples. [40] Blood group frequencies, and the gene frequencies for the different blood groups, have been worked out in great detail. Boyd has also studied the tissues of Egyptian mummies, preserved for a great many centuries but which still afford information concerning the blood groups of the human beings they once were.

෴ ෴ ෴

Looking back at the development and use of blood groups, one cannot help being struck by several outstanding features. In the first place, this discovery, hailed the world over as one of the great 20th-century achievements in practical medicine, and the basis of the Nobel Prize in medicine awarded in 1930 to Dr. Landsteiner, was made by him because of his interest in chemistry, in the serological differences in human blood, and in the general immunological problems connected with the study of the blood. He was never much concerned with doing transfusions before his discovery, or even afterwards with the application of the blood groups to transfusion procedure. The commonly used methods for testing blood groups were developed by other investigators. The reason is probably that Landsteiner was in Austria until after the First World War, and, as we saw earlier, continental developments in transfusion practice were meager. Landsteiner himself always felt his greatest contribution to medicine was that of the concept of specificity, a topic to which his last publication was devoted.

Over the years, Landsteiner's interest in blood groups brought forth new discoveries, for example the three additional agglutionogens $M, N,$ and $P,$ which he discovered working with P. Levine in 1928. In 1940, Landsteiner and A. S. Wiener demonstrated the existence of yet another agglutinogen, the Rh factor. Curiously enough, before the new Rh blood factor had been announced, Levine and R. E. Stetson had reported on a blood incompatibility that suggested a line of thought that ran parallel to our present knowledge of $Rh.$[41]

The importance of the discovery of the Rh factor, in contrast to the four primary blood groups, is that whereas the latter are vital in preventing deaths that might arise from blood transfusions, the Rh factor must be taken into account in normal childbirth, even if no transfusion enters the picture. It would be an unwise obstetrician indeed who would neglect the Rh factor in any woman's second pregnancy today. The most astonishing aspect of this new advance, if not the incompatibility between the blood of a mother and her fetus, is perhaps the fact that the discovery was made by investigating the blood of a rhesus monkey, therefore the name, $Rh.$

Landsteiner's great original discovery would certainly be classified by anyone acquainted with the facts as a fundamental finding about the nature of the blood of animals and human beings. Its importance, and the importance of other recent advances, such as the *Rh* factor, in saving lives, indicate the large-scale vital value of the work. Landsteiner certainly knew, when he began his investigations on the blood, that any discovery he might possibly make would have a practical importance if it was truly fundamental. Most research in experimental medicine or physiology partakes of this double aspect, in being at once a contribution to knowledge and a source of practical procedure. For this reason, and because of a limited understanding of the dual nature of all scientific discoveries, medicine has frequently been called an "applied science." But in the light of our discussion here it should be clear that such a statement has little meaning. The fact of the matter is that fundamental discoveries in medicine or physiology, in so far as they add to our basic knowledge, constitute fundamental discoveries of exactly the same sort as those in physics, chemistry, biology, geology, and astronomy. The only difference is that in the other sciences the practical application of the discovery may not be apparent (and, in fact, may not be found) for many years to come. But in medicine or physiology such discoveries are of comparatively immediate applicable value.

Of course, before the discovery is made, no one knows what its value will be. When Landsteiner began his researches on the nature of the blood, he did not know that he would solve the problem of successful blood transfusion. No one, obviously, knew as yet that blood groups existed. Nevertheless, it was clear that any discovery of an important kind about the nature of the blood would be of use to all practicing physicians, no matter what that discovery was, because of the very nature and function of the blood in all living organisms.

CHAPTER II

The Story of Hybrid Corn

> Experience has shown that . . . few scientific re-
> searches are conducted, whose economic bearings
> do not sooner or later become manifest, though
> their true economic worth may not be recognized
> for years.
> — GEORGE HARRISON SHULL (1907)

CORN IS ONE of the most characteristic products of the New World. The true test of the Americanization of immigrants may well be their willingness to eat corn on the cob and the extent to which they enjoy it. Not only is corn the foremost American cereal, but the story of its development and use from the time of the arrival of the white man on our shores to the present is also the story of American agriculture.

Corn is grown in every one of the forty-eight states; somewhere in the neighborhood of 100 million acres are planted each year. Corn far exceeds in production and market value the combined annual crops of wheat, oats, barley, rice, and buckwheat. Its principal use is as feed for livestock, and about 80 per cent is fed to stock on the very farms on which it is grown;[1] it is used for various commercial and industrial processes; a huge quantity of sweet corn is eaten as a vegetable every summer; and a large industry is devoted exclusively to canning corn for home consumption.

The word itself comes from the old Saxon or Teutonic "Korn," which is a general term for any cereal. In many countries the word "corn" designates the particular cereal most consumed for human food in that country. In England, for example, "corn" and "corn trade" are generally used in reference to wheat. By corn, in concurrence with the usage just described, we will mean the cereal sometimes designated as "maize," a name that derives from the Arawak (Indian) word, many forms of which are encountered today in South America and the West Indies.* Some scientific writers have tried to introduce this word as a substitute for the more general word "corn," but to all Americans corn will ever designate the particular variety which we eat served "on the cob."

For reasons which we shall presently discuss, corn has been studied more than any other American cereal. Evidence leads us to believe that if corn is not the oldest cultivated plant in the whole history of man, it may well be the oldest cultivated cereal. In the form in which we find it today, it is totally unsuited to exist in the wild, and its continued growth requires the agency of human hands. This is in distinction to almost all other cereals and almost all other plants. If we leave a field of wheat or barley unharvested, the seed will fall to the ground, germinate and take root, and be the source of a new growth or stand the following year. Thus in many cultivated fields, seeds from earlier harvests give rise to some unwanted growths. Corn is quite different. If the ears of corn are not picked, but are simply allowed to stay in the field, there will not be a new growth of corn the following year; that would require the grower to unwrap the ears, pick off the seeds, and put them into the ground.

Since plants existed before man cultivated them, some wild ancestor of corn, unlike the corn we know today, must have been able to grow year after year as other cereals do, without human agency. Some of the relatives of the corn family still grow wild; the most outstanding example is *teosinte,* so common in Mexico.

One very probable hypothesis concerning the origin of corn was first proposed in the nineteenth century, and is supported with considerable new evidence in our own time by Paul Mangelsdorf of Harvard University and R. G. Reeves of the Texas Agricultural Experiment Station.[2] According to this hypothesis, the beginnings of corn go back to the extreme southwestern part of the basin of the Amazon River. Since this region has not as yet been fully explored, wild corn may still be found there. Whatever theory is finally vindicated concerning its origin, no one will deny that the time required for corn to reach its present state has surely taken many thousands of years. Since corn is a product of the New World, this may place the beginnings of American agriculture at a much earlier

* *Mahiz, marisi, marichi, mariky, mazy, maysi.*

date than any evidence would warrant for the beginnings of agriculture in Europe or Asia.

Corn has played a great role in American history. When the first settlers landed in New England, one of the foods which prevented their expedition from ending in the tragedy of starvation was the corn they obtained from the Indians. Governor Bradford, in his *History of the Plymouth Plantation,* relates how on 15 November 1620, a party of Pilgrims led by Captain Myles Standish spied some Indians whom they followed all that day. The next morning they found "new-stuble wher corne had been set y⁰ same year . . . and heaps of sand newly padled with their hands, which they, digging up, found in them diverce faire Indean baskets filled with corne, and some in eares, faire and good, of diverce collours, which seemed to them a very goodly sight (haveing never seen any shuch before)." ⁸

Corn, one of the staples of the early New England diet, is particularly American in the following ways: it originated in the New World; it was extensively cultivated by the Indians; it was the staple food in the New England colonies; and America is still by far the greatest corn-producing country.

The first American settlers knew four types of corn: popcorn, flint corn, dent corn, and soft corn. Sweet corn, the fifth, was discovered in cultivation among the Iroquois Indians by Captain Richard Bagnall.⁴ He brought some from western New York to Plymouth and grew it in his garden. These five still stand today as the chief types.* The dent corn receives its name from the in*denta*tion present in every kernel. This is caused by the shrinking of the soft, starchy parts of the endosperm. Today dent corn forms the bulk of the American corn crop.

ᔕᔕ   ᔕᔕ   ᔕᔕ

"History," wrote the great French naturalist, J. H. Fabre, "celebrates the battlefields whereon we meet our death, but scorns to speak of the plowed fields whereby we thrive. It knows the names of

---

* Those with a flair for "botanizing" may be interested in the family names:
  Zea mays everta, popcorn
  Zea mays indurata, flint corn
  Zea mays indentata, dent corn
  Zea mays amylacea, soft corn
  Zea mays saccharata, sweet corn

the King's bastards, but cannot tell us the origin of wheat. This is the way of human folly." [5] With corn as with wheat, few know much about its origin. An even smaller number of us are aware of the steps by which the splendid production of today was developed from the type of corn grown by the Indians and adapted so quickly to the needs of the first white settlers.

The early work on corn improvement made use of "practical methods," chief among which were "mass selection" and "ear-to-row selection." Mass selection consists of choosing plants from a crop and planting en masse the seed harvested from them. This method was used by corn growers from the very earliest times. A farmer would naturally select the best plants and obtain his seed from the ears growing on them.

The ear-to-row method was based on a means of determining the relative planting value of different ears. The farmer, or experimenter, would plant only a portion of the seed from likely ears, using a separate row for the seed from each ear. Hence the name, one-ear-to-a-row. The remainder of the seed from each ear was stored in a carefully labeled box or bottle. At the end of the season, each row would be harvested separately, so that the yield of seed from any of the ears could be compared to that of the others. The theory behind this was that one could select seed from the most productive rows, or plant the remaining seed from the mother ears with the highest yield, continuing the process for a number of years in order to improve the yielding ability. [6]

The ear-to-row method of selection was inaugurated by Cyril G. Hopkins, who began in 1896 to try to improve corn at the Illinois Agricultural Experiment Station. Hopkins, a chemist by training, was interested in altering the chemistry of the corn kernel so as to increase its fat and protein content. In order to carry out his experiments, he devised the new technique, sometimes denoted the "Illinois ear-to-row method," and still in use. Hopkins took enough kernels from each test ear to enable him to plant a row with about twenty-five hills. Each row was harvested and studied separately, and its performance compared to that of another row on the breeding plot. Since only a few kernels of each ear were necessary to make a row, later generations could always be checked back against the original ear. [7] In this way Hopkins achieved partial success. But the over-all protein content per acre remained substantially the same because, while the protein content of the corn went up, the total corn yield per acre went down.[8] Corn was evidently a difficult cereal to improve.

The most successful nineteenth-century corn growers (apparently because of some God-given insight never scientifically investigated) were able to guess which particular ears would give a good yield the following year. But despite a certain measure of success achieved, a great stumbling block was the habit of all corn of not "breeding true." What this means in practice is that one can take kernels from an ear of corn, large and well-made, growing on a plant which produces a large number of ears, and plant the kernels from those ears the next year, only to find that the product from this seed is totally different. In order to understand why this is so, we must pause for a moment to learn something about the actual structure of the corn plant.

అ   అ   అ

In the corn plant the male and female reproductive organs grow on the same plant but are situated in separate male and female flowers. Many readers may wonder why this is an important characteristic to be noted, since the common belief is that this situation obtains in all plants. Yet some species have the male and female organs growing in the same inflorescence. And others are of a different sort altogether, and produce male plants having only male reproductive organs, and female plants having only female reproductive organs. One of the commonest examples of plants of this latter type is the date palm. A male tree yields no fruit; neither will a female tree unless it is fertilized by the pollen from a male tree. The ancient Assyrians were well aware of this fact so long ago as the time of Ashurnasirpal, 885–860 B.C. Bas-reliefs from that time depict workers in the groves practicing the art of "artificial" or "hand" pollination, bringing the male flower with its pollen to the female.[9]

In corn, owing to the separation of the male and female flowers, which grow on separate inflorescences of the plant, and the fact that pollination occurs by the action of the wind in blowing the pollen grains to a receptive female flower, self-fertilization of the corn plant would be extremely difficult. Most of the pollen that fertilizes an ear of corn comes from some other corn plant growing either in the same field or in one that is near by.[10]

Selecting seed on the basis of examining the ear alone thus implies that no attention is paid to the pollen which produces the fertilization. Those who argued against picking next year's seed on the basis of this year's ear could compare such a procedure to growing livestock by carefully choosing the cow, mare, or sow, but paying no attention whatever to the choice of bull, stallion, or boar. No progress could be made in improving corn scientifically until a method was devised whereby the grower could control the male as well as the female progenitors of his seed.

The curious fact is that this important development did not come directly from the work of any of the people whose primary concern was to increase the annual corn crop. Had the investigators who successfully solved the problem of corn improvement been interested simply in getting a better corn crop, and confined themselves to that limited objective, the practice of corn breeding would today probably be no further advanced than it was fifty or even a hundred years ago!

Let us see how this improvement came about. We must actually change the subject just a little, carrying ourselves back to the middle of the nineteenth century, to the town of Brünn, Czechoslovakia, capital city of the province of Moravia. There Gregor Johann Mendel, an Augustinian monk, abbot of the monastery of Brünn, discovered the key to the whole problem of the meaning of heredity. Mendel worked with peas, making crosses or hybrids between different varieties and different colors in order to seek out the laws regulating inheritance.* His subsequent discovery of what are today known as the "Mendelian Laws of Heredity" constitutes one of the great landmarks of nineteenth-century thought. And yet the scientific world was not ready to receive the laws.

Mendel published his findings, and was in communication with Karl von Nägeli, one of the leading botanists of the world, to whom he sent accounts of his research. Nobody paid the slightest attention

---

* He also studied stem height, inflated pods, starchy versus sugary cotyledons, as well as the arrangement of the flowers.

to his published articles. For all the good they did, he might just as well have kept his discoveries to himself and never allowed them to venture into the world beyond his commonplace book.[11] It was only years later, at the very beginning of the twentieth century, that Mendel's work became fully appreciated. Then three other investigators — De Vries, Correns, and Tschermak — simultaneously and independently rediscovered the very same laws of heredity and, looking backward, found the work of Mendel and rescued it from the obscurity to which it had been relegated. Here we see an apt illustration of the point we made in an earlier chapter about the way a discovery must fit the times. When the total scientific situation became receptive to Mendel's discovery, the laws of heredity were discovered again by three independent investigators.

Two of the three men who rediscovered the Mendelian laws of heredity used corn as one of the subjects of their research. That they were not interested in the practical aspects of corn growing is attested to by the fact that they were living in countries where corn was not an important economic crop. They used corn in their research because it has useful properties for experimentation: for example, the seeds are large; the male and female parts of the plants are separated from each other so that one can mechanically control fertilization most easily; and the heritable characteristics of the seeds and plant are easily observable and very marked.

The rediscovery of the laws of Mendel stimulated a vast army of research workers who were interested in extending knowledge of the new principles and applying them to various problems of science, especially such problems as were related to Darwin's theory of evolution. One such experimenter was George Harrison Shull, working at the Station for Experimental Evolution at Cold Spring Harbor, established by the Carnegie Institution of Washington in 1904. Shull was the first staff member in residence, arriving 1 May 1904, before the laboratory building was finished.[12]

Shull's aim was to study the inheritance of the number of rows of kernels on the ears of corn as affected by cross-pollination and self-pollination. In his experiments he used the principles of inbreeding, whereby the ears of corn on a given plant are caused to be fertilized artificially by pollen collected from the stamens of the very same plant. One of the first facts encountered by Shull was that self-fertilization or inbreeding results in a deterioration of the product.

In an early paper, published in 1908, Shull mentioned that the cause of this deterioration was unknown. But he also pointed out that many of the hypotheses that had been advanced could hardly stand in the face of the large number of plants that normally are self-fertilized. A noteworthy few, he added, have given up sexual reproduction entirely, and without "in the least degree lessening their physiological vigor or evident chances of success in comparison with sexually-produced plants." Shull declared that even though the dandelion produces its seeds without fertilization no one save the advocate of an unwarrantable theory would "maintain that this plant is on that account undergoing a process of deterioration which threatens it with summary extinction." He observed that many species of violets produce most of their seeds from flowers that never open, in which cross-fertilization could not take place; and the same thing occurs in one of the forms of the small-petaled evening prim-rose, *Oenothera cruciata cleistantha.* Furthermore, in the planting of tobacco crops, cross-pollination within the limits of a single strain produces an inferior offspring, and only self-fertilization could give an offspring with the highest degree of vigor.

How did Shull produce inbreeding in corn? When the silks or ear shoots first began to form and when the stamenate inflorescences or tassels first appeared, he tied a bag about each ear shoot and each stamenate inflorescence so that the pollen would not be allowed to spread and the silks would not receive any pollen. As the male flower grew and the pollen developed, Shull would shake the bag so that the pollen would fall off. When an ample amount of pollen had col-lected in the tassel bag, Shull removed the bag from the ear shoot and immediately covered its green sticky silks with the tassel bag *from the same plant,* thereby forcing upon the plant self-pollination. He then covered the young ears with bags once again so that no other and unwanted pollen could get to them. He planted the seed obtained in this way and the next year repeated the process once again, thus continuing his inbreeding for several generations.

He declared that although "a study of the injurious effects of self-fertilization was not the aim of the investigation, it was immediately apparent in the smaller, weaker stalks, fewer and smaller ears, and the much greater susceptibility to the attacks of the corn smut. These results were almost as marked when the chosen parents were above the average quality as when they were below it, which in itself refutes the idea that the injurious effect is due to the accumulation of deficiencies possessed by the chosen parents." [13]

As Shull's experiments continued, he found that the several inbred lines produced from an original corn plant differed from one another in definite, easily distinguishable traits; and that each line bred true to its own distinguishing characters — that is, in each separate line the offspring would exactly resemble their parents. This seemed to prove that the ordinary, open-pollinated corn which one encounters in a field is not a pure strain at all, but a mixture of many hybrids. Inbreeding offered a relatively simple method for reducing these hybrids to the pure lines which were continually intercrossing in the natural process of promiscuous cross-pollination. The production of many pure (inbred) lines made it possible to obtain new types of hybrids by combining these pure lines in various ways. Significantly, Shull entitled his publication in which these results were embodied and which he read at the 1908 meeting of the American Breeders' Association, "The Composition of a Field of Maize."

In 1909 Shull presented to the American Breeders' Association two further papers on the same subject. His later experiments had shown conclusively that if crossings are repeated between two given inbred lines, the results will invariably be the same. If the pure inbred lines are continued pure by inbreeding, then no matter how often, year after year, one crosses them to produce a hybrid, that hybrid will tend to have the same properties and characteristics.

One of the interesting results noted by Shull was that the hybrid produced by crossing two inbred lines might be not only far superior in size, quantity and quality of yield, and resistance to disease, to each of the two pure types which had produced it, but it might also be superior by far to the *original corn* (itself a hybrid) from which the pure lines had been obtained by inbreeding. Of course, only *some* hybrids produced in this way are superior; others are decidedly inferior. Shull "advocated making many hybrids, and testing them to find *the* superior ones. Only the *best* hybrids exceed the original cross-bred corn." [14]

Thus not only was Shull able to adumbrate a method whereby one could produce a superior type of corn by hybridizing pure inbred types, but his method had the positive virtue that the corn so produced would invariably have the same quality and could be relied upon to supply a superior harvest year after year.

The importance of this discovery can hardly be overestimated. For the first time in the history of corn breeding, a method had been evolved by means of which the product could be guaranteed to yield the desired results, whereas in all previous methods, seed from satisfactory ears of corn was apt to yield an indifferent crop.

The paper delivered by Shull to the American Breeders' Association at the December 1909 meeting in Omaha, Nebraska, was a masterly plea to corn breeders to adopt his methods. He made a great impression, especially since he had with him a splendid exhibit showing the effects of hybridization of inbred lines. On viewing the exhibit, Professor N. E. Hansen declared to Shull: "You have all the other corn breeders skinned a mile." [15]

Shull was the first person ever to make a cross between two pure or inbred lines of corn. Apart from the extreme value to biological science of his work on inbreeding, and his analysis of the composition of a field of maize, he had completed the initial step in the development of our new corn. Yet there were practical problems to be solved before the superior kind of corn produced by Shull could be made available to the farmers. The seed produced by a cross between two pure or inbred lines would give a good yield to farmers when planted. But because the ears on inbred plants are small, there was very little such seed *available* for planting. The maximum production of seed was from five to ten bushels per acre; [16] would the increased yield be sufficient to warrant the extreme cost of producing it? In addition, could you expect farmers to go through the complicated process of continually breeding pure inbred lines and controlling their crossing year after year? And could you produce enough seed in this way to satisfy the needs of the "corn belt"?

Even to this day, the method of crossing inbred lines in the form proposed by Shull has never found widespread application, except in the canning industry. Processing for canning demands that the ears of corn be of very nearly the same size. If they are too large, the machines that cut the kernels off the cob will cut off some of the cob as well, thereby spoiling the product for the housewife; if the ears are too small, the same machines will cut off only the outer part of the kernels. Since Shull's method yields a very uniform ear, the canners have adopted it and supply their own seed to the growers, who otherwise would balk at the high price of fifty cents per pound for seed.[17]

Shull had shown the virtues of hybrid vigor and had whetted the corn growers' appetites for a method of making controlled hybridization, starting from inbred lines, feasible. Beginning with a genetic study related to experimental evolution, Shull had encountered the remarkable effects of "heterosis," the extraordinary quality by which a hybrid is vastly superior to the inbred lines which produce it. Here is an example, then, of an investigation in fundamental science pointing to a practical innovation. Only it wasn't practical yet. Further research was required before the farmer could plant and grow on a large scale a new type of corn based on Shull's discoveries.

At this point we many introduce Edward Murray East, whose place in the story, although different from Shull's, is nevertheless equally significant.

Young East began his scientific career as a chemist at the Illinois Experiment Station in 1900, where he was assistant to Cyril G. Hopkins, whose work on the improvement of the protein and fat content of corn has been referred to earlier in this chapter. East was employed to make chemical analyses of the corn, and he became so much interested in botany that he took advanced work in this subject at the University of Illinois and ended up on the faculty of the Bussey Institution of Harvard University as one of the world's leading plant geneticists.

East noted that all of the high protein lines of corn produced by Hopkins went back through several generations to a single ear, and he wondered how best to use the potentialities of this unusual ear. Together with H. H. Love (now the distinguished plant breeder at Cornell), East drew up a plan for studying the effects of inbreeding

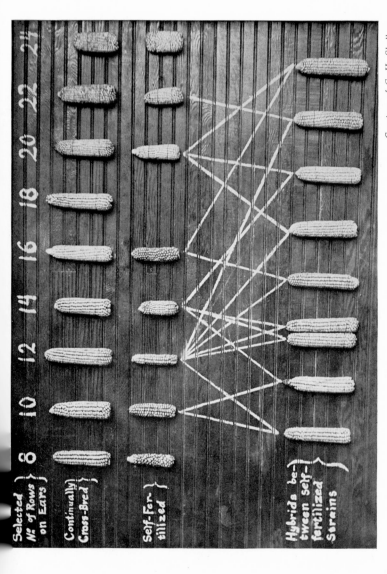

Courtesy of G. H. Shull

SHULL'S FAMOUS OMAHA EXHIBIT

or close breeding, hoping to find some new method whereby they might preserve the high protein content of the unusual ear and yet avoid the low yield. East had previously started a small inbreeding program of his own but, when shriveled kernels appeared on some of the ears, he had dropped the entire project.

Interestingly enough, Hopkins had himself been inbreeding corn "as a sort of check study" in connection with his corn program. Mr. Richard Crabb, who had made a thorough study of all the early work in corn improvement, has found it difficult to establish the exact year when Hopkins began inbreeding, but he has been able to conclude that "the program had assumed definite and stable proportions by 1901." [18]

Sometime in 1904 or 1905 East broached his new plan to Hopkins and in 1905 Hopkins agreed that East might begin an inbreeding program, which he started in the spring of 1905.

Unfortunately, Hopkins lost faith in the project and ordered it discontinued. Soon after, East accepted an appointment to go to Connecticut to the Agricultural Experiment Station. There, he continued the inbreeding experiments he had begun in Illinois.

Years later, referring to the program of inbreeding he had begun in Illinois in 1905, East wrote, "The most extended researches on inbreeding are those on Indian corn, which were begun by the writer in 1905. . . ." [19]

In late July and early August of 1907, East produced his first hybrids from the inbred lines which he had begun in Illinois. In contrast to Shull's single cross between two pure or inbred lines, those produced by East were chiefly "top cross" hybrids, that is, crosses between his inbred lines and open-pollinated corn. His inbreds yielded 62 bushels an acre; but the top-cross hybrids yielded 142 bushels per acre as compared to the Connecticut open-pollinated corn's 121 bushels per acre. [20]

But East also made single-cross hybrids in this late July and early August of 1907 and these yielded 202 bushels an acre. Although the two inbred strains yielded only 62 and 65 bushels an acre respectively, the yield from the single-cross hybrid was almost 100 bushels an acre more than the best open-pollinated corn in his plot.

In January 1908 East attended the annual meeting of the American Breeders' Association held in Washington, D. C., where he heard the famous paper read by Dr. Shull.

Although fully aware of the importance of Shull's work, East differed with Shull as to the practicality of inbreeding and making a single cross, Shull's "pure-line method of corn breeding," as a means of bringing the farmers a new kind of corn. After all, East was thinking in terms of a technique to be adopted by the individual farmer and he knew from bitter experience how reluctant the farmers would be to adopt the "complicated job of developing inbreds or even producing seed corn where they were supplied with the inbred lines." [21] Furthermore, East doubted that the inbred lines could ever yield a sufficient quantity of seed to make single-cross hybrids practical for large areas.

After East had been at the Connecticut Station for some years, he received the offer to come to Harvard University, at the recommendation of the great English geneticist, Bateson. Many people forget that East was for years a "practical" man, interested primarily in getting better corn into the hands of the farmers. They tend to think of him wholly in terms of his later career as a theoretical geneticist at Harvard, neglecting the earlier years entirely. But even after East came to Harvard he continued to direct the corn program he had begun in Connecticut and, in fact, chose the men who carried on that work. The first was H. K. Hayes, famous today for his important work on breeding Thatcher wheat. The second was Donald F. Jones, who, like Hayes, spent part of the year at the Station and part at Harvard as a graduate student working for his doctorate under East.

Although Jones knew practically nothing about corn when he began to work under East's supervision, it was he who cut the Gordian knot and made the new hybrid corn practical. Jones made two important contributions. The first was the so-called method of the "double cross," and the second his thesis on inbreeding and cross-breeding.

The method of the double cross is simple to understand. Let us suppose we have four unrelated inbred strains or pure lines, which we may call *A, B, C, D.* When we plant seed from them, we get four plants. We detassel A and C and cause them to be fertilized, respectively, by B and D. Thus, at the end of the season, we have seed from A that was fertilized by B (denoted $A \times B$) and seed from C that was fertilized by D (denoted $C \times D$). These are single-cross, or first-generation, hybrids. The following year we plant seed from $A \times B$ and from $C \times D$, detassel $A \times B$ and cause it to be fertilized by pollen from $C \times D$, thereby producing a double cross. The whole process may be most easily seen in the following diagram.

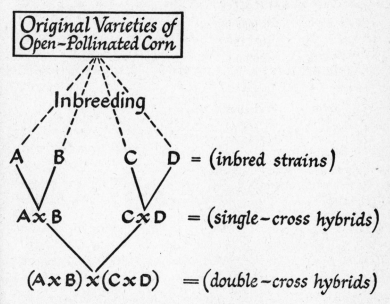

In order to see the significance of Jones's method of the double cross as compared to Shull's method of the single cross, examine the plate facing the next page. This plate has been made from an exhibition in the Botanical Museum of Harvard University, and shows actual ears of corn. At the extreme left we have four rows of ears, corresponding to the inbred strains A, B, C, and D. For each of these four strains, four ears are shown so that it may be seen that the ears in question are not exceptional or unusual. Whether the ears of, say, inbred strain B have been formed by self-pollination or cross-pollination, these ears will be small and poor as contrasted to either the single-cross or double-cross hybrids. Hence we can never get much seed from such an ear. If the ear has been formed by cross-pollination with the inbred strain A, then the seed on this ear is $A \times B$ seed. When we plant it, we get an $A \times B$ corn plant. Typical ears growing on such a corn plant are shown in the top row of the center group. In contrast to the seed parents, these ears are large and well formed. Thus the ears on an $A \times B$ plant are in marked contrast with the parent ears, whether A or B, demonstrating hybrid vigor or heterosis. The same holds true for $C \times D$. And it may be noted that the hybrids $A \times B$ may be formed by pollinating A with B, or B with A; and $C \times D$ by pollinating C with D, or D with C.

The ears on $A \times B$ may be formed by pollinating the $A \times B$ ear shoots with pollen from the $C \times D$ plant, as a result of which the ears on $A \times B$ will contain $(A \times B) \times (C \times D)$ seed. This double-cross or $(A \times B) \times (C \times D)$ seed which is produced on the $A \times B$ plant is harvested, and sold to the farmer. When he plants a field of this seed, and allows the corn to be open pollinated in the field, he will get the type of ear shown in the row on the extreme right. The ears produced on single-cross hybrids, as shown in the two rows in the center of the page, are large and yield plenty of seed.

Jones, working under East's direction, had solved the problem of how to produce a sufficient quantity of seed. By continuing the process of hybridization one step further than Shull, or even East himself, Jones had brought the possibility of a new corn closer to the goal.

Yet even Jones's method was hardly one to be adopted by individual farmers. Although the seed produced by the double cross of inbred lines would yield a magnificent harvest, the farmer who put aside a certain number of the good ears and planted them in the following year would again get an indifferent yield. The only way to ensure a continued high yield was to grow inbred strains, produce single crosses and also double crosses. If East had found Shull's method impractical for the farmer, what could he help but think of the method proposed by his pupil which was at least four times as complex! [22]

Jones also succeeded, where East and Shull had been pioneers, in putting an explanation of hybrid vigor on a Mendelian basis. As

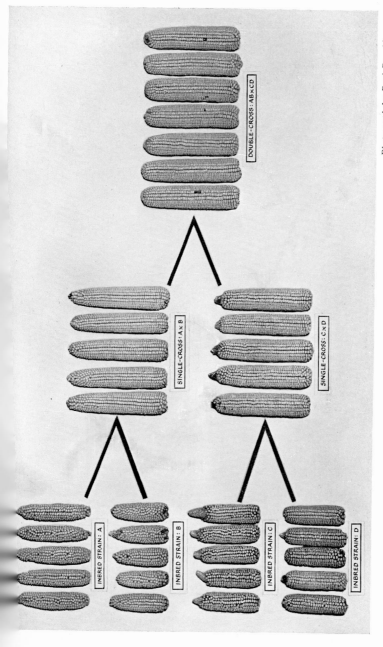

AN EXHIBITION OF THE DOUBLE CROSS METHOD

Reproduced through the courtesy of the Botanical Museum of Harvard University

Photograph by Paul Donaldson

Jones himself tells us, "This new interpretation showed how heredity could be controlled by inbreeding and utilized to the maximum degree. . . . The double cross method of using successive combinations of inbreds and single crosses to build up size and vigor in the seed and seedlings made the theoretical principles workable." [23] Professor Paul Mangelsdorf of Harvard is inclined to think that Jones's interpretation of hybrid vigor may, in the long run, be considered the more important of his two contributions, because the corn people all over the country were more readily inclined to adopt and work with something they understood, rather than something that seemed to work on principles that couldn't be explained.[24]

East at first objected to Jones's theory of hybrid vigor — a phenomenon which he personally believed was due to the stimulation coming from the mixture of unlike germ plasmas. Yet his graduate student convinced him after a long discussion, and together the two incorporated the new ideas in a joint book on *Inbreeding and Outbreeding*.

Like Shull before him, Jones began to propagandize his method of corn breeding. He lectured all over the Middle West, wrote articles for scientific journals, breeders' and farmers' magazines, and one for the old *Breeders' Gazette*. One problem that is minor now, but was important then, was the control of certain diseases of the corn crop, notably smut. The fact that Jones's method of the double cross made it possible to breed disease-resistant varieties naturally appealed to the plant pathologists, who commenced inbreeding experiments, especially in Indiana.

It was Shull who first brought the attention of the public to the importance of the method of inbreeding as a possible means of corn improvement and who first produced a hybrid by crossing two inbred lines; as it was Shull who first analyzed the composition of a field of maize, and who propagandized the method of crossing inbred lines. Yet the problem was not solved when Shull left the field and East knew it, because there was no way of getting a sufficient quantity of cheap seed into the hands of the farmer and out on the fields. But for the one exception of the canning industry to which we have referred, Shull's method of crossing two inbred lines has never been of much use to the farmer.[25]

The important point about East's work is that he provided the continuity; he kept the problem alive when even Shull himself had given it up. He kept the inbred strains begun at Illinois growing at Connecticut, and continued to supervise the work there even after he had gone to Harvard. His pupils, generation after generation, spread out through the country and became the plant breeders and geneticists that are the pride of American science and American agriculture. Had East too given up, we might never have reached the most important achievement in applied biology of the twentieth century. Jones's magnificent work done under East's supervision provides a splendid example of the way in which a sustained piece of research work finally bears fruit.*

There were still great problems to be solved before the new type of corn could be introduced. One of these was the peculiarity which restricts the use to the first generation following the second crossing and requires that each year new seed be obtained. How could you persuade farmers in the Middle West to abandon the old traditional method of mass selection, of picking the best seeds from the best ears of corn in the crop, and using them for seed the following year? When it was finally introduced, many farmers used the new corn for a short time, were enthusiastic about it the first year when the yield far surpassed their expectations, but gave it up in disgust when the following year the seeds obtained from the new corn yielded a much inferior crop. East was right; they had no patience with complex procedures. But a method of supplying them with seed developed which East had not foreseen. There sprang up companies to produce hybrid seed.

The first hybrid corn from inbred lines to be produced commercially was the Burr-Leaming cross developed by the Connecticut Agricultural Experiment Station in 1917, and the first commercial

* Of these three men who were chiefly responsible for the great achievement of "hybrid corn," two are still alive. Shull is professor emeritus at Princeton University and was awarded in 1945 the John Scott Medal for his part in the development of hybrid corn. Donald F. Jones is head of the Department of Genetics at the Connecticut Agricultural Experiment Station and was in 1947 awarded an honorary degree by his home college, Kansas State, for his part. Of the three, only Edward Murray East, who died in 1938, has never been given any official recognition of his important role. How fitting it would be for Harvard, which is celebrating the centenary of the Lawrence Scientific School, to honor her deceased faculty member who contributed so notably to this important practical development, by awarding him a posthumous honorary degree, or by some other suitable form of memorialization!

crossing field for the production of hybrid seed was that of George S. Carter of Clinton, Connecticut, in 1921.[26] The second hybrid to be produced and sold commercially was a single cross between one of the inbred lines of Leaming developed by the Connecticut Station and an inbred line from the Chinese Bloody Butcher produced by Henry A. Wallace of Des Moines, Iowa. This cross was developed by Wallace under the name of Copper Cross and was sold in the spring[27] of 1924 by the Iowa Seed Company of Des Moines; later Wallace organized the "Pioneer Hi-Bred Corn Company" to market the seed.

Encouraged by H. D. Hughes[28] at the State College at Ames in Iowa, Henry Wallace began crossing hybrids produced from inbred lines, not because he was interested in science or the advance of truth but simply because he was determined to breed superior corn for yield. With two corn growers who, having seen the results, were confident of the practicality of the new idea, Wallace organized a seed company which advertised their Copper Cross as "Developed not discovered"; "Made to order, not found by chance."[29]

Within a short time others followed in Wallace's footsteps. As the farmers became convinced of the superiority of the new type of corn, in which the cost of the new seed each year was more than absorbed in the additional profit accruing from the increased yield, companies were organized to produce the hybrid seed. At the time of the AAA program, some people protested that farmers could comply with the AAA restrictions for cutting down their corn acreage but still, with smaller acreage and less labor, raise more bushels than previously by using the hybrid corn. Some even said that the AAA restrictions were simply measures to force farmers to buy hybrid-corn seed from Secretary Wallace's seed company, but eventually these die-hards too were finally converted. Their argument was likened to that of the old woman who pronounced the Daylight Saving Law a scheme of the Government's to make people buy new clocks.[30] No amount of protesting or grumbling could long argue against "the overpowering fact of sixty bushels per acre."

That a method of improving the yield of the foremost American cereal crop by 25 to 35 per cent was an achievement of great practical value no one would deny. As long ago as the eighteenth century, Dean Swift wrote that whoever would make two ears of corn or two blades of grass grow where only one grew before would deserve better of mankind and do more essential service for his country than the whole "race of politicians" put together.

The development of hybrid corn is, in the opinion of Paul Mangelsdorf — a pupil of East who has played an important part in developing hybrid corn for the Southwest and for Mexico — "the most important development in applied biology in this century." He adds that he makes this statement with full cognizance of the work done during our century in the field of medicine, because hybrid corn "has saved more lives than all the research in medical biology put together." Last year we sent Europe 18 million tons of food in order to prevent widespread starvation. We had 72 million acres planted in hybrid corn, and on the average each acre produced 10 bushels more than open-pollinated varieties — that is, a quarter of a ton of corn (since 40 bushels make a ton). The increase in our total production of corn was, therefore, approximately 720 million bushels or 18 million tons. Our total export of food during the year ending July 1947 was simply the "profit" accruing from scientific research on corn — our generosity didn't cost us one iota of what would have been our previous food supply.[31]

It was not a simple step from the work of Donald F. Jones to the universal adoption of his methods; almost twenty years elapsed before that came about. Chief among the reasons, of course, was the normal resistance to any radical innovations on the part of the corn growers and the workers in the agricultural experiment stations in the "Corn Belt." Another was the fact that Jones's Burr-Leaming double cross, eminently suited to the climatic and soil conditions of New England and New York State, was not adapted to conditions prevailing in the more southerly and western parts of the country. East and his two pupils, Jones and Hayes, knew that the breeders must become sufficiently convinced of the superiority of the double cross to begin inbreeding programs aimed at producing the most suitable hybrid corn for each region. That this was finally done is a tribute to the breeders and those who made the seed available, and also to the powers of persuasion of Donald F. Jones. Henry Wallace's contribution, according to Mr. Crabb, "was his unlimited faith in the future of hybrid corn years before the farmers of Iowa had ever seen a field of it or even heard of it except from him. Wallace was truly the John the Baptist of the hybrid corn movement in the great Corn Belt area."[32]

In Jones's work, chance had favored him to an extraordinarily high degree. His first double cross, produced from a single cross of inbred Burr lines and a single cross of inbred Leaming lines, both available to him at the Connecticut Station, blended into a perfect double-cross hybrid, yielding 20 per cent more than the best Connecticut open-pollinated Leaming. It was later learned that only a rare or occasional combination of this kind will produce a useful double-cross hybrid.[33] Jones might well have worked for a lifetime to produce as good a product as his first Burr-Leaming double cross and, indeed, the failures — so much more likely than his immediate success — might have effectively discouraged him or anyone else from pursuing the problem further.

CHAPTER 12

The Fortune at the Rainbow's End

> Genetics stands second to physics as the most fruitful
> department of science during the last quarter of a
> century. Physics has given us a new chemistry, a new
> thermodynamics, in fact a wholly new philosophy
> as to the nature of matter. It has made possible such
> marvellous inventions as the aeroplane, the cinema,
> and the radio. The achievements of genetics are not
> so spectacular, but hardly less broadly constructive.
> The established facts concerning variation, heredity,
> and development provide a new orientation in
> sociology.
>
> — EDWARD M. EAST (1927)

OUR STUDY of hybrid corn in the previous chapter is an excellent
example of how difficult it may be to bring to final fruition
a practical development based on fundamental research, even when
the goal is clear. Both Shull and East knew the kind of hybrid corn
they wanted to produce; and the methods of getting it seemed, for
many years, always within sight and just out of reach — like the
fortune waiting at the rainbow's end.

It should, by now, be clear to the reader *why this important discovery was not made by any of the corn planters or practical breeders.* Shull was, then as now, a man whose primary interest was considerably removed from the economic sphere. He tells us that hundreds of "clever corn men" had been striving for a method to insure
a uniform maximum yield and maximum quality to their corn
crops. All of them failed. Had his "objective been one of private
gain," he too would have been foredoomed to a like failure. The
reason is that poorer and poorer quality *always* results from continued inbreeding.*

---

* Shull writes: "The deterioration due to inbreeding is greatest in the first generation and becomes increasingly diminished with each succeeding year of selfing. This
was one of my most significant discoveries, which led my mathematical mind immediately to the conclusion that such deterioration approached gradually a definite
asymptote or limiting value and that in time there would be no further deleterious
effect of inbreeding." [1]

Anyone who began a program of inbreeding would soon be struck, as Shull was, by the fact that although his method offers a means of obtaining seed that will "breed true," pure inbred lines are decidedly inferior corn. As we have had occasion to note in the last chapter, East — in his early years at the Illinois Station, when he was still a "practical man" — was·so discouraged by the unproductive inbred lines that he stopped at the third generation of inbreeding.

Shull wasn't discouraged, because he was *not* primarily interested in improving the corn crop; he was anxious to discover fundamental facts about inheritance, and corn appeared to be an excellent organism for research in genetics. He had been working with the primrose, *Oenothera,* before starting to work with corn. He tells us, "The work with corn was in fact begun as a second thought to *parallel* the program already in progress in *Oenothera.* The discovery of the genetical basis of variations in a 'field of maize' completely disqualified corn as an organism for the special problem I had in mind. . . ." [2]

Why, then, did he keep on with his work on corn? The answer Shull gives is that this part of his research "was continued only because of its economic significance." [3] And here we see a new element introduced into the picture. At a certain stage of fundamental research, a portion of the results obtained have the possibility of being useful for man, and at that moment a new motive, in addition to the search for truth, is added to the pursuit of science.

It was never true that Shull was the kind of scientist popularly caricatured as being interested in truth for its own sake at the expense of *any* application. In the early days of his inbreeding experiments, and even before he had achieved sufficient results to formulate his famous communication on "The Composition of a Field of Maize," he read a paper before the American Breeder's Association on "The Importance of the Mutation Theory in Practical Breeding." This paper begins with a statement of Shull's scientific creed, and it exemplifies to a high degree the understanding that many men of science have of the dual significance of fundamental research: at once advancing knowledge and providing a source of material benefit to man.

"The time is long past," Shull wrote, "when the practical man who is looking for immediate values is inclined to ignore the work done by the devotee of pure science. Conversely, the scientist appreciates as never before, the reciprocal relationship existing between his work and that of the man who would turn every available resource to the production of something useful to man." [4] He went on to point out that just as all active breeding must be, in as great a degree as possible, as scientific as possible, so all scientific work relating to breeding is likely to prove of practical value in the long run. "While it is not fair to the scientist," he continued, "to insist that he shall be able to point out the economic value of all his results — in the search for truth he must not be so hampered — it is fair to ask of science that when any of its results have a large and important bearing upon economic problems, these results shall be made as available as possible for the use of those who can turn them to immediate practical account."

When Shull wrote these words, he could hardly have had an inkling that he was about to attain the first stages of just such a discovery — his statement was simply a creed based on a secure understanding of the ways in which fundamental research in the sciences produces useful results. When he first crossed his inbred strains and noted the vigor of the hybrid, he acted accordingly.

After completing his work on corn, Shull went to Princeton and turned to other aspects of genetics and evolution, still continuing his fundamental investigations of the primrose, *Oenothera*. Eight years ago, he was asked by Dr. William J. Robbins, then newly appointed Director of the New York Botanical Garden, why he had stopped working with corn. (It was a natural question, since Dr. Robbins has always been interested in the advance of fundamental knowledge and its application to human needs.) Shull replied that he had stopped working with corn because he had completed his part of the program.[5] He had discovered the basic principles, formulated them into twelve succinct statements, invented a method of procedure, and pointed out the important additions which the proposed program offered to agricultural practice. It assured greater yield and greater uniformity; it enabled corns to be produced tailored to fit different regions, different climates, and different soils; it enabled strains of corn to be produced having, to a "superior" degree, any desired chemical content, or other stipulated qualities. On the completion of his work, just before the First World War, Shull had urged the agricultural experimental stations in the Corn Belt states to work out the problems remaining to be solved if these principles and methods were to be utilized in practical corn production. Such applications lay, he had always believed, outside his "own responsibility as staff member of the Station for Experimental Evolution, a laboratory established by the Carnegie Institution of Washington for research in basic biological science." [6]

Shull had done all he could. He had appealed, alas! almost in vain,* to the breeders to continue and to extend his methods. There was a time when he lost faith, when, to use his own words, East, "the most effective opponent of my 'pure-line' method . . . convinced me myself that my proposed method was impractical." [7] In 1914, Shull wrote to East's pupil Hayes, then at the Connecticut Station: "I never believed that my pure-line method was practical. It was scientifically essential for the solution of the particular problem I had in hand. . . ." I consider "the pure-line method of theoretical rather than practical interest." [8]

But although Shull doubted the practicality of his single-cross method, he held grimly to his original belief in the ultimate value of hybridization — a belief finally vindicated by East's pupil Jones. In the very month in which Shull wrote the letter to Hayes from which we have quoted an extract above, he wrote to E. D. Funk, the great Illinois seedsman, urging him to undertake experiments *in order to discover how hybridization could be made most useful.* [9]

It is valuable to reconsider the development of hybrid corn because it reveals a very significant truth not generally recognized. Could we but write that Shull had completed the foundation of this knowledge and all that was required was a group of practical men who had the vision to apply his results, we could say he was simply ahead of "the times." But what was needed in this instance was a very special kind of "practical man," one who could understand,

* Among those who were strongly impressed by Shull's report on his experiments were the workers in the Nebraska Agricultural Experiment Station, in particular T. A. Kiesselbach, who became, in the words of Mr. Crabb, "the foremost authority on corn in the great Missouri River Valley."

on the scientific plane, everything that Shull had been doing and who, at the same time, had had the kind of field experience obtainable only by working at an agricultural station. East, who began inbreeding independently of Shull, had, by the time he was appointed to Harvard, become a geneticist of marked ability. Jones profited not only from East's grasp of this branch of science, but also from the latter's invaluable experience in the world of hardheaded corn breeding. East kept the inbred strains growing at New Haven because he hoped that additional knowledge concerning the underlying principles involved in inbreeding and cross-breeding would eventually make available to the farmers of the world the advantages of hybrid vigor. Somewhere the rest of the key, of which Shull had discovered a significant part, would be found to unlock the puzzle.

Such a situation is in marked contrast to the applications of the auxins, to which we devoted an earlier chapter. It was inevitable, once plant physiologists had begun to study the substances causing growth phenomena, that they would discover how the formation of roots is affected by auxin. The logic of these discoveries would thus certainly have led to the application of auxin to promote the rooting of cuttings.

In the same way plant physiologists could not have avoided studying the distribution of auxin throughout the whole plant. It was inevitable that they would, sooner or later, find the phenomena whereby auxin inhibits, as well as promotes, growth — immediately applicable to the storing of plants and the preventing of the pre-harvest drop of apples. There was no possible escape from the discovery of the toxic action of relatively strong concentrations of auxin, and also the action as auxins of certain synthetic chemical compounds. It is inconceivable that the somewhat selective action of several such synthetic auxins could long have passed unnoticed. With no other motivation than the relentless pursuit of plant science, each step following naturally from the preceding ones, and at the same time suggesting the next, this whole group of the applications of auxin would have become evident in short order.

The discovery of the basic principles of electromagnetism and their elaboration into a mathematical theory by Maxwell, upon which the art of radio communication was founded many, many decades later, offers a pattern with the same ineluctable logic displayed by the story of the auxins. Mind you, we are not saying that radio and radar followed upon Maxwell's theory as simply and as directly as weed killing followed on our knowledge of the auxins. Far from it. But just as certainly as the plant physiologist who found that auxin may inhibit growth was bound to get to the problem of pre-harvest drop, so surely was some physicist bound to try to prove or disprove the existence in space of the electromagnetic waves that Maxwell had hypothecated.

But the resemblance ends here. Maxwell made public his electromagnetic theory in a paper which he read before the Royal Society of London on 8 December 1864, and the full theory was expounded in his monumental treatise on *Electricity and Magnetism* of 1873. Not everyone accepted Maxwell's daring "electromagnetic theory of light." In his *Baltimore Lectures,* delivered at the Johns Hopkins University in the autumn of 1884, for example, Lord Kelvin admitted, "If I knew what the electromagnetic theory of light is, I might be able to think of it in relation to the fundamental principles of the wave theory of light." But some five years before Kelvin's lectures Helmholtz had decided to put the theory to the test and, as we saw earlier, had set an experimental problem connected with the new theory for one of the great prizes of the Berlin Academy. In 1887, fourteen years after the publication of Maxwell's treatise, Hertz demonstrated the existence of electromagnetic waves in space. Twelve years after Hertz had performed his brilliant experiments, in 1899, Marconi bridged the English Channel by wireless communication, and in 1901 sent signals from Cornwall across the Atlantic to Newfoundland.

The very fact that a prize was offered indicates that the existence of electromagnetic waves in space — as well as in Maxwell's mind — was due for proof. The time was ripe. But the successful demonstration needed a man of very specific qualifications — one sufficiently well grounded in theoretical physics to be able to understand and respond to Maxwell's abstractions, and sufficiently well skilled in both mechanical invention and experimental dexterity to perform the decisive experiment.

But after Hertz had shown that electromagnetic waves could be generated, sent out through space and detected, someone — certainly not just a mere gadgeteer or mechanical inventor like the famous "inventor of a better mouse trap," but a man well grounded in physics, and possessing creative imagination — would have thought of using this phenomenon for "wireless" communication and made it practical. Many in fact did, chief among them Marconi. And so we are back again to the remorseless logic by which, after a significant scientific truth about the world around us *has been* made manifest, the shrewd minds of men will hew and hack at it until they have extracted the applications to their lives that are immanent within it. Yet let us not by too easy talk of the "inevitable" forget that it was a long way from the raw facts of nature as presented by Hertz to the cabinet instrument that reposes splendidly in your parlor. That bridge was built by the courage, perseverance, daring, ingenuity, and enterprise of a great many notable men — some of them working in fields of applied research, others merely operating at the level of mechanical dexterity, and still others pursuing fundamental research and adding further knowledge to be applied.

It casts no discredit on these brave pioneers to point out that *after* Maxwell, and *after* Hertz, there was certain to be radio. Had not those men (who built on the foundations laid by Maxwell and Hertz) appeared, others would have taken their place. Likewise, *after* Carothers had demonstrated that linear super-polymers could make a fiber where God had not, there was certain to be nylon. Once it was known that electron diffraction was produced by the surfaces of metals it did not require men of remarkable vision or sustained courage to ensure that the phenomenon would be used in a tool to study such surfaces.

By contrast, in the long search for the secret of hybrid corn, had East given up where Shull turned from corn to other problems; had he not been a guide to Jones and, despite his own pessimism as to results, continued growing so that the inbred lines with which Jones was eventually to make the discovery of the double cross were there for Jones to use, *then* the heroic labors of Shull, and of East himself, would have come to nothing.

But only temporarily to nothing. For I do not believe that the world would not, sometime, have had hybrid corn. We might have waited ten, twenty, or even thirty, additional years. But a certain logic operates here, too. After all, anyone who had seen the extraordinary vigor of the hybrid produced by crossing two inbred lines could not help but be impressed. The facts were on record — largely in Shull's publications — and in time someone would have found the way to get a sufficient quantity of seed.

The key phrase is "in time." We really needed hybrid corn in the last few years. If our agricultural production had flagged, rather than increased, an untold number of European human beings would have starved. The man who today lies ill and at death's door may derive a certain amount of consolation from the conviction that his fellow men a hundred, or even twenty, years from now may no longer suffer from the same disease, but it doesn't help *him* very much. Since some 200,000 deaths occur due to cancer each year in America, if we can advance the date of the discovery of its cure by so little as five years, we can save one million lives in our country alone! There is obviously no exaggeration in the statement that each of us has a vital stake in scientific progress.

PART FOUR

Practical Innovations Based on Existing Fundamental Knowledge

What is true of the electrical art is also true of all the other arts and applied sciences. They are all based upon fundamental discoveries made by workers in pure science, who were seeking only to discover the laws of nature and extend the realm of human knowledge.

By every means in our power, therefore, let us show our appreciation of pure science and let us forward the work of the pure scientists, for they are the advance guard of civilization. They point the way which we must follow. Let us arouse the people of our country to the wonderful possibilities of scientific discovery and to the responsibility to support it which rests upon them and I am sure that they will respond generously and effectively.

— JOHN J. CARTY (1916)

CHAPTER 13

Practical Innovations Based on Existing Fundamental Knowledge

> The book is written; the die is cast. Let it be read now or by posterity, I care not which. It may well wait a century for a reader, as God has waited six thousand years for an observer.
> — JOHANN KEPLER (1618)

EACH OF THE case histories that we have studied in the last section illustrates an example of basic scientific research which led, in some instances directly, in some by difficult and devious routes, to a useful result; in each the application fulfilled a need of which men had been conscious long before hope of its satisfaction was made of anything but wishes.

What farmer — his sleep troubled by his aching back — has not dreamt of the earth's return to a state of Eden when weeds and thistles will shrivel and die and the soil joyfully yield up its fruit? (See the chapter on auxins.) A corn that could feed the hungry world is a more glowing vision than the pot of gold. (See the chapter on hybrid corn.) Persistent belief in telepathy is poignantly significant of man's old desire to speak, one with another, across the empty distances. (See the chapter on radio communication.) Doctors struggled to transfuse blood two centuries before the discovery of citrate made it feasible or the understanding of grouping made it safe; and the promise of nylon appeared just when the war threatened the disappearance of Japanese silk from our markets.

By the time that the principles of induced currents discovered by Faraday had been developed to the state where a practicable generator of electricity had been made by Gramme, the world was quick to accept and use the new source of power; and any discussion of whether the new "electromagnetic engine" would replace the steam engine became a practical, rather than a purely academic, question.

In the same way, the commercial companies needed no urging to get the weed killers on the market — as soon as the scientists in the laboratories had shown that a synthetic auxin could *selectively* inhibit plant growth. Du Pont, you may be sure, lost no time at all in developing the fiber that was to become nylon!

By contrast to such instances of a world anxious to embrace new benefits, there is a considerable body of exact knowledge uncovered by fundamental research which, so to speak, lies fallow for a time and does not find a practical application for years, decades, or even a century. We are not referring here to the supposed time lag of ten years between Fleming's observation of the action of *Penicillium notatum* and the introduction of penicillin for therapeutic purposes, because in that instance the "discovery" was not complete until the work of Florey, Chain, and their co-workers some ten years later. Nor are we referring to the delay between Faraday's discovery of induced currents and Gramme's successful generator; during all that time men were busy at work perfecting the new machine which could not be used before it was ready.

Here we are interested in the curious fact that a phenomenon may be well known and almostly continuously studied for as long as a century before anyone finds a practical way in which to use it.

∾   ∾   ∾

One of the most interesting examples of such a *true* lag between a scientific discovery and its application is afforded by the history of a curious and generally little-known effect, called "magnetostriction." It refers to the distortion of a body when magnetized. This may take the form, in the case of a rod, of a shortening or a lengthening. Since any shortening of a metal rod must take place against the enormous elastic forces of that body, the effect must be necessarily small unless these elastic forces can be balanced out in some way. The shortening (or lengthening) is usually of the order of about one millionth of its length for a moderate magnetic field (strength: 1 gauss). With stronger magnetic fields, the static effect may be increased to *as much as* a few parts per million.

The history of this subject has been carefully investigated by Professor Louis W. McKeehan, now director of the Sloane Laboratory of Physics at Yale University. He found that our knowledge of magnetostriction effects may be said to begin with an observation in 1837 by C. G. Page of New Haven, who noted that a horseshoe magnet, placed in the magnetic field produced by an electric current flowing in a spiral conductor, under proper conditions would be caused to emit a characteristic sound. We know today that these sounds were due to certain changes in dimensions accompanying the changes in magnetization induced in the horseshoe magnet; by first the application, and then the removal, of the magnetic field of the spiral. Others observed similar sounds, but the first quantitative measurements were made in the 1840's by James Prescott Joule of Manchester, one of the discoverers of the theorem of the conservation of energy. His papers, according to Professor McKeehan, "set a standard in the measurement of small linear displacements which was not bettered for many years, and the simple directness of his methods (every relevant variable being measured) leaves nothing to be desired."[1]

In a lecture delivered in April 1926, Professor McKeehan, then a research physicist of the Bell Telephone Laboratories, was still able to point out that, although it was customary when discussing experimental research in pure science to say something about the services which the work in question has rendered to the useful arts, it was impossible to do so in the case of magnetostriction because "no important application of the facts of magnetostriction . . . has yet been made." Within a year, however, the situation had altered considerably; application had been made manifest and a patent applied for.

Professor G. W. Pierce of Harvard had been applying a *changing* magnetic field to various kinds of rods. Let us examine the significance of the word "changing." We can wind a coil around a nickel rod and attach the coil to the A.C. lines. The current flowing through the coil will then alternate 60 times a second, causing the magnetic field produced by the coil to change accordingly, and the rod thereby magnetostrictively to change its length. One can also perform the experiment with a current flowing through the coil at a much higher frequency, hundreds of thousands of times per second.

The interesting thing about a rod which "oscillates" (or changes its length magnetostrictively, first becoming elongated and then shortened) is that there is a "resonant" frequency, characteristic of each rod; that is, there is a certain rate of change at which the cyclic variations in the length of the rod (contraction and expansion) introduce so-called dynamic or inertial forces which tend to balance or cancel out the elastic forces of the rod. As a result, changes in length made to occur at the resonant frequency may be much greater than at other frequencies and much greater than in the static case of applying a steady magnetic field. At the resonant frequency, these changes in length may be more than 100 times as great as those obtained by suddenly applying a steady or constant magnetic field, or suddenly removing same.

Professor Pierce described to me the way in which he drew together his experimental findings and ordered a magnetostriction oscillator to be constructed to the following specifications. Thirty-six rods, each 3/16 of an inch in diameter and 2 inches long, were welded side by side to a frontal steel plate ⅛ of an inch thick and bolted to a rear steel plate ¼ of an inch thick. A coil was wound around each of the rods so that they would be made to oscillate in unison, and at the resonant frequency, thereby pushing the steel plate back and forth.*

In the most important practical application of the magnetostriction oscillator, the frequency is considerably higher than the waves of audible sound, being in the so-called "ultrasonic" range. An oscillator is placed under water, say protruding below the hull of a ship, with the steel plate to which the nickel tubes are fastened facing out. As the rods oscillate magnetostrictively in unison, the plate moves back and forth many thousands of times in each second and with an enormous force. This movement produces pulses of alternate compressions and expansions under water which travel out from the oscillator plate, forming a beam.

Such a steady beam of pulses sent out under water can be used in very practical ways. For example, the impulses travel at definite, known speeds. If they are sent straight downward from a ship, they will reach the ocean floor and be reflected back up again, arriving

---

* Professor Pierce applied for a patent for his magnetostriction oscillator on 3 January 1927, serial no. 158, 452; it was granted 11 March 1930. Although his oscillator was probably the first practicable magnetostriction transmitter, Professor Pierce does not claim to have been the first ever to have thought of making such an instrument.[2]

after a measurable time interval. Knowing this time lapse and the speed at which the impulses travel, the depth of the ocean at that spot can readily be determined. Again, by making use of the fact that such a beam will be reflected by a submerged submarine, a device

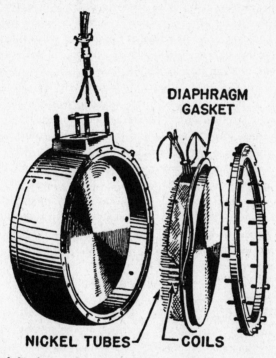

An "exploded" view of the essential parts of a magnetostriction transmitter. Reproduced from the August 1946 issue of Electronics, by permission of the copyright owner, McGraw-Hill Publishing Company, Inc., New York, New York.

was perfected for submarine location — a sort of under-water counterpart of radar, known during World War II as "Sonar."[8] Sonar transmitters and receivers were built not only using the phenomenon of magnetostriction, but also an effect which we shall discuss in just a moment, the piezoelectric effect.

Other uses of the magnetostriction oscillator include the stabilization of high-frequency currents, a means of measuring the elastic constants of metals, and a variety of purposes to which are also applied a phenomenon whose history is much like that of magneto-striction — the so-called "piezoelectric" effect.

⌘   ⌘   ⌘

The piezoelectric effect was discovered by that extraordinary genius, Pierre Curie, whose greatness is somewhat obscured in many people's minds by the greater popular fame of his wife, Marie. Some-time around 1880, Pierre Curie had been studying crystals of all kinds and was interested in their behavior in an electric field. One of the questions he studied was: What would happen if one places a nega-tively charged plate on one side of a quartz crystal and a positively charged plate on the other? Investigating this subject with his brother Jacques, Pierre Curie found that a crystal, under such con-ditions, undergoes a very minute compression, so small as to be roughly of the same order of magnitude as the changes in length observed in magnetostriction.[4]

Soon afterwards, the converse effect, foreseen by another investiga-tor, Lippman, was found also to be true. If one were to put a mechan-ical strain on the crystal, say by squeezing it, one side would become positive and the other negative.[5]

This discovery was not used in a practical way until the time of the First World War, when the submarine menace was almost as acute as during the Second World War, if not more so. The French physicist, Paul Langevin, applied Curie's discovery to the very same purpose that we have already described for magnetostriction. By building up a mosaic of piezoelectric crystals, which were placed in a changing electric field, Langevin was able to send out, underwater, pulses of very high frequency. Although this device appeared capable of detecting a submerged object at a distance of half a mile or more away by the use of a beam of high-frequency sound waves, it was perfected too late to be generally applied.[6]

During World War II, Sonar gear of both types was employed — some using magnetostriction oscillators and some the crystal.

Today we use the piezoelectric effect in a variety of ways. One which affects the average person the most is the so-called "crystal pickup" on electric phonographs. As the needle moves in the grooves of the record, it produces a varying mechanical strain on the crystal, this in turn producing a pulsing electric current which can be ampli-fied and be made to produce sound waves in the diaphragm of the loud-speaker, just as the pulsations of current in the telephone enable us to hear someone else's voice.

High-frequency oscillators, built around the resonance frequency of such crystals, are so stable, and vary so little, that they provide the scientist today with the most accurate instrument for measuring time at his disposal. So accurate is this clock that it enables us to measure the wobbling of our unsteady earth as it rolls in its somewhat irregular way about its axis. This effect of crystals is also used extensively in the telephone industry.[7]

As a third and last example of a discovery which, like magneto-striction and the piezoelectric effect, was not used practically for many years, we may cite the photoelectric effect. The latter phenomenon refers to the emission of electrons by certain materials under the influence of light and its history begins with an observation made by Hertz in 1887,* and extended a year later by Wilhelm Hall-wachs. During the period 1900–1905 the photoelectric effect and its interpretation gave nineteenth-century physics a rude jar. On the basis of it, and the famous quantum theory formulated by the late Max Planck, in 1905 (the same year that he published his Special Theory of Relativity) Albert Einstein showed why one must assume a corpuscular as well as a wave theory of light. But although the photoelectric effect was studied largely for its theoretical significance, since it was one of the most important phenomena demonstrating the dual aspect of nature in partaking at once of wave and particle properties, the effect in time found practical use.[8]

During the last twenty years or so, the photoelectric effect has been applied in many ways familiar to us all: in door-opening mechanisms in railway stations and department stores, in photographic light meters, and in many automatic control and testing devices used in industry.

The importance of this type of phenomenon for the lay administrator lies in the fact that science not only uncovers new truths that may be used almost at once, so to speak, but also continues to

---

* The work of P. Curie and H. Hertz, referred to in this chapter, illustrates once more a point we have made again and again in this book: that truly great scientists are usually remembered for more than one discovery.

accumulate knowledge that may not be used until sometime in the future. We cannot tell in advance whether a given research project will turn up something that can be applied speedily, or whether the findings will be ready and available for use only at some time in the future when a need for them will arise. No one has the gift of prophecy to enable him to tell, even after a discovery has been made, whether it will be used immediately, in the near future, in the distant future, or perhaps even never at all.

The three chapters which follow illustrate the way in which fundamental knowledge is available and at hand at the time it is needed. The first illustrates how, at a time when there was a demand for petroleum on a larger scale than ever before, the studies of microfossils had provided the knowledge on which to base a wholly revolutionary procedure in oil prospecting. The second shows how the organic chemist, constantly studying new compounds, builds up a vast supply of knowledge to be used by industrialists and his fellow scientists when the time arrives. In the last chapter of this section, we shall see how an important problem in radio communication arose, was made acute by the advent of World War II, and was in large measure solved by existing studies and techniques on the part of the astronomer.

CHAPTER 14

Microfossils and Oil Prospecting

> To those young men and women who are hesitating
> in the choice of a future career, that of the research
> worker is here recommended for consideration. It
> means a lifetime of devotion to a cause which
> probably will bring neither fame nor fortune. One
> who chooses it must find most of its rewards within
> himself. . . . When he has gone on to the limit of
> his strength . . . he will feel within him, whether
> the world says "Well done" or not, that he has been
> true to the inner urge of his own soul and his
> reward is in the knowledge that he has carried the
> standard of science a little further into the unknown.
> — JOSEPH A. CUSHMAN (1938)

TWENTY-FIVE YEARS ago the word "foraminifera" was known only to
biologists and a few paleontologists. Today the word is current
throughout the whole practical world of petroleum engineering and
prospecting, and it is also the name of a subject studied widely in
our institutions of higher learning and research. The development
and application of knowledge concerning the foraminifera constitute
one of the most astonishing examples of the way in which scientific
research of apparently no practical value whatever suddenly assumes
vast economic importance. Let us see what foraminifera are, and
then examine the useful application that such apparently recondite
studies have found.

The foraminifera are tiny animals, most of which live in the sea,
although a very few are found in brackish or even fresh water. They
are single-celled, belonging to the protozoa (see Chapter 2). Although the commonest varieties can be laid out in a row, 50 or 100
to the inch, most of them have a fully developed "test," which is the
name given to the covering of the animal, the equivalent of the shell
secreted by special organs in the mollusks and other shelled denizens

of the sea. Some of the so-called "giant" foraminifera grow to two or three inches in diameter, a size encountered in living specimens discovered in the Philippines and East Indies.[1] In the oceans the foraminifera still occur in enormous numbers, and in water from the continental shelf to depths of 2000 fathoms or more their tests form the thick ooze of the ocean floor. Tests are preserved as fossils in many of the geologic formations since Cambrian time, a period which began about 540 million years ago. The fossil forms are abundant in almost all past geologic ages since Cambrian; their economic use is premised on both that abundance and their wide distribution.

Most of us know something about fossils, at least we know they are remains of animal and plant life from bygone ages. Thus fossils may consist of actual remains of organisms; impressions left by organisms in what are now rocks, such as tracks, trails, or burrows; artificial structures made by organisms; or replacements of the hard parts of an organism by the infiltration of mud or sand, and the chemical deposits of mineral matter, or by the petrification of skeletons.[2] In California asphalt pits, the material which is today hard and solid, many thousands of years ago was soft and sticky. Animals of a bygone era were caught in these sticky pools and died, leaving their bones in great numbers. These asphalt pits have yielded to our museums a great host and variety of bones of extinct animals, the most famous of which are the bones of saber-toothed tigers.

Another fossil preservation occurs in amber. The amber used for cigarette holders, beads, and other ornaments is a hardened gum from trees that lived a long time ago. In those days, when the gum was sticky and soft, flies or other extinct insects became caught in the sticky mass and died. More of the gum oozed out and covered them. Hardened and preserved through the centuries, amber frequently contains in perfect preservation the insects of older times. Sometimes all the details of their delicate wing structure can be seen if the amber is of the clear variety.[3]

Dr. Joseph A. Cushman, the leading micro-paleontologist of our day, describes, in a most graphic manner, slabs of red sandstone at the Museum of the Boston Society of Natural History.[4] They come from the Connecticut Valley and are millions of years old. Once these slabs of stone were merely soft sand, which, like the sand of today, was marked by footprints of animals. You can actually measure the length of step from one footprint to another, and determine which prints were made by large animals and which by small. Likewise you can see the fine markings where crabs or worms once crawled across the mud; and sometimes the trails of the larger animals pursuing them. Then perhaps a shower came up, and you can still see the markings of the raindrops. One side of the raindrop markings is deeper than the other, showing which way the wind was blowing at the time. From such slabs of rock an observer can, with study and imagination, tell many things that took place in that faraway time. A record has been inscribed on rock for one who is trained in the language to read.

One of the interesting things about fossils is the way in which they fit into the geologist's clock; they provide a method for correlating events of similar age in widely separated localities. The early Paleozoic rocks, laid down sometime between 225 million years and about 540 million years ago, contain certain primitive forms of fossil plants and animals living at that time. As one examines more and more recent geological strata, just as the forms of life changed from one era to another, so the types of fossils encountered will change. The age of the rocks in which the fossils are found is determined, as we saw in Chapter 9, by the lead-uranium ratio in certain minerals.

The trained paleontologist cannot, in general, determine whether a certain type of fossil comes from the coal fields of England or those of West Virginia, but he can usually tell in what particular geologic time the fossil in question was laid down. An oil operator who comes from Pennsylvania may find in California an oil-bearing sandstone formation that looks very much like an oil bed in Pennsylvania. But even though they may appear to be superficially identical, there is no connection between them because the California oil deposits were laid down millions of years later than those in Pennsylvania. The difference between the two formations is immediately apparent to the paleontologist on examining the strikingly different fossil formations contained in them.[5]

Coal consists of the remains of fossil plants that lived in the Carboniferous period, which began about 300 million years ago and lasted almost 100 million years. The crude oil from which gasoline is made is also a product of fossil plants and animals that lived a long time ago. Many beds of limestone are made up almost entirely of the shells of fossil animals that were buried in the mud, ages past. They became cemented together and hardened, and then, as mountains were built up by crustal movements, they might be raised far above the sea in which they were formed. If during this process they were heated under sufficient pressure, they turned into marble. Even the common chalk which we use to write on blackboards is made of such tiny shells; the fossil animals can be seen under the microscope. The great pyramids of Egypt are built of limestone made of tiny fossils of the simplest and lowest forms of animal life we know anything about: the foraminifera.

The fossil tests, or shells, of the foraminifera are found in dredgings from the ocean floor and along beaches. Along seacoasts, the tests of the foraminifera are frequently washed up onto the beach in large numbers. These tests, or shells, are very light; each wave carries them up and deposits them at its highest point. When the wave recedes, a whitish line is found on the beach, often largely composed of foraminifera. This material may be scraped up and taken away for further study. Sometimes the collection for foraminiferal tests deposited in this way on the beach is a mixture of recent species as well as fossils.

If anyone wants to see these tiny fossils for himself, he can collect them on the beach and follow a simple procedure. First, the material must be washed with fresh water; then it should be put in a cup and covered with carbon tetrachloride, sold commercially as cleaning fluid under the name of "Carbona," and the sandy material stirred vigorously. After a few minutes, a scum will appear on the surface, which can be poured off onto a cloth to dry. When fully dried out and examined, it will be found to contain a large number of fossils which appear to the naked eye as so many sand grains. But under a microscope (a fourteen-power magnifying glass, such as a linen tester, will do) they are seen to be shells; each perfect and well formed, but each no bigger than a grain of sand.

The tiny shells resemble many of the larger and more familiar varieties. Some of the chambered forms look like miniature replicas of the chambered nautilus, and, indeed, in the eighteenth century, the foraminifera were thought to be, and were called, "nautilus."

At the Cushman Laboratory for Foraminiferal Research, a special exhibit has been arranged to impress visitors with the very small size of foraminifera tests or shells. Dr. Cushman originally prepared the exhibit for a visiting group of the American Legion. He took the head of a common pin, painted it black, covered it with a gummy substance, and carefully placed on it nearly 100 specimens, some white, others yellow, and some rosy-pink in color. The fact that so many can be put on such a small base makes vivid their minimal size. As a souvenir of my visit to the Cushman Laboratory, I was given a bottle containing about 500 specimens, collected at a depth of 20 fathoms from off the coast of Ireland, and containing some 75 different kinds of foraminifera. This collection, if spread out as thinly as possible, would barely cover the surface of a half-dollar!

Our knowledge of foraminifera really began in about 1731, when an Italian paleontologist named Beccarius described the various minute shells from the yellow sands near Bologna. Eight years later, in 1739, a memoir was published by another early pioneer named Plancus, who stated that he had found on the Adriatic shore of Rimini as many as six thousand specimens in a single ounce of sand. Some early writers thought the foraminifera were worms, or cephalopods, or even corals, and it was not until 1835 that Félix Du Jardin demonstrated that the foraminifera belonged to the protozoa.[6]

The first record of foraminifera in the history of civilization is probably the account given by Herodotus, who in 450 B.C. observed the fossilized tests or shells of nummulites, a species of foraminifera growing to a diameter of about an inch. But the first discovery of a *microscopic* fossil test appears to have been made by that universal genius of seventeenth-century England, instrument maker, architect, physicist, and microscopist, Robert Hooke. His famous treatise, published in London in 1665, was entitled *Micrographia: or some Physiological Descriptions of Minute Bodies made by Magnifying Glasses. With Observations and Inquiries thereupon.* In "Observation XI" Hooke tells the reader:

It were endless to describe the multitude of Figures I have met with in these kind of minute bodies. . . . But amongst others, I met with none more observable than this pretty Shell . . . which, though as it were light on by chance, deserv'd to have been omitted (I being unable to direct any one to find the like) yet for its rarity was it not inconsiderable, especially upon the account of the information it may afford us. For by it we have a very good instance of the curiosity of Nature in another kind of Animals which are remov'd, by reason of their minuteness, beyond the reach of our eyes. . . .

I was trying several small and single Magnifying Glasses, and casually viewing a parcel of white Sand, when I perceiv'd one of the grains exactly shap'd and wreath'd like a Shell, but endeavouring to distinguish it with my naked eye, it was so very small, that I was fain again to make use of the Glass to find it; then, whilest I thus look'd on it, with a Pin I separated all the rest of the granules of Sand, and found it afterwards to appear to the naked eye an exceeding small white spot, no bigger than the point of a Pin. Afterwards I view'd it every way with a better *Microscope,* and found it on both sides, and edge-ways, to resemble the Shell of a small Water-Snail with a flat spiral Shell. . . . I could not certainly discover whether the Shell were hollow or not, but . . . tis probable that it might be *petrify'd* as other larger Shells often are. . . .

In the last hundred years more than 1000 different authors have published approximately 5000 works on the foraminifera. There have been proposed close to 1500 generic names and approximately 18,000 specific designations, so that the mere cataloguing of the foraminifera requires 30,000 pages.[7] But the greatest single step in the advance of knowledge about foraminifera was that taken by Dr. Joseph A. Cushman, and at once placed the study on a wholly new basis of scientific accuracy and made possible their economic exploitation.

When Dr. Cushman came to Harvard in 1899, he intended to study cryptogrammic botany, a subject whose name derives from the fact that the sexual organs of the plants it studies are hidden from view. A course in paleontology, or fossil life, under Dr. R. T. Jackson in 1902–1903 changed the whole trend of his life. He became interested in the foraminifera and wrote a thesis for his S.B. degree and another for his Ph.D. under Dr. Jackson on this subject.

The two leading experts on the foraminifera in this country at that time were Dr. J. M. Flint, a retired naval surgeon, whose microscope had uncovered foraminifera in samples of dredgings from the ocean floor, and Dr. R. M. Bagg, a paleontologist who taught biology at the Brockton High School. Dr. Cushman went to Woods Hole for two summers, in 1904 and 1905, to collect specimens for the Boston Museum of Natural History, and to study living foraminifera at the laboratory of the United States Bureau of Fisheries. In Woods Hole, a chance acquaintance with Miss Rathbun, herself a distinguished biologist, assured him of a further supply of foraminifera through the agency of her brother, Richard Rathbun, director of the National Museum at Washington. Cushman made a trip to Washington, where he met, and was greatly stimulated by, Dr. Flint. He found that the United States Geological Survey was anxious to have him work on the fossil representatives of the foraminifera group. Cushman became a member of the U. S. Geological Survey and continued his study of microfossils. But first he undertook an investigation of the Pacific species since he believed he should know the living forms better before going deeper into the fossils. Later he agreed to study, for the U. S. Geological Survey, the species from the later geological eras.

Many people at that time thought, largely because of the abundance of foraminifera, that most of the forms were extremely long-lived and that they "ranged all the way from the top to the bottom" in all geologic formations. Soon Cushman knew better. It became apparent to him that the range of many species, given frequently as "Cambrian to Recent" (which means species found from a half billion years ago to today), was erroneous and had to be corrected. His idea was to split each form into numerous species, and he was roundly criticized for it by many writers over a period of years. His detractors saw no reason for the infinite labor of trying to divide each apparently long-range or long-lived species into new species of shorter range.

≈   ≈   ≈

Cushman's approach to the problem was of vast importance, not only in advancing our knowledge of foraminifera and their distribution, but also in making possible the use of foraminifera in determining the age of rocks, or in geological correlation of strata.

As early as 1877 an Austrian water-well driller, operating near

Vienna, attempted to use the foraminifera to determine the geologic age at which the rocks he encountered had been formed.[8] But clearly, if it was believed that the foraminifera encountered were the same a half billion years ago and today, they could hardly be used effectively for such a purpose. Although Cushman's attack on the general problem was completely nonutilitarian, the later large-scale commercial applications of his discoveries proved the general validity of the course he pursued.

On the basis of "species splitting," Cushman revised all previous classifications of foraminifera; the general theoretical background was slowly worked out by him in the decade before 1914. Cushman's work in dividing up the types of foraminifera made it possible completely to identify each species or form, to give positive identification to each one and to distinguish it from others, and to determine exactly, from the presence of a particular kind, during what geologic stage the formation in question had been made.

One of the first vindications of Cushman's new idea occurred just before the First World War when a group of drillers were engaged in digging a water well near Charleston, South Carolina. There are several types of water, differing greatly in mineral content. Some water is useless, being not even good for machinery, since it scales the boiler or forms a scum. Some water can be used for machinery but not for human consumption, whereas other water may be used for drinking purposes. The well people appealed to the United States Geological Survey and sent samples from the drilling for identification. The ordinary experts on fossils could be of little help since the drill had broken up the samples of rock and shale, apparently destroying any fossils present. But the minute foraminifera were complete and intact. Dr. Cushman was able to identify each stratum of rock by analyzing the types which he found. Cushman's analysis was published by L .W. Stephenson in 1914, as part of the description of the geology of the deep well at Charleston. It marks the first instance of a detailed micro-paleontological analysis of strata penetrated in a well.

It was just one simple step from a water well to an oil well.

The exact year can no longer be ascertained, but soon after the work on the Charleston well, the United States Geological Survey sent Cushman samples from Texas oil-well drillings for age determination. Cushman found that his theoretical work had laid the background for the same accurate determination of the strata of oil wells that had marked his previous experience in the case of the water well. From this time on the science of micro-paleontology, as well as its applications to geological problems, grew by leaps and bounds.

Since Cushman's methods yielded certain results, and were of enormous commercial value, and since he was, at that time, just about the only person engaged in, or able to do, the work, his services were in great demand. Cushman left the U. S. Geological Survey and went to work as a consultant to oil companies. He had a number of reasons for this move. The opportunities offered him to do field work offered a proving ground for his ideas on a scale unobtainable in any other way, and he was assured of sources of foraminifera to investigate which would not otherwise have been available. The bargain was a good one. Cushman rendered yeoman service to the oil companies, but he never forgot that he was primarily a scientist rather than a prospector and he kept in mind that his experience must always be thought of in relation to his scientific career. The practical success vindicated his scheme of classification, and the fees he obtained enabled him to retire after several years and to establish and endow the Cushman Laboratory for Foraminiferal Research.

The search for oil in all parts of the world is going on today at a greater rate than ever before. Many people have attempted to estimate the total oil reserves of the earth, and some of the startling conclusions which have been arrived at tell us that the supply of oil over the entire globe may be exhausted within two or three centuries.

Kirtley F. Mather, professor of geology at Harvard University, in a recent study of the resources of the earth, points out that the "proved reserves" of petroleum beneath the surface of the United States as of January 1944 may be reliably estimated at about 20 billion barrels. Various estimates have been made concerning "the additional quantity that may be discovered in areas not yet adequately explored with the drill, or in deeper reservoirs not yet reached by the deepest wells in known fields." In addition, there is "the possibility of increasing materially the percentage of recovery from reservoir rocks." Professor Mather is inclined to accept the larger figures for the quantity to be added to our petroleum reserves from these two sources. Thus we may add to the "proved reserves" of 20 billion barrels an additional 15 or 20 billion, so that "the present store of available petroleum beneath the surface of the United States is 35 to 40 billion barrels." By the end of 1943, when over 400,000 wells were in operation, we had taken out of the earth nearly 28 billion barrels since the drilling of the first oil well in 1859 — some two fifths of all the oil beneath the continental United States. On the basis of the average annual production of petroleum in this country during the period from 1938 to 1942 (1,314,400,000 barrels *per annum*) "the domestic stores of this essential material would be exhausted in 25 or 30 years." [9]

Such a statement must be interpreted very carefully. It does not mean, for example, that the oil fields in the United States will be completely exhausted within thirty years, because with a dwindling supply we shall depend more and more on foreign sources; the total American production is envisaged as declining gradually while the largest portion of oil used in the United States in the future will come from sources without our national boundaries. In 1940 America produced 61 per cent of the total oil of the world, and the total United States production to date is about 64 per cent of the total world production.

The nature of the problem in the future will depend on many factors; for example, whether or not American chemists and geologists can find ways to use low-grade sources such as oil shale more efficiently than hitherto, and also on the possibility of the American public being willing to assume the higher cost of oil produced from sources which today are not profitable to work in the face of competition from the normal oil well.

A tremendous amount of crude oil has been obtained since the beginning of the industry, a quantity estimated by Professor Kirtley F. Mather to be about 32.7 billions produced in the United States alone from the late 1850's to the end of the year 1946.[10] It seems a huge figure, and yet this quantity would not fill a box one mile square and one mile deep. The rate of increase of oil production has advanced from about 2000 barrels of 42 gallons in the 1850's to 1.2 billion barrels in 1932 [11] and 1.75 billion in 1946.[12]

                                 ~   ~   ~

Many of us think of oil as being found in large underground lakes, but the oil pools which occur underground are always within some kind of porous reservoir rock. The oil fills the spaces between the particles of sand, limestone, or shale, rather than being a free lake in the ordinary sense. After an oil field has been exhausted, a porous rock skeleton remains; the oil can never be entirely drained, and a considerable amount of oil always remains, wetting the surface of the rock.

The earliest form of oil prospecting depended upon surface indications in the form of seepages of oil, asphalt deposits, gas, saline ground water, stunted vegetation, or a combination of all of these. The existence of oil is not, however, limited to such places, nor are deposits always found under seepages, since oil migrates through the lower earth layers over great distances.

The old-time prospector was called a wildcatter, a man who "took his courage in his hands and drilled a well with nothing but a hunch to guide him."[13] In the early days one of the instruments used by the wildcatter was a device called variously a divining rod, wiggle stick, or doodlebug. This was a forked twig, which, in the hands of an "experienced" man, supposedly would point to the ground when carried over a spot under which oil or water was present. No scientific evidence has ever been found to indicate that the use of such instruments had any basis in fact, and the number of errors committed with the divining rod was probably enormously greater than the number of successful determinations.

The interpretation of surface indications requires a great deal more experience. Dr. Gustav Egloff, the Director of Research for the Universal Oil Products Company, tells us that the famous Oklahoma City oil pool was found by drilling in a section of ground covered with scrub oak. It was discovered because a geologist with wide experience in another oil field noticed that scrub oak was there associated with oil, and making a case study of the earth and surrounding country decided that Oklahoma City had a first-class oil pool. But another geologist who had his home in the middle of the same scrub oak saw nothing to indicate that he was living on top of one of the greatest oil fields uncovered in the United States in recent times.[14]

For a great number of years an active controversy raged between various schools of thought concerning the actual origin of petroleum: whether this origin was inorganic (that is, purely chemical) or whether, like coal, oil had its origin in organic living material of bygone ages. Because, unlike coal, oil does migrate in the earth and is usually not found in the exact place where it was formed; it is very difficult to examine the circumstances under which it was formed. Today most oil geologists believe that the formation of oil occurs by a slow chemical or biochemical decomposition of the remains of primitive forms of organic life which were entombed in sedimentary rock. Sometime long past, seaweeds or sea grasses, tiny marine animals, and tiny plants, were entombed in the sediments at the bottom of shallow seas under stagnant conditions which prevented complete decomposition before they were buried by further sediments. Somehow or other this organic material was transformed, either by chemical change or by bacterial action, into globules of oil and gas. Then, as ages rolled past, the original mud was compacted into shale, and the globules of oil, together with salt water, were squeezed out until they found convenient resting places in sand or porous limestone.

In this process, the globules of oil and gas may be widely dispersed, but since the oil and gas are lighter than water, they tend to float or trickle up to the top of any given layer of sand until further upward progress is blocked by an impervious cover of such solid rock as shale. These layers are usually not horizontal but are tilted by the process whereby mountains are built. Thus in front of the major mountain ranges of the world, the strata of rock are thrown into a series of folds or may be curved into a dome-shaped structure called an anticline. The crests of the anticlines are traps for the oil and gas which float up and become concentrated there. The most usual type of oil accumulation is under an anticline or dome.

The task of the prospector is to find regions under the earth where the structure of the strata forms such domes or anticlines and in which oil may possibly be found. Contour maps are made of regions by means of aerial surveying. Then the geologist goes to work with magnetic and gravitational instruments, and sets up earthquake waves which he records on a seismograph. These and various other geophysical methods give a considerable amount of information about the general structure of the strata of rock far beneath the surface of the earth. If the indications appear favorable for the type of structure in which oil may be found, sample borings or drillings may be made in order to determine the exact composition of the layers.

In analyzing the sample drillings the prospector must be able to determine whether beds that elsewhere have proved to be petroleum-bearing lie below, and if there is below the earth the dome-shaped structure in which oil is usually found. In both of these investigations the foraminifera, or "forams" as they are called colloquially, play an important part. By analyzing the occurrence of

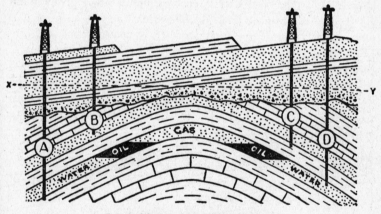

LOCATING AN ANTICLINE

Reproduced from Natural History *through the courtesy of the American Museum of Natural History.*

these tiny fossils in the various strata, the geologist is able to tell in exactly what geological period the various rocks were formed, and to give information about possible oil-bearing rocks underneath. The forams likewise afford precise information about the existence of an arch or dome-shaped structure (an anticline). Looking at the figure, we can see exactly how such determinations can be made. If the drill samples at points *A, B, C,* and *D* contain identical forams but at depths in proportion to the structure of an arch, then the geologist knows that one and the same stratum of rock has been encountered at the different points A, B, C, and D.[15] Without this positive identification by the use of fossils, a sandstone obtained at these different points might or might not be exactly the same stratum. But if the same index fossils are found in each one, then there is 100 per cent assurance that the strata of rock encountered at each of the four points form a continuous single layer — that is, an arch or dome; and the chances are good for oil.

The strata, or layers, of rock are frequently folded over each other and it is important to know if the successive layers that the drill meets are folds of layers encountered earlier or higher; here again a positive answer may be given by the presence of fossils. Likewise one may correlate oil-bearing rock formations many miles apart by discovering in them the exact fossil formations, which give absolute information concerning their identification.

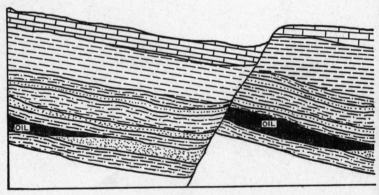

A FAULT, SHOWING THE ACCUMULATION OF OIL

Drawing by Elmer Rising

Another geological process connected with oil geology is that of faults, or planes of rupture in the rocks, due to the slipping or sinking of one stratum upon another, and caused by the movement of the earth. A fault like that in the figure is very common, and oil which is buried deeply will often migrate along the fault plane to beds higher up, and enable production to be obtained at a shallower depth than expected. In the vast oil fields of Mexico the largest oil accumulations occur along such fault planes.[16] In such a fault as may be seen in the figure, it is necessary to correlate the strata on one side of the plane with those on the other, and this again may be accomplished by the positive identification obtained with the use of fossils.

A good account of the state of knowledge and practice in 1924, when the value of microfossils in petroleum exploration was first becoming generally recognized, is afforded by a review article contributed by the late Charles Schuchert to the American Association of Petroleum Geologists in that year. Dr. Schuchert described the work of various persons engaged in using microfossils for prospecting; their number was small. Dr. Cushman at that time was having unparalleled success in working out the stratigraphy of the Tampico oil region of Mexico for the Marland Company, and others whose names we need not catalogue here were exploring other regions by using microfossils.

Yet there were still many who were not fully convinced of the value of using small foraminifera as a means of identifying geological strata. One eminent geologist had in fact declared the year before that he very much doubted whether the foraminifera could be used at all in precise identification of geological strata; he had stated unequivocally that the evidence obtained by finding similar forams in different strata indicated nothing more than a similarity in ecological conditions rather than a positive identification in age. Those who had begun to use the forams, especially in the wells of Texas, Mexico, and Louisiana, replied that the study of several thousands of tiny samples proved that the identification by forams was by far more positive than the doubters would have supposed.

The trouble was that many people continued to believe that certain older species, still living today in the oceans and also found as fossils, would *nowhere* have any geologic correlation value. But the workers in Texas were not much concerned with the world distribution of the particular forams they found in well cuttings. Their sole interest was to study the particular species brought up by the drill and their relation to the rock assemblages from which they had come. Taking advantage of Dr. Cushman's fundamental work in defining species, they were able to distinguish between the species with a fineness beyond the published classifications of the old literature. The fossil material used in such study of geological formations was classified into many new species and varieties, which, although proposed by Dr. Cushman, had not as yet been generally recognized. This very "splitting of old species into new and more localized groups" was the one factor that "made it possible to use the foraminifera in detailed stratigraphic correlations." [17]

Dr. Cushman wrote at this time, in a private letter to Dr. Schuchert, "The greatest success that I may have had over others in stratigraphic correlations on the basis of Foraminifera is partly due to the very thing for which I have been criticized, especially by European workers on the forams; that is, the tendency to split species to a much greater degree than has been done by others. The time value of forams, however, is entirely dependent on this splitting, for putting together species which are of short range into one long range would defeat the purpose of close correlation. . . . I have felt for a long time that the forams are just beginning to come into their own, as far as their value in economic work is concerned, and I am very sure that careful, trained workers, who have powers of close discrimination, would prove that they are one of the most valuable sources of information for close correlation in economic work." [18]

The reader must keep in mind, as Dr. Cushman pointed out in 1924, that the work in correlation for petroleum uses must be often of a very exact character. "It is not usually a matter of the age of a certain formation, but just where in one well section does a certain sample from a certain section from another well in the same field correlate? Are the beds becoming higher or lower? What is the angle of dip of the producing sand between two wells? In such cases no abstract method of age determination will do, but there must be a very careful and detailed examination of the contained specimens. . . . The worker is not worried as to what the percentage of living species may be, or the exact vertical range of a long-lived species in his sample, if he can find the exact point at which contact occurs between materials bearing two distinct faunas whose position in the section is already well known to him. Then he can say that the strata between the two wells are rising and the oil possibilities are thereby measurably increased in certain directions, and that water sands should be cased off at certain points. It is this practical side which gives to the petroleum industry such far-reaching results from the use of the foraminifera." [19]

           ∾   ∾   ∾

The importance of fossils in oil geology was recognized when, in 1926, at a meeting of the American Association of Petroleum Geologists held in Dallas, Texas, a dinner was arranged for a score of persons who were interested in paleontological and stratigraphic research. A paleontological society was formed and a journal of paleontology inaugurated, edited by Joseph Cushman.[20] The president of the new society was J. J. Galloway, author of a manual on the foraminifera and one who, together with Dr. Cushman, must be included among the pioneers in advancing the study of foraminifera and their application to oil geology. The name of the organization was the Society of Economic Palaeontologists and Mineralogists.

In these early days, as contrasted to the present, the number of active workers was few, and the type of work required an extensive knowledge not only of geology but of the special technique of micro-paleontology, which could be obtained only at the expense of years of arduous study. Today, workers have at their elbow the splendid manual of Dr. Cushman's, containing a descriptive account of the foraminifera and their economic use, pictures of the chief types one may encounter, and also a description of the different families and the various types of genera and species. The systematic array prepared by him renders the task of the micro-paleontologist in the field relatively simple compared to what it was twenty years ago. Yet even today those who approach this work must have college training, or its equivalent, in geology or mineralogy, plus study on the graduate or post-graduate level of several years' duration, usually culminating in a Master's or a Doctor of Philosophy's degree. Dr. Cushman today receives more requests for trained micro-paleontologists than he can meet. The demand by far exceeds the supply.

           ∾   ∾   ∾

The greatest difficulty in practical work derives from the smallness of most common foraminifera. The large species can be treated in the same way as ordinary shells — sorted by hand into trays and comparison easily made from one specimen to another. With small species the mechanical handling becomes much more difficult, and the specimens must be mounted for microscopic study. The worker will never find it easy to carry in mind visual images while transference of slides takes place, and a series of specimens is compared with the original. Furthermore, the characteristics are very fine and the sculpture of the fossilized shells is easily obliterated. Many of the species lack external ornamentation, and are therefore more difficult to distinguish than the large varieties. Since Dr. Cushman's manual was designed for workers in the field and in the laboratory, where the whitish or pinkish foraminifera tests or shells are mounted on black slides so that they will stand out and be more clearly marked, the many beautiful plates in that manual are published in white against a black background, as in the one reproduced facing this page. The figures delineated in the plates thus have the exact appearance of the material as examined by the worker under his microscope.

Although there are some strata of rock barren of all fossils, which at times may be many hundreds of feet thick, foraminifera are more often found in strata than not. Usually the micro-paleontologist can determine accurately the faunal differences in each successive four hundred feet, and it is not rare to determine zones two hundred feet thick or even less. This faunal, or foraminiferal, evidence must be correlated with other evidence about the type of rock in which it is found, in order to provide the most accurate determination. As material from a section or well core comes in, the micro-paleontologist quickly determines the vertical distribution of the fossils. By referring to the figures of the different varieties, he may note changes from one depth to another and the new species which occur. From this data he constructs a chart showing the distribution of certain important species in the particular section or well. Such a chart is reproduced here and indicates the particular fossils uncovered in samples at every ten feet of depth. The names at the top are those of species of foraminifera, and the letters C, F, and R opposite each depth indicate whether the particular species was common, frequent, or rare.[21]

In any section there are some species which are so rare as to be of

Courtesy Cushman Laboratory for Foraminiferal Research

Photographs made through a microscope of a series of foraminifera tests or
shells. This plate of photomicrographs, made at the Cushman Laboratory, was
chosen for me by Dr. Cushman who describes it as "his favorite."

Depth	Nodosaria Xy-1	Nodosaria Xy-2	Nonion Xy-1	Nonion Xy-2	Bolivina Xy-1	Vernewilina Xy-1	Textularia Xy-1	Spirillina Xy-1	Clavulina Xy-1	Robulus Xy-1	Globigerina Xy-1	Pyrgo Xy-1	Cassidulina Xy-1	Eponides Xy-1	Oxbulina Xy-1	Ammobaculites Xy-1	Dentalina Xy-1	Dentalina Xy-2	Glandulina Xy-1	Globulina Xy-1	Frondicularia Xy-1	Lagena Xy-1	Uvigerina Xy-1	Pyrulina Xy-1
210'	F	C		c						F	C									F				
220	C	C		C							C													F
230	C	C		C							C													
240	F	F								C	F			F				R					C	
250	R	F								C	F												C	
260	F	R	R			R				R	R							R		C			C	
270	R	F								R	F			R									F	
280	C	F								F	F	C								C				
290	F	F								c	c	c												
300	C	F					F			F	C										F			F
310							F			R	C							R			F			
320	R			R			R			F	F			R							C			
330	C	F					F			C	F										F			
340	C	F					c			F	C						F							
350	C		R				C			F	C			R			F	R						R
360	F						C			C	F						F							
370	F		R				F				C						F							
380								C	F		F										F			
390								C	F	F	F													
400		R			R			C	F	F									F					
410			R						F	R	R			R			R		F					R
420		R								R					F				F					
430			R							R	F			F										
440			R							R	F			C										
450										R	F			C										
460														C									F	
470										R	R			F									F	

A typical micro-paleontologist's work sheet. It gives a rough tabulation of the occurrence of different species (whose names appear at the top of the chart) in each ten feet of a 260-foot section of core. R means that the species is rare, C common, F frequent. Reproduced from Cushman's Foraminifera, courtesy of Harvard University Press.

little use in determining the position of samples. Even if their ranges are very short and accurate, the actual time consumed in finding them in any given sample, and the possibility of missing them altogether, may make their value very slight. On the other hand, species will be encountered whose ranges are very long, and which may be present through too much of the section to be of use in detailed work. (One such may be seen in the accompanying chart.) Yet in every section species will be encountered whose ranges are relatively short, and which are abundant enough to be found quickly in a sample if they are present at all. This type of species is ideal for correlation purposes.

The chart reproduced here gives the reader an idea of the report which the micro-paleontologist makes of a given section. A similar report made on a near-by region may be quickly correlated with this one, and the strata which occur in successive levels at a certain depth in this chart may be quickly identified with those occurring at a different level on the other chart.[22] This exact information makes the use of foraminifera such a valuable tool for the oil geologist, and explains furthermore why it is that every one of the large oil companies now employs on its staff a number of trained micro-paleontologists, and maintains well-equipped laboratories for the microscopic examination of fossils obtained in drilling for oil.

After Dr. Cushman had put in a number of years as a consultant in the field, he gave up the practical work and returned to his original fundamental studies. He organized and built near his home in Sharon, Massachusetts, the now famous Cushman Laboratory for Foraminiferal Research, and began publishing in 1925 the famous series known as the *Contributions from the Cushman Laboratory,* the first regular publication to be devoted exclusively to micropaleontology. The laboratory is situated in the middle of a woods about one quarter of a mile from Dr. Cushman's home. Leaving the house, one follows a path through a garden and then a dense grove of trees, until one comes to a clearing where a simple, good-sized white building is located. This laboratory, although supported largely by Dr. Cushman himself, constitutes a regular field station of the United States Geological Survey, of which he is once more a member, and which supplies him with an assistant geologist, Miss Todd, to aid him in his labors. Dr. Cushman has also the help of his daughter, Alice.

The specimens in the laboratory are preserved on tiny slides which can be placed under a microscope for examination. There are altogether about 102,000 such slides, each one three inches long and one inch wide, and each containing from one to a couple of hundred specimens, several million all told. This extraordinary collection has been willed to the Smithsonian Institution, because, as Dr. Cushman explains, "That is where I started."

There are probably in the world today some 2500 experts in the use of foraminifera, of whom say 1500 are in our hemisphere, and the others in the Near East, the Holy Land, North Africa, and West Asia. A large number of them are to be found in West Asia, in Siberia, and more of Dr. Cushman's publications go to the Soviet Union than to any other foreign country.

Today Dr. Cushman is used to the fact that his publications are sent to all corners of the globe, but many amusing events are associated with the early days when his fame was on the rise and the importance of his work was just becoming recognized. Soon after Dr. Cushman published the first edition of his great treatise, *Foraminifera — Their Classification and Economic Use* (special publication number one of the Cushman Laboratory for Foraminiferal Research), in 1928, he received a request that fifty copies be sent to a place he had never heard of. The order was received by him at his summer home in New Hampshire. (Parenthetically one may add that Dr. Cushman can very easily carry off with him a month's work or more in a package of slides that fits in his vest pocket!) He went to the local post office, but the postmaster too had never heard of the strange place from which the order had come. He sent Dr. Cushman to the nearest big town to inquire of the postmaster there concerning the shipping of fifty copies of his book — "What would be the cost and time required for delivery?" This postmaster had a larger collection of postal routes, and after looking through them turned to Dr. Cushman and said, "Depends on whether you use the ordinary route or whether you ship by camel." In this way Dr.

Cushman learned of the far places in the world where the foraminifera were being studied for economic purposes.

In December of 1945 the first oil well was discovered in Chile, in the Tierra del Fuego field. The *New York Times* announced that the government of Chile plans to construct a nationalized petroleum industry integrated through the refining and distribution stage. One of the first steps the government took was to request that a Chilean student studying geology at Harvard go to the Cushman Laboratory to study the use of foraminifera in oil drilling.

ᛅ   ᛅ   ᛅ

To readers of this book, the most interesting aspect of the development and use of foraminifera is that the application came at about the time it did. Had the only utility of foraminifera been in the drilling of water wells, it is quite certain that the extended knowledge and commercial applications of micro-paleontology would be on a much smaller scale than they are today. But the vast development of the oil industry provided a field of work of extensive proportions.

The first oil well was opened up in Titusville, Pennsylvania, by Drake in 1859. One of those who observed the new oil took a can of it because he had an idea that it would make "a mighty fine spread for buckwheat cakes," but actually the first use for petroleum was the production of kerosene to keep lamps burning.

The early refiners had one great problem, namely, what to do with that troublesome by-product, gasoline. They did not know how on earth to get rid of it. It was too explosive to be used in lamps or stoves. Many refiners of kerosene dumped it into rivers and harbors. Since this created a great fire hazard, laws were enacted to prevent the dumping of gasoline into any handy water. In the early 1890's a refiner was a lucky man if he could sell it at even less than a cent a gallon. Very few refiners could sell the gasoline at all, and they dared not dump it overboard.[23]

This was the background of the successful introduction of the gasoline or internal-combustion engine and its application to pumps, but especially to horseless carriages. The plentiful supply of cheap fuel available at the end of the nineteenth century was one of the most important factors in the victory of the automobile and tractor and the resultant "passing of the horse." With the use of internal-combustion engines, the development of various oil-burning engines such as the Diesel, and oil burners for homes and industrial plants, the demand for petroleum and its products grew and grew. At the end of the First World War a mad race was on to discover and produce more and still more oil. The feverish and greedy demand for oil was reflected in the Teapot Dome scandal of the early 1920's, and the dour predictions of those who claimed that we were burning up the oil reserves of the world at a much faster rate than oil could possibly ever be discovered. Much of the political future of the Near East is certainly linked very closely to the still pressing need for oil today, not only as a source of gasoline and fuel but also for the enormous variety and magnitude of chemical by-products of petroleum.

After the First World War there was a demand for oil, and a search for oil wells, on an unprecedented scale, with vast expenditures for prospecting. The world was ready for the application of any new techniques which would improve the state of oil prospecting, and provide more accurate knowledge which would prevent the needless spending of perhaps millions of dollars. At that very time, when the need became acute, the knowledge was already available to the scientists.

∞   ∞   ∞

Of course the use of microfossils is not the only new technique applied in the last twenty-five years to oil prospecting, but the story is the most spectacular as an example of how apparently useless knowledge is put to use.

Another of the important sciences is that of igneous petrography, described as the study of small sand grains and rocks under the microscope. Some sandstones contain definite proportions of certain minerals, of which many are easy to detect while others are not. The heavy minerals such as tourmaline, zircone, and the minerals composed of iron in the form of magnetite, hermatite, or pyrite, are usually easy to distinguish. These are used by the petrographer as the basis of comparison and examination. Dr. Gould, director of the Oklahoma Geological Survey, tells us, "It is no unusual occurrence, after a certain ledge of sandstone has been encountered, for drilling operations to stop, machinery to stand idle, and workmen to loaf on the job, while a sand sample from the bottom of a five thousand foot well is sent hundreds of miles to the laboratory where the petrographer makes his tests, and studies the grains of sand. The question as to whether or not another $10,000 or $20,000 shall be spent in the deep hole in addition to the $75,000 or $100,000 already expended, frequently rests upon the examination of the particular type of sand grains under the microscope." [24]

Still another of the new techniques applies geophysical methods, the applications of physics to geology. One of these involves the explosion of small charges of dynamite in the ground which produce on a small scale the earthquake waves usually associated in the public mind with disaster. The pattern of these waves is recorded on seismographs, which tell the geologist a good deal about the structure of the earth in the vicinity. [25]

Cushman's studies of the foraminifera, culminating in his important conclusion that the accepted species must be split, and the work of all his predecessors in the field of micro-paleontology, had been carried on without any thought of economic gain, or even of practical applications. Who, indeed, in those early days, would have thought that the study of tiny, microscopic-sized shells would contain the key to oil prospecting? Yet, when the demand arose, the knowledge was already at hand and was applied.

Just as our knowledge of magnetostriction and the piezo-electric effect was on record by the time it was needed, so also our knowledge of the foraminifera was available for use in oil prospecting at the time when the oil companies set out to discover sources of petroleum on a larger scale than ever before and needed new techniques to make their prospecting more effective and more secure.

CHAPTER 15

The Organic Chemist's Job of Work

> I would ... establish the conviction that Chemistry, as an independent science, offers one of the most powerful means towards the attainment of a higher mental cultivation; that the study of Chemistry is profitable, not only inasmuch as it promotes the material interests of mankind, but also because it furnishes us with insight into those wonders of creation which immediately surround us, and with which our existence, life, and development, are most closely connected.
>
> —JUSTUS VON LIEBIG (1851)

A FEW YEARS AGO a rough estimate based on published records revealed that about 450,000 organic chemical compounds had been "discovered." The number was only 15,000 in 1883, 150,000 in 1910, and about 350,000 in 1936. This huge collection has been put together by investigators working all over the world: in universities, research institutes, and industrial establishments.[1]

The gigantic collection of publications, including both periodicals and books, in which this work is described requires considerable library facilities. The published material is currently digested in journals like *Chemical Abstracts,* and the *Chemisches Zentralblatt,* which together run to the neighborhood of some 300 bound volumes. In addition, a famous collection known by the name of the original editor, Beilstein, and whose official title is *Handbook of Organic Chemistry,* attempts to keep abreast, in so far as possible, of all material in this field. Now in its fourth edition, and although at least twenty-five years behind, the price of this handbook at one time passed the mark of $1500.[2]

Organic chemistry as a separate branch of the science is a little more than a century old, although the subject of chemistry itself goes back almost to the beginning of our culture. In the early stages of civilization, the extraction of metals from their ores, and the art of working them, were carried out by men who, although they had no theoretical understanding of the arts they employed, showed by their considerable skill a sound appreciation of the properties of metals.

One of the great modern books on the history of chemistry was written by J. R. Partington, Professor of Chemistry at the University of London. Dealing entirely with the origins and development of applied chemistry, it will ever remain a monument to his enterprise and learning.[3] Partington surveyed the industrial activities of the ancient nations and discovered that "the technical arts of the Classical Period in Greece and Rome, formerly regarded as the spontaneous expression of a higher civilization, are really rather decadent forms of crafts practised many centuries before in the Bronze Age cultures of Egypt and Mesopotamia."[4] The early civilizations developed an extensive knowledge of applied chemistry in the use of metals, in the manufacture of pottery, the production of glass, and the development of dyes.

The name "chemistry" first appears in human records in an edict of the Emperor Diocletian in A.D. 296, in which the books of the Alexandrian Egyptians, on the subject of *chēmeia,* are ordered to be burned. Although used by the Greeks, this word appears to derive from the native designation of Egypt — which country (according to Plutarch, in a treatise written about A.D. 100) was called *chēmeia* because of the black color of its soil.[5] Thus "chemistry" goes back to the "Egyptian Art."

The treatises of the later Greek chemists contain much practical information, as well as diagrams of chemical apparatus and operations: fusion, calcination (oxidation), solution filtration, crystallization, sublimation, and distillation. In the curious circuit by which scientific knowledge reached Europe from the Greeks, by way of the Arabs, the various terms frequently had added to them the definite article "the," in Arabic *al-,* and thus the Alexandrian-Greek word *chēmeia* became alchemy — a blend of experimental science, magic, and superstition.

As the centuries passed, the alchemists discovered many important chemical reactions and added greatly to the store of knowledge accumulated by the ancient craftsmen. None of them, of course, ever achieved his ambition of transmuting "baser" metals into the more "noble" gold. Little contribution was made before the seventeenth century, however, to a theoretical science of chemistry in the modern sense; indeed it may seriously be questioned whether any true chemical science, as such, existed prior to the seventeenth century. Examining the admixture of empirical techniques and recipes and "magic" one may well agree with M. M. Pattison Muir, "Chemistry has appeared to be sometimes a handicraft, sometimes a philosophy, sometimes a mystery, and sometimes a science."

In this chapter we shall be concerned with the latter and most recent phase. Robert Boyle, that seventeenth-century genius whose name has appeared frequently in these pages, is often considered to be the father of modern chemistry. One of his claims to that high post of honor is the distinction he made between pure substances and mixtures. Today we know that pure substances may be either elements or compounds (which are chemical combinations of elements).

The difference between a mixture and a compound is usually demonstrated to classes in elementary chemistry by a very simple experiment. A small quantity of iron filings is mixed with powdered sulphur and the resultant mass is placed on a piece of paper. The question is then put as to whether the iron and sulphur have formed a chemical combination. The class is told that a chemical combination of elements is one which cannot be separated into the component parts by nonchemical means. The instructor now draws a magnet through the mixture; the magnet attracts to itself all of the iron filings and leaves the sulphur behind. Then the filings are wiped off the magnet and mixed once again with the sulphur. This time the flame of a Bunsen burner is applied to the mixture, whereupon the magnet no longer is able to separate the particles of iron from those of sulphur; hence we say that the two elements — iron and sulphur — have united to form a chemical compound called iron sulphide. To separate them we must now use chemical reagents.

In the century following Boyle, the list of chemical elements was enlarged and the proportions by weight of the elements which combine to form chemical compounds were determined. By the end of the eighteenth century, chemistry as an independent science had made such great strides that it could face the problem: Does a difference exist between the mineral and the vegetable or animal substances? Most scientists agreed that the *elements* which made up vegetable and animal, or organic, compounds were the very same as those of which mineral, or inorganic, compounds were made. Yet everyone seems to have believed in an "important difference" between compounds of the animal and vegetable (organic) types as opposed to the mineral (inorganic).

∽   ∽   ∽

Within the sphere of living nature, most chemists believed, the compounds were formed by a process in which the chemical elements obey laws totally different from those operating in the inorganic world. The compounds found in plants and animals were thought to be produced by the action of a so-called "vital force." Thus, although an existing organic compound, obtained from a plant or animal, might be changed into an entirely different organic compound, it was believed that no *organic* compound could be made in the laboratory by beginning with its component parts; because this composition of all organic compounds supposedly depended on the operation of the vital force which, obviously, only God was a clever enough chemist to control.

The idea of a vital force received a severe blow in the year 1828, the date sometimes given for the birth of organic chemistry. In that year Friedrich Wöhler made the discovery that cyanate of ammonia generally regarded as an inorganic compound, could be converted in the laboratory test tube quite simply into urea, an organic compound, a substance hitherto only known as a product of animal metabolism.

Wöhler communicated his discovery to the Swedish chemist Berzelius, declaring, "I can prepare urea without requiring a kidney or a living creature, either man or dog." A complete investigation could not dispute the identity of the synthetic and naturally occurring organic compound. Alas, Wöhler's synthesis was not as complete as he thought, because although ammonium cyanate was regarded as an inorganic compound, its preparation in Wöhler's day required the use of dried blood, hoofs and horns, and so on. As

Douglas McKie points out, Wöhler could make urea without "a kidney or a living creature, man or dog; but, be it noted, not without dried blood, horns, hoofs, and such 'organic material.' " [6]

Yet Wöhler had made a beginning, and in 1845 a compatriot did produce an organic compound, acetic acid, wholly from inorganic substances. As the century rolled on, not too much attention was paid to these two syntheses, because they were isolated phenomena. Not until some years later did the great French chemist, Marcellin Berthelot, show how, in general, one could start from elements and mineral substances, and cause carbon to be combined step by step with hydrogen, then with oxygen, and then again perhaps with nitrogen.[7] Berthelot's *Organic Chemistry Founded on Synthesis,* published in 1860, truly overthrew the vital-force theory and laid the basis for experimental synthetic organic chemistry.

Let us follow one of Berthelot's syntheses step by step. He began with pure carbon (charcoal or coke) which he heated in an electric arc surrounded by an atmosphere of pure hydrogen. As a result, the atoms of hydrogen and carbon combined in pairs to form molecules of acetylene, which we write C_2H_2 to indicate that each molecule is composed of 2 atoms of hydrogen and 2 atoms of carbon. By another process, he was able to cause each molecule of acetylene to combine with 2 more atoms of hydrogen to become ethylene C_2H_4. This substance he dissolved in sulphuric acid. When the ethylene was dissolved in sulphuric acid, it underwent chemical change; a new substance was formed from which, by the action of water, alcohol was obtained, each molecule of which has 2 more atoms of hydrogen than ethylene and also an atom of oxygen, and is therefore [8] written C_2H_6O.

To this day the organic chemist continues to synthesize important organic compounds found in nature, such as the vitamins, the hormones, penicillin, and quinine. Sometimes he begins, as Berthelot did, with the elements themselves, carbon, hydrogen, and so on, and step by step builds up complex molecules. At other times, his procedure more nearly resembles that of Wöhler and builds complex molecules on the basis of simpler (and perhaps cheaper or more readily available) ones. And, in addition, as we have seen in the earlier chapters on the auxins and on synthetic rubber and nylon, the organic chemist also constructs important compounds containing carbon which are never found in nature at all.

~ ~ ~

After Wöhler had synthesized urea, the next immediate step was taken by him in concert with the scientist who, more than any other, established organic chemistry as a science — Justus von Liebig. Liebig began his chemical career by experimenting on silver fulminate, an explosive compound produced by the action of alcohol on silver nitrate.

Liebig's career is an interesting reflection on the times because, in order to pursue his studies, he had to go to Paris. Germany, which in the later years of the nineteenth century and the early part of the twentieth was to become the great lodestone attracting to itself all chemists who wanted to study at the feet of the masters, and which developed the most advanced chemical industry, had at the time of Liebig *not one single institution* in which there was practical or laboratory instruction in chemical science.

Liebig went to Paris in 1822 and studied in the laboratory of the great French chemist, Gay-Lussac. There he went on again with his investigations on the fulminates, and in 1824 returned to Germany to accept a chair at Giessen, where he remained for twenty-eight years, until 1852, at which time he went to Munich.[9]

Besides his purely scientific research, Liebig greatly influenced the chemistry of agriculture by introducing the now common use of mineral fertilizers, and his work in physiological chemistry was very stimulating to generations of scientists. But his greatest contribution was the improved method of organic analysis (by combustion with copper oxide and the oxygen of the atmosphere), which led him to a curious and important discovery which at once placed organic chemistry on a footing far beyond that of Wöhler, and established a phenomenon which baffled chemists for many years.

~ ~ ~

In 1824 Liebig completed an analysis of fulminic acid and discovered that it contained the same proportion by weight of the constituent elements as a totally different compound, cyanic acid, which had been analyzed the previous year by Wöhler.[10] When the results came to the hands of Berzelius, he naturally enough thought there must have been a mistake. But further research showed that no mistake had been made, and in 1827 Berzelius gave the phenomenon a name, *isomerism:* "It would seem as if the simple atoms of which substances are composed may be united with each other in different ways," he wrote.[11]

We know today that the occurrence of isomers is of great significance in compounds containing at least one atom of carbon in their molecules. We may now state the basis for current distinction between "organic" and "inorganic" chemistry, the names of which have no longer their earlier significance and are merely the vestigial remains of an outmoded idea. Discarding the vital force altogether, today we mean by organic chemistry nothing more than the chemistry of carbon compounds.

∽   ∽   ∽

One of the great advances that enabled chemists to understand isomerism, and also the very nature of their science, is related to a dream. The dreamer was Friedrich August Kekulé, who was born in Darmstadt in 1829. He studied architecture at the University of Giessen and, under the influence of Liebig, turned to chemistry. He had his famous dream while working in London after the completion of his doctorate.

This dream, described by him in a speech delivered before the German Chemical Society in 1890, follows:

During my stay in London I resided for a considerable time in Clapham Road in the neighborhood of the Common. I frequently, however, spent my evenings with my friend Hugo Müller at Islington, at the opposite end of the giant town. We talked of many things, but oftenest of our beloved chemistry. One fine summer evening I was returning by the last omnibus, "outside," as usual, through the deserted streets of the metropolis, which are at other times so full of life. I fell into a reverie (*Träumerei*), and lo, the atoms were gambolling before my eyes! Whenever, hitherto, these diminutive beings had appeared to me, they had always been in motion; but up to that time I had never been able to discern the nature of their motion. Now, however, I saw how, frequently, two smaller atoms united to form a pair; how a larger one embraced two smaller ones; how still larger ones kept hold of three or even four of the smaller; whilst the whole kept whirling in a giddy dance. I saw how the larger ones formed a chain, dragging the smaller ones after them, but only at the ends of the chain. I saw what our Past Master, Kopp, my highly honoured teacher and friend, has depicted with such charm in his "Molekularwelt" but I saw it long before him. The cry of the conductor: "Clapham Road," awakened me from my dreaming but I spent a part of the night in putting on paper at least sketches of these dream forms. This was the origin of the Structurtheorie.[12]

Kekulé's *Structurtheorie* affords the chemist a means of envisaging the structure of organic molecules, in terms of such formulas as we have already encountered in the chapter on synthetic rubber and nylon. Let us see how they account for isomerism.

We represent each individual atom by a letter and the bond that holds the atoms together to form a molecule by a short line. Common marsh gas, or methane, is composed of 4 atoms of hydrogen and 1 of carbon, CH_4, and its structural formula is:

$$\begin{array}{c} H \\ | \\ H-C-H \\ | \\ H \end{array}$$

The number of lines emanating from each atom denoted by a letter is called its valence. Carbon has a valence of 4, hydrogen 1.

Not only can the bonds emanating from carbon atoms extend to hydrogen atoms, but they can also extend to other carbon atoms. Thus a compound composed of two atoms of carbon and six atoms of hydrogen (C_2H_6) can be represented by the Kekulé formula:

$$\begin{array}{c} H \quad H \\ | \quad | \\ H-C-C-H \\ | \quad | \\ H \quad H \end{array}$$

Note that 4 bonds extend from *each* carbon and 1 from *each* hydrogen, and that each bond extends from one atom and terminates on another.

To the last formula which we have written we may add an atom of oxygen to give us the compound (C_2H_6O) which we write as follows:

```
      H   H
      |   |
  H—C—C—O—H
      |   |
      H   H
```

This formula represents a molecule of ordinary ethyl alcohol. We note that such a molecule has all together: 2 atoms of carbon, 6 of hydrogen, and 1 of oxygen.

The problem that vexed Liebig and Wöhler was how two compounds could each contain the same relative composition, or, in modern terms, how molecules of two decidedly different substances could contain the same atomic composition. To show how Kekulé's structural formulas account for such isomerism, let us write the formula for another molecule: one that, like ethyl alcohol, is made up of 2 atoms of carbon, 6 of hydrogen, and 1 of oxygen.

```
      H       H
      |       |
  H—C—O—C—H
      |       |
      H       H
```

The substance represented is methyl ether, and the reader should satisfy himself that it contains the same number of carbon, hydrogen, and oxygen atoms per molecule as ethyl alcohol. But now the carbon atoms and the one atom of oxygen have taken up new positions, and the result is a molecule wholly different in all its properties. Since oxygen has a valence of 2, note that 2 bonds extend from the O.

The method of structural formulae gave the chemist one of his important tools in the determination of the structure and nature of organic (or carbon-containing) compounds. Kekulé, the erstwhile architecture student, to paraphrase J. R. Partington,[18] became master of a more refined architecture than any before him.

            ❦   ❦   ❦

The determination of the structural formula of a compound helps the organic chemist to find a way to make this compound from others which may be similar to it but more easily obtainable. We saw

Carothers follow this type of procedure when he adapted Nieuwland's discoveries in acetylene to the production of the first satisfactory synthetic rubber. But clearly, although the structure must be
known before a process can be developed, the mere knowledge of a
structure does not in itself suggest a process for synthesis. It may be
a necessary, but not a sufficient, condition. For example, a great
number of different synthetic processes might be — *and are* — used
to effect the synthesis of the same structure.

As Robertson puts it, "It became possible to specify a particular
arrangement of atoms which meant a useful drug, a gorgeous dye,
or a potent insecticide; and, more important, to demonstrate the
course of manufacture in the laboratory or manufacturing plant.
Without such chemical architecture the conversion of ineffective
natural gasoline, whose molecular design is suggestive of strings of
beads, into modern aviation gasoline, designed more like bunches
of grapes, would have been impossible." [14]

The use of these structural formulae helps the chemist to explain
the difference between isomers; the nature of organic compounds,
their reactions and properties; and they also make possible the eventual synthesis of many organic compounds. Yet it should not be
thought that the chemist's job is a simple one, like putting together
the parts of a "Meccano" set to conform to a given pattern. Many
important substances have yet to be synthesized, such as the protein
molecule itself, certain of the vitamins and antibiotics, and so on. The
horizons of chemistry are almost infinite. The synthesis of quinine
remained for many years an outstanding challenge until it was accomplished in 1944 by Dr. Robert B. Woodward. In addition to synthesizing known or naturally produced substances, today the organic
chemist has constantly before him the practically limitless task of
making in his laboratory organic compounds that man has never
found in nature. Any one of these may completely revolutionize
some aspects of our lives, or become the foundation of a new ten-
million-dollar industry.

∾   ∾   ∾

The greater part of the chemical industry is concerned with inorganic chemical processes (which include metallurgy), but probably
the greater part of industrial chemical research is concerned with

organic chemistry. Both the academic and industrial chemists, investigating the countless possible combinations of compounds of carbon, have built up a vast storehouse of compounds to be drawn upon when needed for practical purposes.

As an example of the way in which the knowledge accumulated by the organic chemist suddenly takes on a great practical value, let us consider a story involving Chaim Weizmann, the Russian-born Professor of Chemistry at the University of Manchester. In the early days of the First World War the British Navy was faced with a most serious problem. Shells fired at a range of five thousand yards in a battle off the coast of South America plunged into the ocean at half that distance. A board of inquiry investigated the cause of this disaster and finally fixed the blame on the poor quality of acetone which is used as a stabilizer in the loading charge. In the gloomy winter of 1916 when all of the leaders of the English war effort were concerned about the production of acetone, someone thought of Dr. Weizmann, who had been experimenting with various organic reactions and fermentations, hoping to synthesize rubber. It was generally believed that although he had not found what he wanted, he *had* discovered a means of making acetone.

Weizmann knew it was possible to synthesize rubber from butadiene if one could only obtain a supply of butyl alcohol.[15] In the usual fermentation process that takes place in sugar or starch, *ethyl* alcohol is produced by the action of yeast bacteria. Weizmann had been seeking another form of bacteria to produce *butyl* alcohol. He had found one which he identified and named *Clostridium-acetobutylicum Weizmann*. Its name, like most names of bacteria, is composed of three parts; the first indicates the general family, the second the specific variety, and the third the name of the discoverer. The second part of the name, aceto-butylicum, reveals that this particular bacterium produces not only butyl alcohol, but also acetone. In fact, it produced twice as much acetone as the butyl alcohol which Weizmann desired.

Years later, when the Weizmann process for producing butyl alcohol and acetone formed the basis for the original activities of the Commercial Solvents Corporation, these bacteria were called "B–Y's" — B for bacteria, and Y for Weizmann, since the letter Y was the first syllable of his name as pronounced in English.[16]

The fact that Weizmann's process produced acetone, and especially that twice as much acetone was produced as the butyl alcohol for which Weizmann had originally sought, very much interested Arthur James Balfour, then First Lord of the Admiralty, and Weizmann was called to London. A special laboratory was set aside at the Lister Institute, and during the autumn and winter months of 1915–1916, research was advanced to the point where, early in 1916, the first commercial unit for the production of acetone by the Weizmann process was set into operation. In the spring of 1916 additional units were set up in Canada, and soon after America entered the war, two large distilleries in Indiana were set aside for this purpose, one for British armament, and one for American.[17]

Once it had become clear that Weizmann's research had solved the British acetone problem and had solved a problem of munitions for the British Navy, the Prime Minister, Lloyd George, sent for the chemist and, according to the usual story, offered to recommend to the King any honor he might wish to have bestowed upon him: knightship, a baronetcy, or an annuity to guarantee the possibility of research until he died. Weizmann replied that he wanted no honors for himself, but if there was to be any reward he would like it to be the use of the influence of the British Government in setting up Palestine as a Jewish homeland.

In point of fact Weizmann's was a timely request. Only the day before a number of members of the cabinet had advanced the thesis that the adoption of such a position would be of great value for Britain in international politics. The cabinet had not agreed, and Lloyd George himself had been undecided. Three weeks later the Balfour Declaration promising that England would establish in Palestine a national homeland for the Jews was made public.[18]

When the war was over most of the acetone plants using the Weizmann process were shut down, but those in Peoria, Illinois, and Terre Haute, Indiana, were purchased from the Allied War Board by a group of farsighted capitalists who organized themselves into the Commercial Solvents Corporation.[19] This company continued to make acetone, and was concerned to find a use for the by-product butyl alcohol, which, up to that time, had been considered waste.

The first application they found was in the manufacture of quick-drying lacquers, with amazing results.

The automobile industry, in particular, had long been seeking a quick-drying paint because, as the mass-production process developed and the speed of manufacture of automobiles accelerated, the painting remained the slow part, or bottleneck. One manufacturer in the early twenties was reported to have twenty million dollars of capital tied up in automobiles which could not be delivered because they were still drying. The new process of using quick-drying lacquer meant that this last bottleneck was removed and cars could be painted and even dried on the same assembly line belt on which they had been put together.[20]

The story is told by Williams Haynes that, at the time the lacquers were first developed, an executive of the General Motors Corporation drove one of the plant engineers, Charles Kettering, later to become one of America's foremost scientists and president of the American Association for the Advancement of Science, to lunch at the Detroit Club. The executive remarked to the engineer that he wished he could have his car repainted but he could not afford to have it laid up for three or four weeks in order to give it a new coat of paint. Kettering asked him what color he would pick if he were to have it done over and the executive replied, "Black."

The luncheon was a long one with a considerable discussion of many different engineering problems on which Kettering's research department was then engaged. As Haynes tells us, "Kettering does not admit unduly stringing out that conference, but though he keenly loves a joke, he is also a cautious man. No doubt he was certain that the car had returned from the experimental laboratory before they left the table. When they walked down the front steps, there it stood, no longer a shabby red but now finished a glossy black. It was an impressive demonstration of what the new lacquer finish could do." [21]

The development of the lacquer business, based on the apparently useless butyl alcohol, came about so quickly that in order to supply the large quantities needed by the automobile industry Commercial Solvents soon found that now they had an excess of acetone! The original product had become the by-product.

Those who are interested in how this renewed imbalance was

solved may be referred to a very well written and interesting book devoted to the history of the Commercial Solvents Corporation by Frederick C. Kelly, entitled *One Thing Leads to Another*.

And so we see how the applications of scientific discovery were available twice in succession. At the time during the First World War when there was a crying need for acetone, Weizmann had already accumulated the fundamental knowledge on which to base a commercial process for producing it. Later, with the development of fast-drying lacquers, when the need arose for butyl alcohol the same process was at hand and able to be put into operation. When Midgley needed thousands of compounds at his disposal in order to test them for antiknock properties, the organic chemists had already synthesized them. They were ready for Midgley to use. When a process for producing acetone and butyl alcohol was urgently needed, the scientific information to be applied had already been obtained in the laboratory and was ready and available.

Yet the stored chemical knowledge is so vast that probably 95 per cent or more of all the known organic compounds listed in Beilstein may be completely useless as far as any application outside of the realm of chemistry itself is concerned. But never think that this knowledge, accumulated by thousands of investigators, has not therefore a very real practical value. As Professor Robertson tells us in his delightful essay on *The Task of the Organic Chemist,* "When an investigator tries to identify a complex natural substance, he often pulls the unknown molecule to pieces, isolates and purifies the pieces, and then searches for data on these fragments. It is then very convenient to have a depository, a chemical museum, let us say, containing scores of thousands of well-described compounds ready for comparison. Once these fragments are recognized, the main problem is well along towards solution. It is not even necessary to have the actual substance at hand. Accurate descriptions traced through Beilstein do very well." [22] Of course, final proof that two substances are identical does require a *direct* comparison.

Many urgent practical problems are solved in just this way. One of the most egregious examples is that of R. R. Williams, a chemist employed by the Bell Telephone Company, who in his spare time finally made possible the synthesis of Vitamin B_1 so that it would be available in cheaper form than it was in its naturally occurring state in fruits and vegetables. Williams found that the Vitamin B_1 could be split into two parts by the application of sodium sulphite, a common chemical used by photographers. By further treating these two parts, he was able to produce substances which could be identified in chemical literature, and in this way worked out the B_1 structural formula. As Professor Robertson says, "It is thus presumptuous to declare that any organic compound is entirely useless. Not all useful things are in retail stores." [23]

Dr. Linus Pauling, a distinguished chemist of the California Institute of Technology, tells his students that the organic chemists work in two principal ways which the reader may now be in position to appreciate. The first of these may be illustrated by the investigation of some naturally occurring material, such as may be obtained from a plant, and which is found to have beneficial properties in the treatment of some disease, say malaria. The chemist will start his research by using various methods of separating or dividing this extract into what he calls "fractions." Following each fractionation, he makes tests in order to determine which part or fraction still contains the active principle or active substance. If he is fortunate, he may be able to carry the process far enough along to obtain a pure substance, perhaps in crystalline form.

The next job, according to Dr. Pauling, is to make an analysis of the crystalline substance: determining its molecular weight, the kind of atoms of which a molecule is composed, and the number of each kind of atom in a molecule. This work enables the chemist to write a formula, but he has still to obtain more information before he can write a structural formula; and, as we have seen, it is the latter which tells the story.

In order to obtain the requisite information for writing the structural formula, he splits the molecules of the pure substance into smaller molecules of known substances. In identifying them, he will rely on the published literature and it is here that the accumulated labors of the organic chemists who have described organic compounds becomes of great value.

After he has identified the smaller molecules he has formed, the chemist puts together all the information he has gathered and determines the structural formula of the pure substance in which he is interested. Then, and only then, is he in a position to attempt to synthesize the substance and to show how to manufacture it in larger quantities and at lower cost than would be possible when the substance was obtained from a plant.

But, Dr. Pauling reminds us, there is also a second way in which organic chemists work, one that involves "the synthesis and study of a large number of organic compounds and the continued effort to correlate the empirical facts by means of theoretical principles." The chemists who do this sort of work aim at understanding the physical, chemical, and physiological properties of organic compounds in terms of their molecular structure. Our chemists have gone a long way toward the goal of understanding just how the physical and chemical properties of organic substances depend on the structure of their molecules. Yet only a brave beginning, we are told, "has been made in attacking the great problem of the relation between structure and physiological activity. This problem remains one of the greatest and most important problems of science challenging the new generation of scientists." [24]

In the same way, developments in scientific technique become extremely valuable tools in the hands of the skilled investigator, not only for the advancement of science but also for the development of utilitarian products. During the nineteenth century, organic compounds which occur naturally were found in abundance. Tartaric acid was obtained from grapes, and nicotinic from tobacco. Since there was an ample supply of material the quantitative analysis necessary to produce the condensed chemical formula indicating the proportions of the different elements which made up the compound was a simple one. For the two check-determinations involved in this process about one half a gram, the equivalent of one sixtieth of an ounce, was all that was required.

With the advent of the twentieth-century research on the vitamins and hormones that were obtainable only in minute quantities, a completely new style of chemistry became necessary on what has been described as a microscopic scale. One of the great developments toward this end was that of the famous Kohlmann chemical balance, which is sensitive to 0.001 milligram, or about 1/30,000,000 of an ounce. The research work of Fritz Pregl at the University of Graz in Austria developed completely new techniques of analysis of small samples so that analytical work could be reduced by a factor of 100, and 2/1000 of a gram could be dealt with as simply as 2/10 of a gram had been handled before. Because of the remarkable results which he achieved, Pregl was awarded the Nobel Prize in 1923. The use of Pregl's technique enabled Richard Kuhn at Heidelberg to analyze and decipher the structure of riboflavin or Vitamin B_2, at present a component of so-called vitamin-enriched bread, as well as a constituent of the vitamin pills which have become for so many of us as much a part of breakfast as coffee. Kuhn obtained his sample by working up the albumin of 33,000 eggs. From this fantastic quantity he isolated only 1/10 of a gram of this vitamin, yet sufficient for the purpose of analysis by the use of the new technique. For his brilliant achievements Kuhn was awarded the Nobel Prize in 1939. But on orders from Berlin, he disdained to accept modern science's greatest honor.[25]

Another example is afforded by the research of Kögl and Haagen-Smit in Holland. We have discussed in an earlier chapter their isolation and identification of auxin A and auxin B. After about six years of research and expenditure in American cost-equivalent of $56,000, these investigators produced approximately 700 milligrams of auxin A and 300 of auxin B. In order to see how small a quantity this represents we may notice that its total weight is about 1/30 of an ounce. That would not fill a small teaspoon! By the old-fashioned methods there would have been enough auxin A for three analyses. By skimping considerably one might have been able to perform the necessary two analyses on the 300 milligrams of auxin B. This performance would have been wasteful since, although it would determine the condensed or empirical formula yielding the proportions of the component elements of the compound, it would have left no material at all with which to decipher the structural formula. As we have seen, this is the real scientific job. It is the structural formula which tells us *why* a particular compound works in the way it does and thus yields the clue to its eventual synthesis. In any case, this whole discussion, as Professor Robertson tells us, is in a sense absurd. The quantity we refer to was *that obtained in a six-year period*. Kögl and Haagen-Smit never had enough material *in any given single year* to perform an old-fashioned full-scale determination. Furthermore, they would certainly have been reluctant to save up the substance since the earlier supply might deteriorate in storage and simply be a waste of precious materials.[26] Thus in the development and application of our knowledge of the growth hormones in plants, the factor which made for eventual success was the *prior* research of Kohlmann and Pregl by which the Kohlmann balance was perfected and from then on allowed investigators to perform chemical experiments on microscopic samples.

In such ways do the practical applications of much of organic chemistry take place! Just as those who studied microfossils for over a hundred years accumulated knowledge which was ready and available when it was urgently needed by the oil prospectors, so organic chemistry continually accumulates a vast store of scientific knowledge and information that is always ready, and waiting for the moment when it will be used.

CHAPTER 16

The Solar Corona and Radio Communication

> Most of the great discoveries in science that have been put to practical use had their origin in a laboratory where the scientist labored, not for money, but for the love of finding out about nature.
> — DONALD H. MENZEL (1939)

DURING WORLD WAR II, one of the most urgent problems was the planning of radio communication, the choice of the proper frequency or wave length "appropriate to the occasion and the route." The selection of the wave length was extremely critical, especially for communication over long distances; if too short or too long, the radio waves might not arrive at their destination at all! To make the task more difficult, the wave lengths appropriate for any particular route varied from one season to another, and were different at night and during the day.

The wartime achievements in radio of our physicists and electronics engineers are known to us in terms of such marvels as the prodigious feat of engineering that made possible a midget-sized radio in the "proximity fuze"; and of course, the development of radar. But the problem of choosing the proper frequency or wave length did not depend on the design of new types of equipment, or even on the introduction by the radio engineers of new principles, but rather on utilizing both the scientific knowledge of basic natural phenomena already in the possession of physicists, astronomers, and so on, and the techniques which they had developed in their own work and which were now, at a moment when they were bitterly needed, ready at hand.

∾   ∾   ∾

In order to understand what astronomers were able to contribute to the engineering problems of radio communication, we must tackle first the question of how long-distance radio communication is possible at all!

In Chapter 7 we showed how the Hertzian Waves, predicted by Maxwell, are a form of electromagnetic waves traveling through space. This family includes visible light, infrared (or heat) radiation, ultraviolet light (causing sunburn), x-rays, and some of the radiation from radioactive substances. All of these many forms of electromagnetic waves travel through space at exactly the same speed, usually denoted by the letter c, 186,000 miles per second — the constant that appears in Einstein's equation for mass and energy: $E = m\,c^2$.

We usually think of light waves as traveling in straight lines, a property exemplified for us in the sharply defined shadow cast by an opaque object. Well, we may ask, if radio waves are like light waves, and also travel in straight lines, how can we possibly communicate by radio between two points so far apart that the curvature of the earth itself precludes straight-line communication? To take a most extreme possible example, how can waves which travel in straight lines originate at the Equator and be heard at the South Pole? About two decades after the first radio-communication demonstrations, when radio sets were to be found in many homes and ships, and when stations were beginning to make regular broadcasts, it was still something of a mystery just how radio communication was possible at all.

This riddle was one of the four "Unsolved Problems of Wireless," to quote the title of a lecture given by R. H. Barfield in 1924, before the Radio Society of Great Britain. The problems were:

1. How is long-distance radio or wireless communication possible?

2. Why are radio signals apparently stronger at night than during the day?

3. Why do radio direction finders have large errors at night and only negligible errors during the day?

4. What causes fading? [1]

During the ten years following this lecture, the questions raised were solved more or less satisfactorily from an engineering standpoint, but the most interesting results of the investigations since

1924 properly belong in the domain of fundamental science. The solutions to these and allied problems arose from research in a great variety of fields, including physics, geology, meteorology, and astronomy, which were in no way directly connected with problems of radio engineering. New experimental tools and methods were developed, permitting exact measurements in atmospheric physics. Related experimental and theoretical research included work on cosmic rays, terrestrial magnetism, solar activity, auroral displays, atmospheric temperatures, luminous clouds, thunderstorms, meteor trails, air-mass movement, earth currents, stratosphere meteorology, and elastic deformations of the earth's crust.[2]

On 12 December 1901, Guglielmo Marconi received radio signals transmitted from Poldhu, Cornwall, to St. John's, Newfoundland. The transmitting antenna was 150 feet high and the receiving antenna was elevated to 400 feet by means of a kite. Now the rotundity of the earth produces an elevation of some 125 miles or more between the two points, which are separated by approximately 2000 miles. How did the radio waves get through this bump? If they had traveled in a straight-line path, they would have had to pass through the earth itself, which is impossible.

The reader may wonder how Marconi ever *thought* that he would have been able to send his radio signal so far. The fact seems to be that Marconi had not at first given this obstacle any consideration. His early experiments were carried out over very small distances, so small that they were measurable in feet rather than in miles. (In 1895, he sent his signals about 300 feet.) Then, with each successive trial, he increased the distance, until, in 1901, he was able to send messages successfully as far as 150 miles.[8] Yet between two points separated by 150 miles, the elevation of the earth rises to about three quarters of a mile! Thus, according to R. N. Vyvyan, one of his co-workers in the transatlantic experiments, "The fact that Marconi had been able to telegraph by wireless satisfactorily up to a distance of 150 miles, convinced him that the curvature of the earth presented no obstacles to the extension of wireless communication to still greater distances. He therefore decided to make a serious attempt to telegraph by his system across the Atlantic."[4]

Our question number one was raised by scientists immediately after Marconi's successful experiment. The first answer proposed was that of the English physicist, Lord Rayleigh, who explained away what others had called the "theoretical impossibility" of the phenomenon by a diffraction theory. Later, Lord Rayleigh's hypothesis was elaborated and improved upon by the best minds in the field of mathematical physics.

Diffraction is the process whereby rays are bent, and depart from the straight-line path. It occurs in all types of wave motion, such as light and sound, and also in electron waves. The phenomenon of electron diffraction (discussed in Chapter 5) has come recently to be of great practical importance.

In the case of light, the wave lengths are very small and the bending effect takes place on a similarly small scale. If we examine under a microscope the shadow of an opaque object, we find that there may be a diffraction or "bending" of the light waves into the shadow area. But as we go on to longer wave lengths, such as we encounter in radio, the bending grows more pronounced, or occurs on a larger scale. In the case of the long waves used for broadcasting purposes, waves may bend around a not inconsiderable portion of a sphere the size of the earth. But as such a wave travels in the neighborhood of the earth throughout all of its path, it suffers a continual loss of energy absorbed by the earth, and eventually dies away altogether. In the broadcast region, the distance covered by such a diffracted wave depends upon the power of the transmitter, the nature of the aerial, and the nature of the terrain. The range of such radio waves may be as much as 100 or 200 miles. This type of wave propagation occurs in the range used in the United States for local broadcasting.[5]

But even if the diffraction theory accounted for local transmission, it could not readily account for the fact that signals could be transmitted across the Atlantic Ocean, nor for other curious effects.

෴   ෴   ෴

In the years following the First World War, it was generally agreed that radio waves whose wave lengths were shorter than 200 meters were useless for communication. The entire region of radio waves below 200 meters was allotted to amateurs, for whatever they could make of it, by the terms of a law passed by Congress in 1912.

What the radio "hams" did with the now-famous region assigned to them forms one of the most exciting chapters in the history of modern science.

The amateurs were organized in 1914, into an association known as the "American Radio Relay League," founded by Hiram Percy Maxim, the famous inventor, who became its first president.* Radio enthusiasts, both men and women, of all ages and nationalities, and representing every conceivable trade and profession, soon swelled its ranks and have continued to do so ever since. To this day, the League maintains a technical staff, and has continued to relay messages from one member to another, to and from all parts of the world, near or far, gratis. Since its inception, its journal called *QST* has remained one of the leading publications in experimental radio, and its annual *Handbook* is used by everyone from the young ham seeking to learn enough fundamentals to obtain his license, all the way to the professional radio engineers and designers.[7]

Only in one other field, astronomy — where national organizations such as the American Association of Variable Star Observers have done extraordinarily useful work — have amateurs made such consistent contributions to knowledge.

In 1922 there were about 5719 amateur radio stations in America, representing 56 per cent of all stations licensed by the United States Government. These amateurs were free to enjoy sending and receiving radio signals in the region of short waves.

Those who were interested in distance were called "DXers," they logged the distant stations as they obtained reception from them. As DX, or "distance," grew from 1000 miles to 1500 miles and 2000 miles, the amateurs began to dream of establishing two-way amateur contact across the ocean. The problem was how to do it. The new improved types of radio receiver had increased the efficiency of receivers to an unheard-of degree and the power output of many amateurs was up to, if not beyond, the legal upper limit, which had been set at one kilowatt of power. The amateurs had found that the distance covered at the "worthless" value of 200 meters — worthless according to the authorities — was so great that there might be reason to suppose that the authorities were wrong on other points

---

* The first amateur radio organizations were the Junior Wireless Club, Limited, of New York City, and the Wireless Association of America, both founded in 1909.[6]

too. They decided to try working below 200 meters. By 1923 they had achieved successful results at 90 meters! At 110 meters, the hams established successful amateur two-way communication between France and America. One of the reasons for their success was their refusal to accept the general opinion that wave lengths of less than 200 meters were useless over long distances; another was the fact that they made immediate use of every latest improvement in vacuum tubes and other wartime improvements, while, as Professor Harry R. Mimno tells us, "commercial progress was frequently hampered by patent restrictions and conservative economic policies." [8]

By about 1926, the work of the amateurs in exploring the shorter waves had been made public, and the economic importance of the newly discovered region was generally recognized. The construction of powerful long-wave stations was abandoned gradually in favor of short-wave stations.[9] In the year 1926 H. Rukop wrote a survey of early short-wave research for the *Zeitschrift für Hochfrequenztechnik,* in which he showed that the research divisions of many commercial organizations had long had on hand equipment for the type of short-wave transmission achieved by the amateurs, but that they had never even suspected its possible use over long distances.[10]

The amateurs had found not only that short wave lengths could be used successfully for long distance; they had also discovered that as the waves used were made shorter and shorter, the transmission of signals became less and less erratic, and much stronger. The movement downward continued, "limited only by the design of vacuum tube circuits for increasingly higher frequencies," [11] that is, for increasingly shorter waves.*

Everyone now wanted to use the once-disdained region below 100 meters, and the amateurs dropped "down and down," along the wave-length scale.

But still they talked halfway around the world! At a wave length of 40 meters, successful communication was established between the United States and Australia, New Zealand, and South Africa.

---

* Electromagnetic radiation, or electromagnetic waves, can be described in terms of their wave length or the frequency (number of times per second) with which the waves pulse out. A short wave has a high frequency, and a long wave has a low frequency.

At 20 meters, not only was communication possible between the East and West coasts of the United States, but it was possible in broad daylight, whereas previously such communication had had to be carried on at night only. During the years before the recent war, the amateurs extended the boundaries to shorter and shorter wave lengths, while successive international agreements about frequency or wave-length allocations all but squeezed the amateurs off the air. They retained a bare 10 per cent of the region below the 200 meters which had once been exclusively theirs, and these "few channels were preserved through the friendly efforts of the American governmental representatives." [12] No wonder the story of amateur radio has been entitled *Two hundred meters and down!*

∾   ∾   ∾

None of the proposed theories could be made to account for the results obtained by the amateurs. Lord Rayleigh's theory of diffraction seemed particularly useless, because the effect of diffraction is less and less marked with shorter and shorter wave lengths. According to this theory, the bending, and hence the range, of transmission should have become less with shorter wave lengths; instead, it apparently became greater.

The clue to the whole problem — and the factor that eventually linked together the fundamental research of the astronomers and the practical problems of the radio engineers — came from a curious and "new" effect which the amateurs noticed. At short waves, say 50 meters and below, the strength of the signal rapidly decreased to zero very near the transmitter (within, at most, 50 miles), although under favorable conditions the same signal could be heard thousands of miles away. Apparently you encountered a "zone of silence" once you got a little ways away from the transmitter. [13]

The only other phenomenon in nature in any way resembling this one was the "zone of silence" sometimes encountered with ordinary sound.

At the end of the First World War, many observers noted that when huge ammunition dumps were exploded, the blast could be heard near by, far away, but not in between. This acoustic phenomenon was correlated with studies of the effects of great explosions, such as the Great Siberian Meteor and the explosion of Krakatoa.

More recently our knowledge has been advanced by investigations of meteor trails in the earth's upper atmosphere.[14]

Everyone knows that as one ascends toward the stratosphere, the temperature drops at a rapid rate. Aviators in that region must wear special clothing, and airships must be specially designed and equipped, since the thermometer may fall as low as 60 degrees below zero. But few readers know that if one ascends still higher, an inversion takes place; that is, the temperature begins to rise again rather than continue to fall. Fred L. Whipple of the Harvard College Observatory — who has been making an extensive study of atmospheric temperatures as revealed by meteor trails — informs me that at an altitude of 120 kilometers (about 75 miles) above the surface of the earth the temperature reaches the boiling point of water. Owing to this phenomenon of temperature reversal, first going down lower and lower and then beginning to rise as one ascends higher and higher, the sound waves traveling upward are bent from their normal path, reflected, and returned to the earth some distance from the source. Between the point at which those reflected sound waves return to the earth and the point at which the direct waves emanating from the source, and traveling along the earth's surface, die out and become inaudible, there is a region in which no sound can be heard, a "zone of silence."

Can a similar type of reflection occur in the case of radio waves? The latter, in contradistinction to sound waves, are part of the general family of electromagnetic waves.

J. L. Reinartz, one of the leaders in the experimental two-way short-wave radio communication across the Atlantic, had worked with a group of American amateurs in 1924, making an extended series of "zone of silence" observations. He attributed the phenomenon to the presence of a reflecting region for radio waves in the upper atmosphere — somewhat on the principle of the sound-reflecting layer, but different in so far as this one would reflect radio waves.

The story of knowledge about such a reflecting layer or region begins in 1878, when Balfour Stewart contributed an article to the ninth edition of the *Encyclopaedia Britannica,* in which he suggested that the presence of conducting layers in the upper atmosphere above the earth might explain certain cyclic variations in the earth's magnetism — an hypothesis developed further by Arthur Schuster in 1889. In *The Electrical World and Engineer* of 15 March 1902, A. E. Kennelly of Harvard University suggested that "there is well-known evidence that the waves of wireless telegraphy, propagated through the ether and atmosphere over the surface of the ocean, are reflected by . . . [an] electrically conducting surface." In the same year, the Englishman Oliver Heaviside made a similar comment, noting: "There may possibly be a sufficiently conducting layer in the upper air. If so, the waves will, so to speak, catch on it more or less. Then the guidance will be by the sea on one side and the upper layer on the other." *

To sum up the story of short-wave radio, then, it runs something like this. When Marconi first made his transatlantic experiments, he never bothered about any theoretical difficulties which might argue the impossibility of successful long-distance communication. The first attempt at an explanation of such transmission was the diffraction theory, proposed by Lord Rayleigh. This was followed by the acceptance of an "empirical" result, which set the useful range at a limit of 200 meters. But amateur radio enthusiasts, defying "scripture," experimented in the "useless" range, and discovered that successful two-way communication could be established over long distances at short-wave lengths. These results, plus the discrepancy between the predictions of the diffraction theory and actually observed field intensities, led men to seek a new explanation. The true answer finally was found in the presence of a conducting region in the earth's upper or outer atmosphere, a region which was capable of reflecting radio waves back to the earth. Thus, today, long-distance radio communication is known to be possible because the radio waves bounce back and forth as they are reflected first from the layer, then from the earth's surface, then from the layer once again, and so forth. The failure of all early theories was due to the fact that they did not take into account the action of the Kennelly-Heaviside layer.

* Heaviside's remark comes from an article on "Telegraphy" in the tenth edition of the *Encyclopaedia Britannica,* which Kennelly found had as its "Date of First Publication" 19 December 1902, according to the "Copyright Registry Record Office" in London.

Today we no longer talk about a single Kennelly-Heaviside layer, but rather about a whole region of concentric layers known collectively as the "ionosphere." It is common to consider three main concentric regions, distinguished by the British physicist E. V. Appleton, who, with Barnett, was one of the first to obtain direct evidence of the downward reflection of radio waves and of the virtual height of the reflecting layers, in a series of experiments made between 11 December 1924, and 17 February 1925. These are: [15]

F region	strongly ionized	approximate height 300 km. (about 180 miles)
E region	moderately ionized	approximate height 100 km. (about 60 miles)
D region	weakly ionized	approximate height 50 km. (about 30 miles)

How do these layers in the ionosphere affect radio transmission? Let us follow the course of a short-wave or high-frequency signal. When it is emitted, a "ground wave" follows the earth's surface for only a short distance, because the diffraction effect is on a small

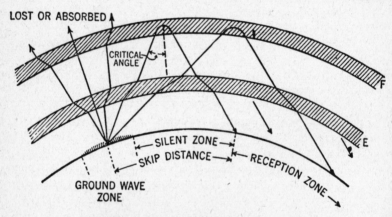

PENETRATION, REFLECTION, AND
CRITICAL ANGLE

Reproduced by permission from Transmission Lines, Antennas and Wave Guides *by King, Mimno and Wing, Copyrighted, 1945, by McGraw-Hill Publishing Co., Inc.*

scale for such short waves, and because the strength of the signal diminishes rapidly as it travels near the earth, which absorbs energy.

A ray which is inclined at a small angle to the vertical (see the figure) is refracted at each layer; that is, it changes its direction slightly and is bent, just as a ray of light passing from air into water is refracted, or changes its direction — a phenomenon which causes an oar dipped into water to appear to be bent at the water's surface.

As the angle to the vertical at which a ray leaves the transmitter is increased more and more, a value is eventually reached at which the wave may be *reflected,* rather than *refracted,* and return to the earth. Now, it may be picked up by a radio receiver, or reflected back out into the atmosphere, to be once again reflected back to the earth. The smallest angle at which reflection of this kind occurs is known as the "critical angle" and it determines the "zone of silence."

∾   ∾   ∾

Since the long-distance transmission of short-wave radio signals depends on the ionosphere, the reader himself may infer that a connection exists between radio engineering and atmospheric physics. But where does the astronomer enter the picture? We have had one hint, a few pages back, when we discussed the relation of the studies of meteor trails to the temperature of the earth's upper atmosphere. But the real key lies in the cause of the very existence of the ionosphere, and the reason for its being a conducting layer.

When Kennelly and Heaviside first proposed such a layer, they could offer no convincing explanation for its existence. For this reason, many scientists did not take their suggestion too seriously. G. W. Pierce, in his *Principles of Wireless Telegraphy* of 1910, had presented Kennelly's hypothesis and pointed out that if it were true, then one might expect "interference" under certain conditions from a "ground wave" and a "sky wave" — that is, between a wave traveling near the earth's surface and one reflected from the Kennelly-Heaviside layer. Two years later, Lee De Forest encountered what he thought to be an example of such interference and sent a letter on the subject to the editor of the London *Electrician.* He wrote to Professor Pierce under the date 24 May 1912, enclosing a copy of that letter. Professor Pierce was unable to reply until 7 September 1912, at which time he made a computation based on De Forest's data, which seemed to place the height of the layer at 196 miles. On 10 May 1946, when Professor Pierce showed me the correspondence, he looked at his computations and found that he had made an error; De Forest's data yielded a height of only 60 miles, which we know today is the location of the E-layer of the ionosphere, from which waves of the length used by De Forest in 1912 *are actually reflected!* This was a somewhat better figure than Kennelly's own rough estimate of 50 miles.

The ionosphere, the region in the earth's upper atmosphere that we have been discussing, receives its name from the fact that in it there are a large number of ions, that is, atoms and molecules that have had one or more of their external electrons stripped off, and the free electrons which are no longer attached to an atom or molecule. The reflecting properties of the ionosphere derive from the presence of these free electrons. They are stripped off the atoms by the action of the ultraviolet light of the sun, including the so-called "soft" x-rays. This ionizing radiation constitutes a major fraction of the sun's radiation, although we are unable to detect it directly on the earth, since it is absorbed during its passage through the atmosphere. Were this radiation able to penetrate to the earth, then life — plant, animal, and human — as we know it could not long exist.

Far beyond 300 kilometers from the earth, the air is very thin and there are relatively few atoms and molecules. The ultraviolet radiation from the sun is stronger in this region than in regions closer to us, because it has thus far traveled entirely through free space and has undergone no absorption. Very few ions and free electrons are produced, because there just isn't much matter to ionize. As we come closer to the earth, the relative density of these ions and free electrons increases until we reach a maximum somewhere in the region of 300 kilometers. It then drops to negligible proportions, because the material composing the atmosphere is still the same, and the frequencies of radiation producing ionization of this material have all been absorbed in the process of causing ions. Certain frequencies are adapted to producing ions of certain materials and of those materials only. If those frequencies are used up in ionizing certain molecules or atoms, they are no longer present and able to ionize further molecules or atoms. This explains the existence of the strongly ionized F-layer at 300 kilometers.

The frequencies which have not been used up in producing the F-layer continue to penetrate deeper into the earth's atmosphere until, at a height of about 100 kilometers, they encounter for the first time a new material in large quantities: molecular oxygen. This oxygen is ionized, absorbing certain other frequencies and forming the moderately ionized E-layer. Radiation of frequencies not absorbed at either the F-layer or the E-layer continues through the atmosphere until — at about 100 kilometers — it encounters ozone for the first time, which it proceeds to ionize to form the weak D-layer. Some frequencies of ultraviolet light are not adapted to ionize any of the materials encountered in the passage through the atmosphere. These are therefore not absorbed, and actually penetrate to the surface of the earth, where their effects are important to animal and plant life.

Thus the presence of the three chief layers of the ionosphere can be explained satisfactorily by the selective action on the molecules of air of the sun's radiation, and it is the action of the sun which is the controlling factor in radio communication.

Now let us see how our knowledge of the sun was applied to the solution of practical problems.

In an earlier section we saw that a wave will be reflected by one of the layers of the ionosphere, or pass out into interstellar space, according to a critical angle. The value of the critical angle is different for various wave lengths and depends on the density of free electrons. Professor Donald H. Menzel suggests that although it is customary to think of the ionosphere as a reflecting surface, or mirror, we may do better to think of it as a sieve of variable mesh. In this analogy we may liken a radio wave to a ball whose diameter corresponds to the wave length.[16]

If the diameter of the ball is smaller than the mesh of the sieve, it will usually pass on through it; if the mesh is smaller than the ball, the ball will be reflected. Thus we see that the issue of whether or not a given wave will be reflected depends not on the angle alone (as we have discussed earlier), but also on the density of free electrons in the ionosphere. For very short wave lengths, the balls are so small (wave length so short) that the minimum size of mesh (maximum electron density) obtainable is nevertheless too coarse to reflect the waves. Thus the very highest frequencies are never reflected by the ionosphere and are useless for long-distance communication. In radar, however, they too find application, because the "mesh" of "solid" objects, and even of clouds, is very very small. Another model of the ionosphere is illustrated in the figure.

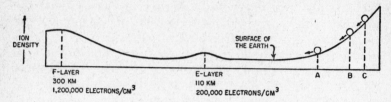

HEIGHT ABOVE THE EARTH

A DYNAMICAL MODEL OF THE IONOSPHERE

The above drawing is a representation of a model of the ionosphere constructed for Dr. J. A. Pierce of the E. R. L. (Harvard). It consists of a narrow metal track bent to the shape indicated. The arrow corresponds to the surface of the earth, and distances to the left of the arrow are drawn on a scale corresponding to distances above the earth. The height of the curved surface corresponds to the density of free electrons on arbitrary scale. Two maximum intensities are indicated: one at 110 kilometers above the earth, and the other at 300 kilometers above the earth. A small steel ball is allowed to roll freely along the track, starting from any position one chooses on the curve at the extreme right side of the drawing. If the ball is released from point A, it will attain a relatively small speed, or small kinetic energy, corresponding to a relatively low frequency or large wave length. This ball will roll partway up the hill at E, but will not have sufficient energy to go over the top; it will slow down, stop, and then return to the point indicated by the arrow. This corresponds to the reflection of radio waves of low frequency or long wave length at the E-layer of the ionosphere. If we start the ball rolling from the point marked B, it will attain a greater speed, or greater kinetic energy, and will go right over the top of the hill at E and partway up the hill at F; then it will slow down, stop, and return, going over the hill at E on the way back. This corresponds to the reflection of radio waves of greater frequency and shorter wave lengths from the F-layer of the ionosphere. It will be noted that these waves pass through the E-layer, although with some reduction of their velocity. If we start the ball rolling from C, it will attain such a speed that it will go over the top of the hill at E and also over the top of the hill at F. This corresponds to radio waves of very high frequency and very short wave lengths, which are reflected by neither the E-layer nor the F-layer of the ionosphere.

Since the electron density in the ionosphere is caused by the action of sunlight, it is greatest at noon, less at midmorning or midafternoon, and least at night. In terms of Professor Menzel's analogy, we would say that the mesh is always smaller during the day than in the night; thus we may use shorter waves by day than by night. This also explains why there is a marked difference between day and night radio communication.

~   ~   ~

In addition to the effects just described — angle, and size of mesh — there is another complication: absorption. As the radio waves travel through the lower fringes of the ionosphere, they encounter a resistance, especially noticeable in the longer waves. These fringes of the ionosphere may once again be likened to a sieve allowing small balls (short waves) to pass through, but effectively stopping and absorbing the larger ones (long waves). Just as the size of the mesh in the reflecting sieve sets a lower limit, telling us how short the waves we may use can be, so the size of mesh in the absorbing layers sets an upper limit to the usable wave lengths. Since the size of this absorbing mesh, like that of the reflecting layer, is a function of the density of free electrons, it too is affected by the sun and is greatest during the day, and almost unnoticeable at night.

Most serious in radio communication is a sudden complete fadeout, which may last anywhere from a few seconds to as long as five or fifteen minutes, and even, under rare circumstances, thirty minutes. These were first accounted for by Dr. Joseph H. Dellinger of the National Bureau of Standards, who suggested that they occurred at the same time as solar flares or eruptions. Solar flares are excessive emissions of light (probably largely ultraviolet) from a very small region or point on the surface of the sun. They produce an enormous amount of ionization in all absorbing layers, thereby altering them so that practically all wave lengths are absorbed, never get to a reflecting layer at all, and are never heard again on earth.

In addition to changes in the ionosphere caused by the daily variation in the position of the sun as the earth accomplishes its rotation, there is a seasonal variation as the earth travels along its annual orbit, and a long-range variation due to the eleven-year solar cycle. We shall not discuss the many other phenomena related to variation in the successful transmission and reception of short-wave radio signals, such as magnetic storms, auroras, changes in meteorological or geophysical conditions, and such. But it may be of some interest to point out that cities in the same latitude, such as Tokyo and Los Angeles, and which therefore might be expected to exhibit the same iono-spheric conditions and the same problems insofar as radio com-munication is concerned, behave in fact quite differently. This in-dicates that the condition of the ionospheric mesh in any locality is not wholly determined by the sun alone. In the case of Los Angeles and Tokyo, the cause may well be, as Professor Menzel suggests, that Tokyo is further from the North Magnetic Pole of the earth than is Los Angeles, and that the earth's magnetic field is composed of lines more nearly parallel in Japan than in California.

ᕒᕔ   ᕒᕔ   ᕒᕔ

To conduct a successful war on a scale such as that of World War II, and waged over so great an area, the problem of planning and maintaining communication was perhaps secondary only to the problem of supply. The Chiefs of Staff set up Wave Propagation Committees on both a Joint (strictly U. S.) and Combined (U. S. and Great Britain) basis, which worked together with similar groups in England, Canada, and Australia. The Joint Committee established an Interservice Radio Propagation Laboratory at the National Bureau of Standards, which, with the aid of the Department of Ter-restrial Magnetism of the Carnegie Institution of Washington, es-tablished several stations to observe the ionosphere. Further data supplied by the Russians and the British helped to complete a pic-ture of conditions throughout the world. Solar observations were given their due importance. The Mt. Wilson Observatory * and the McMath Hulbert Observatory † provided daily sun-spot data, while the Fremont Pass Station of the Harvard College Observatory ‡ provided information about the solar corona. Thus it was possible to predict the state of the sun and, therefore, to a considerable degree the trends of ionospheric behavior.

Information about the trends of the ionosphere was of enormous importance in the planning of radio channels and the selection of a frequency "appropriate to the occasion and the route." If the fre-quency was too low, the wave would be absorbed; if too high, it would simply pass on into the empty space between the stars.

* Of the Carnegie Institution of Washington, at Pasadena, California.
† Of the University of Michigan, at Lake Angelus, Pontiac, Michigan.
‡ At Climax, Colorado. Altitude 11,500 feet. Now jointly operated by Harvard University and the University of Colorado.

Furthermore, different frequencies had to be chosen for day use and for night use. Professor Menzel, for example, on wartime leave from the Harvard College Observatory, had the job of analyzing one particularly difficult circuit, in which transmission was impossible during the major part of the day. A study of the situation revealed "that the frequencies which may have been altogether satisfactory several years earlier when sun spots were more numerous, were far too high. When a new set of frequencies was allocated, contact was possible during almost the entire day."

Ionospheric storms, as they are called, also created serious problems. They cause the mesh of the reflecting layer to open wide, thus allowing a considerably larger number of high-frequency radio waves to pass into interstellar space, while at the same time an increased density of free electrons in the absorbing lower layers causes a much greater absorption. Severe storms of this kind may last for several days or even longer, during which the band of usable frequencies is greatly restricted.

These disturbances are usually accompanied by brilliant outbursts of aurora borealis, or australis, and a noticeable variation in the earth's magnetic field. Their severity is greatest in latitudes bordering on the auroral zones. Sometimes the effect of the disturbance is sufficiently great to interfere seriously with telephone and telegraph, as well as power, lines. No one yet, according to Professor Menzel, knows the exact cause of magnetic-ionospheric storms, although it seems certain that they are connected in some way with the activity of the sun.

                          ∽   ∽   ∽

Fortunately, for the solution of many urgent problems, it is no longer necessary to wait for eclipses in order to study the sun.

We usually consider the sun to be composed of three parts: the *photosphere,* or luminous disk with the spots and other markings; the sun's *atmosphere,* a region of luminous but almost transparent gases; and the *corona,* an outer gaseous envelope of very great height and exceedingly small density. The sun's atmosphere can usually be observed directly with a telescope only during a total eclipse, when the photosphere is hidden from view. But for some years now it has been studied without an eclipse by means of an instrument known as a spectroheliograph, which enables an observer to view the sun through a narrow band of color in the spectrum. If one chooses a color prominent in the sun's atmosphere but not very prominent in the light from the photosphere, the sun's atmosphere can be viewed during ordinary times by thus excluding the light from the sun's luminous disk. But the same procedure cannot be applied to the corona!

Most of the radiant energy from the corona is emitted as soft x-rays or "far" ultraviolet light. If we could "view" the sun in that region of the spectrum without any intervening effect, the corona would undoubtedly appear many many times brighter than the sun itself. However, this radiation from the corona is absorbed by the atmosphere surrounding the earth, and does not penetrate sufficiently to be of use to a terrestrial observer. Thus the corona looks to us like a faint haze, some half a million times less brilliant than the sun itself.

During the fifty years prior to 1929, many of the most able astronomers tried to devise methods whereby the corona or its spectrum might be photographed. But except when the solar disk itself was blanked out during a total eclipse, the faint haze yielded no trace on the photographic plate.

Many people had tried during about seventy years to place an opaque disk somewhere in the telescope aligned with the sun in such a way that artificial eclipses might be produced at will. Unfortunately, however, even when this is done a certain amount of sunlight is "scattered" into the image of the artificial eclipse. In an ordinary telescope this unwanted light, small as it is, is many times brighter than the faint corona.

The problem was solved in an ingenious way by a French astronomer, Bernard Lyot, of Meudon Observatory. Following a suggestion of Professor H. O. Barnard, Lyot made a systematic study of all possible sources of scattered sunlight in a telescope. After extensive research, Lyot was able to construct a telescope whose optical system is almost perfect: it eliminates the scattering of light introduced by diffraction at the edges of the objective lens, by tiny bubbles in the lens (which are usually considered a mark of high quality in photographic objectives, especially those made of Jena glass!), by dust and scratches, and by reflections from the lens's

THE SOLAR CORONA AS SEEN DURING A TOTAL ECLIPSE

Photograph by Irvine G. Gardner of National Geographic Society — National Bureau of Standards Eclipse Expedition, 1936. (c.) National Geographic Society.

surfaces. Lyot's instrument, called the "coronagraph," was installed by him on the Pic du Midi, in the Pyrenees Mountains on the border between France and Spain.

Some time later, a similar instrument was constructed and installed by Max Waldmeier of the Zurich Observatory. Waldmeier, who had worked for a time with Lyot, mounted his coronagraph at Arosa, at an elevation of 6200 feet. In 1932, Slocum and Pettit of the Mt. Wilson Observatory built a Lyot-type instrument which they have used for the study of prominences, rather than of the corona.

       ∾   ∾   ∾

The next such instrument was set up by the Harvard College Observatory, high up in the Rockies at Climax, Colorado, not far from the old mining town of Leadville. This station is the highest permanent observatory in the world; its elevation is 11,520 feet, approximately two miles above sea level! The construction was supervised by Dr. Donald H. Menzel of the Harvard College Observatory, who, as an astrophysicist, had long been interested in the corona and in its relation to the ionosphere. The operation of the new instrument was entrusted to Dr. Walter O. Roberts, who tells us: "The need for clean, dry, and rarefied atmosphere imposed stringent conditions for the location of a coronagraph. The site chosen . . . in the Rocky Mountains enjoys frequent precipitation to clean the air, and at the same time offers a large number of clear days. The observatory is just below timber line at one edge of the community of homes maintained by the Climax Molybdenum Company for its mine employees. The observatory and residence lie directly on the Continental Divide, so that the peak of the roof forms, at this point, the watershed between the Atlantic and Pacific oceans." [17] It is so high as to be considerably above the level at which pilots are advised to breathe the extra oxygen carried in their airplanes.

During the war years, this coronagraph was the only one available to our allies, although Lyot continued to use his in Southern France for his program of basic research. The importance of this instrument in time of war may be seen from the fact that the Germans started construction on a large number of Lyot-type coronagraphs, and had made plans for an extended program of corona observations. By the war's end they had one such instrument in operation.

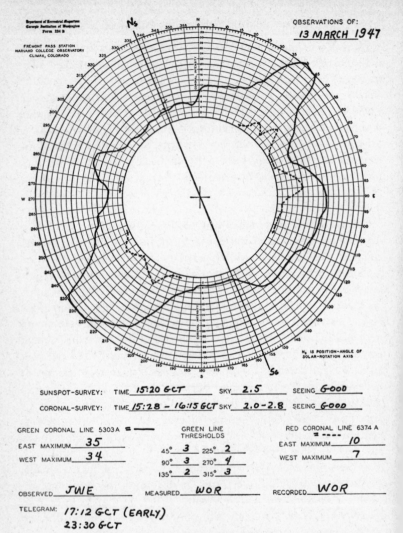

OBSERVATIONS OF:

13 MARCH 1947

Ns IS POSITION-ANGLE OF
SOLAR-ROTATION AXIS

SUNSPOT-SURVEY: TIME *15:20 GCT* SKY *2.5* SEEING *GOOD*

CORONAL-SURVEY: TIME *15:28 – 16:15 GCT* SKY *2.0-2.8* SEEING *GOOD*

GREEN CORONAL LINE 5303A = ———	GREEN LINE THRESHOLDS	RED CORONAL LINE 6374 A = - - - -

EAST MAXIMUM *35*
WEST MAXIMUM *34*

45° *3*	225° *2*
90° *3*	270° *4*
135° *2*	315° *3*

EAST MAXIMUM *10*
WEST MAXIMUM *7*

OBSERVED *JWE* MEASURED *WOR* RECORDED *WOR*

TELEGRAM: *17:12 GCT (EARLY)*
23:30 GCT

TYPICAL DAILY REPORT ON THE CORONA

This report is based on a summary of six spectrograms. The heavy line represents the green line in the coronal spectrum, while the broken line represents the red line in the coronal spectrum. This graph is plotted in such a way that the distance from the center (indicated by a cross) represents the intensity of the light, on an arbitrary scale from 0 to 34, while the angular position corresponds to the place in the corona itself, with regard to the sun's axis of rotation, which is indicated by the line N_s——S_s. It will be seen that the greatest intensities are obtained roughly in the region of the solar equator. — Courtesy W. O. Roberts

Dr. Roberts, superintendent of the Harvard Climax Station, took daily records of the solar corona throughout all the war years. Study of these data revealed very definite relationships between magnetic storms and coronal brightness; for example, during the war years there was a high probability of magnetic disturbance four days after a region of bright coronal emission had passed the eastern limb of the sun. When these coronal data were examined, together with other astronomical data, such as that on sun spots and prominences supplied by the Mt. Wilson and McMath-Hulbert Observatories, as well as magnetic and ionospheric data, the scientists working in Washington were able to forecast ionospheric storms and radio disturbances in advance. The importance of this foreknowledge can hardly be overestimated; it was certainly one of the major factors in making continuous uninterrupted communication possible.

How accurate were these predictions? Can we assume that the job of making such predictions is completed?

Dr. Menzel tells us: "The accuracy attained in the ionospheric forecasts was satisfactory, though not perfect. After all, the weather man makes some mistakes, and the ionosphere is a sort of weather phenomenon. Those who have been closely associated with the work are now concerned with the improvements that will be possible with new and more advanced equipment." One of the major scientific problems for the future is not simply to correlate ionospheric phenomena with other types of phenomena, but to understand the mechanism by means of which they actually happen. Toward this end a brave beginning has been made, although the problem is far from being solved.

Our peacetime problems are much the same as those of the war years. They include long-range planning of frequencies for general communication, choice of locations for effective signal transmission, planning of broadcasting relays (especially those from abroad) based on propagation information to solve problems of interference and on prior knowledge of ionospheric storms, maintenance of reliable communication over land and sea for commercial aviation, more effective ship-to-shore radio service.

The usefulness of a prediction about the nature of the ionosphere, and therefore about the possibilities with regard to radio communication, are probably much the same in peace time as during a state of war. A prediction about radio communication serves much the same purpose as weather prediction. For example, let us suppose that a man wishing to ship his products to Europe by air must get them there before a certain date, say ten days hence. He will not, in general, wish to send out the airships if he cannot maintain continuous and uninterrupted communication with them, just as he would not send them out in the face of an impending hurricane. If he knows that at the end of the ten-day period there will be an ionospheric storm, he will conclude that the airships must be sent out immediately, within the next few days, if he is to meet his dead-line of ten days. Military aviation does not differ so much from commercial aviation; those in command of our air force are just as interested in keeping in communication with their airships as are civilians. Furthermore, just as one takes account of weather conditions in planning military campaigns, so too it may be presumed that one takes into account the predicted state of the ionosphere. One plans a campaign at a time when communication may be assured, or, perhaps, when communication is impossible for the enemy. Plans for radiotelephone conversations between leaders of our armed forces in different parts of the world, or between civilians, must take into account the state of the ionosphere which tells us whether such communication will be possible. Likewise, if one ceases to hear the enemy broadcasting, one must be able to tell whether this fact has something to do with the enemy's plans, or whether it simply is owing to the state of the ionosphere.

What, we may ask, are the needs for future research in this field? The answer as given by Dr. Menzel is: "The present network of ionospheric stations requires extension. Mobile equipment for exploration, especially in the complicated auroral zone, must be further developed. We need special data to increase the accuracy of absorption, reflection, and radio noise prediction. Continued analysis of magnetic variations should give a valuable clue. Extensive solar studies, including those of eclipses, will contribute important information that can be gained in no other way. We must have theoretical studies and laboratory measures of the ionization properties of the common gases. Without these additional phases, we should be forced to follow the blind alley of empiricism. With the broad view there is a reasonable hope that some day we may fully understand the physical, chemical, and astronomical processes that cause the ionosphere and are responsible for its variations."

The reader should not gain the impression that knowledge of whether at a given time and place you can achieve radio communication at a certain frequency can now be assured by the simple process of observing the state of the corona. As we have pointed out earlier, the state of the corona at any given time is but one aspect of solar activity. So little *of a precise nature* is known about the exact relation between the sun and the ionosphere that predictions are based only on empirical laws which, by trial and error, have been found to work for a given period. For example, the relationship between coronal brightness and ionospheric storms which held during the war years and which served as a satisfactory basis for predicting ionospheric storms was no longer valid in the years immediately following the war. There appears to be some sort of cyclic variation in the relationship that nobody understands. But even during the war, although the results were extremely useful, the correlation between coronal brightness and ionospheric storms was at best imperfect. Furthermore, there are alternate hypotheses to explain the state of the ionosphere, such as tides in the upper atmosphere. Yet most scientists believe that the condition of the ionospheric layers does depend upon the state of the sun, and there are theoretical reasons which we cannot discuss here for believing that the corona should affect the ionospheric layers more than the radiation from other parts of the sun.

Let us now place this story in the conceptual scheme of our book. The significance of the work done in studying the solar corona, from the point of view of the lay administrator, is revealed by the time sequence of the events. By the outbreak of World War II, radio scientists had advanced their art to the point where the use of short-wave radio communication was extensive. But before communication routing could be relied upon, scientists working in many other fields of physical science had to discover the mode whereby such communication was achieved, and to learn the important role of the changing ionosphere. An urgent wartime problem was: How could the state of the ionosphere be predicted, in order to know which channels would ensure communication? All eyes were turned to the astronomers, because the state of the ionosphere depends almost entirely upon the activity of the sun. And in their coronagraph the astronomers had ready at hand the means of predicting with reasonable accuracy some of the ionospheric changes.

In just the same way, when the need arose for new methods in oil prospecting, the micro-paleontologists had the knowledge available. And the organic chemists, as we saw in the last chapter, constantly build up a store of knowledge to be used when the occasion arises.

Future research on the corona, the ionosphere, and the earth's atmosphere in general, will be financed by the Armed Forces and the radio companies, because more information is needed. The fundamental research of the future will provide the basis for a more extended practice, based on the new knowledge as it will be accumulated. Yet scientific interest in the sun, its spots, and its corona long antedated the advent and widespread use of short-wave radio communication. Just as radio itself (as we saw in an earlier chapter, 7) developed from research done by such men as Maxwell and Hertz, who were motivated only by "the love of finding out about nature," so our knowledge of the corona and its effect on the ionosphere — so important for the practical art of radio — originated with the seekers after truth rather than with the practical engineers.

PART FIVE
Science, Servant of Man

It is possible to conceive that in criminal hands radium might prove very dangerous, and the question therefore arises whether it be to the advantage of humanity to know the secrets of nature, whether we be sufficiently mature to profit by them, or whether that knowledge might not prove harmful. . . . I am among those who believe with Nobel that humanity will obtain more good than evil from future discoveries.

— PIERRE CURIE (1903)

CHAPTER 17

Science, Servant of Man

> Probably at no time in the world's history has the
> average citizen of this and of most other civilized
> communities felt so insecure against death by
> violence. At no time in the world's history has the
> same citizen had reason to feel so secure against
> death by disease.
> — SIR EDWARD MELLANBY (1939)

No BOOK dealing with the practical applications of fundamental research in the sciences can be complete without a discussion of the
atomic bomb. Here, in a sense, is the very apotheosis of all practical
results. If man wants to blow himself right off the face of the earth,
and perhaps even move the earth out of the orbit to which it has
been constrained to move — this boon too may be made available
by the pursuit of "abstract" truth.

Our knowledge of atomic power, like so many other examples
considered in this book, came about as a logical end product of the
activity of physicists who were interested in exploring the nature of
matter, rather than in producing a new weapon or uncovering a new
source of power. Few, if any, of the physicists preoccupied in the
early '30s with problems of the atomic nucleus even dared to dream
that the age of atomic power was so close at hand. Their work was
in fact frequently cited as an example of the most profoundly abstract and fundamental type of research; it was concerned with the
actual structure of the atoms of matter itself and seemed to be in-
finitely removed from anything that could be translated into
practicality.[1]

When the war began and the physicists, both in the United States
and in Germany, were forced to think of all the possibilities of using
science in war, no matter how remote or fantastic they might, at
first thought, appear, then, and only then, was serious consideration
given to atomic weapons. The "Smyth report" tells us that even

after work was gotten under way, many physicists hoped that the preliminary surveys would show that the manufacture of an atomic bomb was an impossibility.[2] It should thus be clear, not only that nuclear physicists had engaged in their research without having as their aim practical application of atomic energy, but also that the transition from the knowledge existing in 1939 to the production of the bomb was by no means an obvious one. So remote was the bomb from nuclear research that the German scientists who discovered the fission of U-235 missed it altogether.

Long before we gave serious consideration to the use of atomic energy in warfare, the Germans began their studies. They too built a uranium pile, but it never occurred to them that it might be possible to manufacture artificially a new element, plutonium. If they had continued in the direction of *their* research for an additional dozen years, they would never have been able to make an atom bomb nor would they, in all probability, have developed atomic energy. Little practical issue was expected from atomic bomb research in Nazi Germany, even by those engaged in it. When the German scientists held a large dinner to discuss the future of atomic research and the possibility of the military use of atomic energy, the high officials in political and military circles did not think it sufficiently important to attend. Von Keitel, the Chief of Staff of the German Army, and others of similar rank, refused to have anything to do with the project at all, or even to send delegates.[8]

The complete failure of German research may be accounted for in various ways, but the point we wish to emphasize here is that their failure indicates to a high degree that the development of the atomic bomb was far from being an *obvious* application of existing knowledge.

Since the advent of the atomic bomb, we inevitably ask, "Is science a blessing or a curse?" That hoary and hotly debated question is no longer an exercise in rhetoric but in our day has become a real and terrible issue. Are all the benefits of science worth the bomb?

Throughout most of this book we have explored examples which afford evidence of the blessings conferred on humanity by scientific activity. With the exception of a few defensive measures such as radar, we have tried to steer clear of the applications of science to warfare. Yet reviewing the development of science since its inception in the modern era, and indeed even from its beginnings in remotest antiquity, one fact stands out clearly: not only has scientific activity led to "improvements" in the art of warfare, but the socio-economic fact of war itself has been a great stimulus for particular lines of scientific development and for accelerating the application of known findings of science.

Warfare existed as an institution in human society long before the advent of modern science. Destructive weapons were always deadly, and men wounded in battle in ancient times suffered as much as, and probably more than, the soldier during the last war. I must confess that I see little choice between having my breast pierced by a bullet and pierced by a spear; or shall I choose between dying in an atomic bomb explosion and being drenched with boiling oil or molten metal in the good old-fashioned way?

There is current in many circles a point of view described many years ago by J. B. S. Haldane as "Bayardism." This name derives from a hideous form of sentimentalism symbolized by the conduct of the Chevalier Bayard, described by his contemporary soldiers as *sans peur et sans reproche*. He was the soul of courtesy to captured knights and treated them with the greatest respect. Even to bowmen he showed the greatest kindness and military deference. But every musketeer or other user of gunpowder who fell into his hands was immediately put to death. Bayard believed it proper to kill human beings in war by the old tried and traditional methods, but anyone who used the new invention of gunpowder was considered beyond the pale, infra dig, and deserved only summary execution.[4]

Haldane relates a curious example of Bayardism during the First World War. A Turkish aviator had developed a considerable flair for shooting down British observation balloons. A British officer (interested in winning the war!) one day sent up a balloon with a large cargo of gun cotton, which blew up the Turk. But instead of receiving a citation for his clever idea, he was severely reprimanded by the local commanding officer of the R.A.F. — for his "unsportsmanlike" conduct. Haldane tells us, "This gentleman doubtless felt little objection to bombing Turkish transport columns consisting mainly of non-combatants and animals incapable of retaliating, but he objected to airmen being killed except by other airmen. I, fighting in the mud beneath them and exposed to the bombs of both sides (I was wounded by one of our own), felt differently." [5]

A similar form of Bayardism greeted the announcement of the first atomic bomb. Who, of all those who cried out at the use of this terrible weapon, previously raised his voice at the bombing of Japanese women and children by detonating or incendiary bombs? It seems almost unthinkable that so-called civilized human beings in this twentieth century, the age of science, object to one form of destruction rather than another. Have we lost all basic sense of the moral idea? The necessities of war may have made ineluctable the large-scale bombings of civilians. But what ethical or moral principle can possibly justify the demolition of a city and its civilian population by the use of 200 "blockbusters," but not by one atomic bomb!

~~~   ~~~   ~~~

During the First World War, few scientific men in any country doubted that it was their unquestioned duty to apply their special knowledge and skill to the service of their country. Manufacturers were expected to orient their plant facilities for war production, doctors to care for the wounded, the ordinary citizen to serve in the armed forces or in the production line, and the scientist was expected to do war research or to become a technical man in the army or navy. But once the war was over, many people declared that science had been the real source of destruction and it was up to the scientist to make a constructive contribution to finding a remedy. Science became a scapegoat, along with Kaiserism, Junkerism, Militarism, and Imperialism.

One reason why the average American citizen assigned science to such company may have been his comfortable unawareness of the growing potentialities of science — until German scientific activity in World War I made the facts all too clear to him. This point of view was apparent to Joseph Sweetman Ames, Chairman of the National Advisory Committee on Aeronautics in 1918, who said, "It was so evident from the very beginning that Germany had mobilized for the purpose of war all her men of science, and was using the fruits of their investigations in ways entirely unexpected. This was a matter

of surprise to most Americans and illustrates clearly the comparatively insignificant position held by scientific men in the minds of
our people." [6]

Recoiling from an introduction to the powers of science under the
terrible auspices of war, the average citizen cried out, "These men
who make poison gas in their secret laboratories are monsters! If
they had within their breasts a spark of humanitarian feeling, could
they not have stopped war by refusing *en bloc* to have anything to
do with such awful slaughter?"

If all the scientists in all countries refused to support any form of
warfare whatever, very likely modern war, with its great dependency
upon technical skills and developments, would cease to exist. But the
same is equally true of any other group: doctors, teachers, clergymen,
machinists, bankers, engineers, manufacturers, railroad employees.
If all the members of any one of these groups refused categorically
to do any work whatever in time of war, then war would certainly
be impossible. But clearly, such action would have to be taken simultaneously in *all* opposing countries. If only one country refused to
have anything to do with war activity, it would soon be at the mercy
of another, and more aggressive, country. A curious point of view
prevails in many quarters today that American scientists are poorly
advised to have anything whatever to do with the army or navy in
peacetime. Those who hold to this opinion apparently believe that
if the United States ceases to be militarily strong, then war will be
impossible — even if other nations increase their military power while
we do not. The fallacy of such reasoning is apparently not nearly as
obvious as it should be.

Our chief concern here, however, is not with national defense so
much as with the question: Why single out the scientists rather than
any other group?

Like most of the activities of man, science is a double-edged sword
and can cut in either of two directions with equal facility. Science
does not, nay cannot, recognize of itself any distinction between right
and wrong, and hence it cannot concern itself with moral issues.
Science is never an *immoral* activity, but rather *amoral* — completely
removed from the moral sphere. Science says only that if you
follow a certain procedure x, then a certain result y will be sure
to follow, and it will follow whether what you are doing is morally

right or morally wrong. Whatever you may want to achieve, science will tell you that the best way of achieving it is to follow the course marked x. If you embark on that course, the end is inevitable.

Science, the servant of man, will help you to attain whatever end you desire. Do you want to combat a certain disease? Science will find for you the most efficient method of doing so. Do you want a greater yield in a certain industrial process? Science will find out how to get it. Do you want to be forewarned of the approach of enemy aircraft? Science provides the principles upon which radar can be constructed. Do you want to destroy men and cities? Science provides a more efficient means of accomplishing this end than man has ever known before: the atomic bomb.

In every case of an application of science, no matter what the purpose, no blame or praise should properly be imputed to science itself. Science acts simply as a most efficient servant. We may praise the body of scientists for having done the job assigned to them in an excellent manner, or we may blame them for having failed to solve the problem at hand, *but the blame or praise must be based on the accomplishment of the task that was set, independent of whether the end product was a procedure for saving or for destroying life.* If man at large uses the findings of science for purposes of evil when he might equally have used the same findings for the purposes of good, how can we lay the blame at the door of science as an institution, or the scientists as individuals? The sulfa drugs and penicillin were discovered in the laboratory; their effectiveness as curative agents was soon afterwards demonstrated in the clinic. Our society has made use of the two new discoveries as curative agents in the war against disease. This is not alone to the credit of the scientists; the two discoveries might equally *not* have been used and they might have lain dormant in the annals of science, just as DDT lay dormant for forty years or so in *Beilstein* before it was put to use as an insecticide. The credit goes to mankind at large, to the manufacturers who made the new therapeutic agents available, to the doctors who employed them in their daily work. The praise for introducing the sulfa drugs and penicillin must be given to man's desire to alleviate human suffering and sickness, which prompted him to make universal use of the new discoveries. Mankind had the purpose; science, the good servant, provided the means.

Teacher, banker, fireman, policeman: each one of us is responsible for the collective actions of our society. And this includes the scientist. No more nor less than his neighbors is he responsible as a citizen. Well, perhaps a little more; perhaps when an aspect of science with which he is intimately familiar, and of which the general public does not recognize the significance, is uncovered he has then the additional duty of informing the community about the dangers or benefits *for them* which lie within that discovery.* The atomic physicists did just this in relation to the potentialities of their research. They performed a magnificent office to the community, sacrificing time, work, and energy, in a passionate effort to see to it that all members of the community knew the true nature of the "atomic age" of which they had so abruptly become citizens. And then the scientists went back to work. From that point on, guided and advised by them, we carry on. But if we ask those physicists who have so splendidly informed us about the atomic age to exchange the physics of the atomic nucleus for the politics of our salvation, we in effect ask them to give up the field in which they are experts and become amateurs in another profession. Personally, I doubt whether, as politicians, the scientists would do as much good for us as they can accomplish in the laboratory. As Professor Bridgman says, "If I personally had to see to it that only beneficent uses were made of my discoveries, I should have to spend my time oscillating between some kind of a forecasting bureau, to find what might be the uses made of my discoveries, and lobbying in Washington to procure the passage of special legislation to control the uses. In neither of these activities do I have any competence, so my life would be embittered and my scientific productivity cease." [7]

I do not mean that the scientist, having made his discovery and informed the world, should retire to his laboratory, close the door, and leave it up to the world as to what happens from then on. It is his continuous, never-ending responsibility as a citizen to guard, for the community, the advantages to be derived from science and never to stop fighting for them. But this is his work as a citizen and it

* See page 301 of the next chapter for further discussion of this point.

should go hand in hand with, rather than swallowing up, his work as a scientist.

War itself, then, cannot be the responsibility of scientists any more than of bakers and candlestick makers. How can we blame such a collective action as modern warfare on any single group? The scientists serve in war as they do in peace, simply to advance the ends that we as the components of a society (of which they are also members) desire.

Now that the war is over, research will undoubtedly lead the way to using atomic power for beneficial peaceful purposes. If we have another war, the same type of research will lead to using atomic power in even more destructive ways than we know at present. In either case the scientist will make use of his knowledge and techniques to render this new source of energy as efficient as possible, *and for whichever purpose society desires and dictates.*

To all who fondly believe that scientists should, at any rate, *select fields of research* where the results can be used by society only for good purposes and never for bad, Lord Rayleigh replies, "I believe that the whole idea that scientific men are especially responsible is a delusion born of imperfect knowledge of the real course of scientific discovery." [8] A few examples will make this clear.

Modern warfare is based upon the extended use of high explosives. The recent wars, including the last, employed on a large scale explosives which were developed out of the natural trends of organic chemistry, such as we described in Chapter 15. Chemists studying carbon compounds were inevitably led to try the action of nitric acid upon such substances as benzene, toluene, glycerine, and cellulose. No one could have foreseen or predicted the results, which, indeed, were varied. In the case of benzene, the end product was nitrobenzene, one of the "keys" in the development of the synthetic aniline dye industry. In the case of glycerine, the compound obtained by Sobrero in 1846 was nitroglycerine. This discovery was made in the logical pursuit of extending knowledge concerning organic compounds. The discoverer meant no harm to society. He was a great investigator whose work contributed to the advance of civilization; he was certainly not its enemy. His discovery was neglected for almost seventeen years until 1863, when the Swedish chemist Alfred Nobel showed that by mixing nitroglycerine with other substances, solid explosives could be made which admitted of safe handling. One of these was dynamite. It and others proved and continue to prove their value in the arts of peace — for example, in mining, railway and highway construction, tunneling, and the building of dams.[9] Shall we blame science for the use of these explosives in weapons of war?

Let us look at the question of poison gas, responsible, perhaps more than any other single weapon, for science's becoming the scapegoat after the First World War. The use of poison gas (contrary to the agreement of the Hague Conference) profoundly shocked the "decent sensibilities" of the "Allied citizenry." The civilized world has never recovered from that shock. Throughout World War II, newspaper editorialists continued to congratulate themselves and us, applauding the fact that poison gases were never used. Yet no loud voice was ever raised to condemn with equal force the use of flame throwers which roasted our enemies alive. Perhaps two great wars within such a short compass of time have jaded our moral sensibilities.

In terms of actual numbers, the poison-gas toll of casualties in the First World War accounted for considerably less than even 1 per cent of the total, and the great majority of these occurred during the first days of its use, before the protective device of the gas mask had been developed.[10] Thus our outraged horror was surely not justified in terms of numbers; the spectacle of millions of casualties is certainly far more to be deplored than the particular *form* of casualty which effected so small a percentage, however horrible it might have been.

The story of gas warfare illustrates also the essential neutrality of science in war. On the one hand, research introduces new methods of destruction such as poison gas; while on the other it invents new devices, such as the gas mask, to counteract or nullify their effects.

Chlorine, used extensively in gas warfare during the First World War, was isolated, as we have had occasion to discuss in Chapter 3, by the Swedish chemist, Scheele, in the eighteenth century as one of the steps in the investigation of common salt or sodium chloride.[11]

When first found, it was considered an interesting and "curious" substance of no practical value whatever. Yet it soon proved its usefulness, not as an instrument of warfare, but as a bleaching agent, for which purpose it is still used industrially and is the active ingredient of the common household bleaching agent found under various trade names in almost every kitchen and laundry.

If chlorine was not discovered for war purposes, what of the dread mustard gas? Was this not a "scientific devilment" *deliberately* produced in German laboratories in order to cripple, maim, and destroy Allied soldiers in 1914–1918? Those who share this belief may be referred to the 1894 edition of Watt's *Dictionary of Chemistry* under the heading of "dichloriethyl sulfide," the scientific name of mustard gas, described there as "very poisonous; violently inflames the skin." [12]

The incendiary bombs used during the late war have given rise in some quarters to the notion that their chief constituent, thermite, was invented by scientists as a device for spreading fire throughout bombed cities. Yet as early as 1901 the reaction whereby large amounts of heat energy are liberated when aluminum combines with oxygen was well known. In that year Sir William Robert Austin delivered a lecture at the Royal Institution in London in which he showed how a mixture of powdered aluminum and red iron oxide produces a violent reaction, liberating great quantities of heat. The mixture was called "thermite" from the Greek word for heat, the same stem that appears in the word "*therm*ometer." Thermite was soon being used in various branches of the peaceful art of metallurgy, especially welding, long before the invention of the airplane made possible the use of thermite bombs to set fire to cities. [13]

The airplane itself was the culmination of centuries of dreaming that man might conquer the air, beginning with early myths from classical times, such as that of Icarus, the son of Daedalus, who attempted to fly to the sun with wings made of feathers and held together with wax. It was always apparent that the airplane might be used in war as well as in peace. But what other invention or discovery could not equally be used for both purposes? Such apparently innocuous processes as the mass production of clothing and shoes are also important for war, since they make possible the large-scale production of uniforms and footwear required for the modern-size army and navy. Shall all progress stop because any innovation may be used in war as well as in peace?

&   *&*   *&*

The preceding examples show how difficult it would be to control scientific discoveries at the source. In each case we have considered, the application of the fundamental discoveries of science, as well as advances in technology, to the purpose of war not only was far remote from any control of the discoverer, but often not even apparent to him. The same kind of dreamer who produced ether and chloroform in the laboratory also turned up mustard gas. The unexpected application of one to relieve pain, and of the other to produce suffering, would certainly have seemed astonishing to the research workers who were producing these substances for the first time. One was not "a fiend" whose activities ought to have been suppressed, nor was the other "an angel of mercy" whose work should have been encouraged. Both investigators, like all scientists, were activated by scientific curiosity and the desire to find the facts of nature and to master them. Seekers after truth and knowledge, they had no possible means of knowing whether the results of their research would cause future generations to think of them as fiends, or dreamers, or angels. As Lord Rayleigh tells us, "For good or ill, the urge to explore the unknown is deep in the nature of some of us, and it will not be deterred but shows contingent results, which may not be, and generally are not, fully apparent till long after the death of the explorer. The world is ready to accept the gifts of science and to use them for its own purposes." [14]

If science is to stand before the bar of justice for the part it has played in warfare, then judge her by the whole record and not just part of it. It will then be seen that science in war has not been alone destructive. In his address as retiring president of the American Association for the Advancement of Science, Dr. Alfred F. Blakeslee pointed out that statistics from the Surgeon General's office tell an interesting story.[15] Deaths due to injuries sustained in battle were 15 per thousand in the Mexican War, 33 per thousand in the Civil War, and 53 per thousand in the First World War. At the same time, the death rate due to disease decreased from 110 per thousand to 65 and 19 respectively. The net result of scientific activity therefore in improving weapons of destruction, and methods for conquering disease, was that the total death rate in the armed forces decreased from 125 per thousand in the Mexican War to 98 per thousand in the Civil War, and to 72 per thousand in the First World War. The data thus far available on World War II show that the trend has an even more marked decrease in the recent conflict. The chances of death for the diseased and wounded soldiers have become greatly lessened. The complete record shows clearly that science serves man in war as in peace simply as an instrument for furthering the desires of mankind, whatever they may be.

To sum up briefly, then, I believe it to be demonstrable that scientists have no special guilt in modern warfare — not any more special than any other group in modern society. To ask that scientists desist from any activity which may lead to a new instrument of destruction is pointless. A famous mathematician recently declared that he would not publish in the future any work "which may do damage in the hands of irresponsible militarists." [16] Such a statement exhibits a painful lack of understanding of the whole nature of the scientific enterprise. Readers of this book should know full well that it is absolutely impossible in general to predict today what use will be made of fundamental knowledge tomorrow.

The only way to make sure that the fruits of scientific research will *never* be used for destructive ends is to give up science altogether and terminate the "age of science." No one seriously recommends such a program. We want science to go ahead — to find the fundamental knowledge on which to base the cures for the diseases that afflict us and before which we are helpless. We *do* want the better, easier, and more comfortable lives that the fruits of scientific research will make possible. If we wish, at the same time, to eliminate the effects of science in war, let us face that problem as citizens, boldly and with imagination tempered by realism. Let us do all within our power to eliminate war as an instrument of international policy — not by our country alone but by all the countries of the world.

Science will not make our moral decisions for us; these will remain our own personal responsibility. Science provides the power and means of obtaining the good life, but we as individuals, and as groups of human beings organized into political and national units, we the citizens of every country on this globe, must decide whether we truly desire to achieve that goal.

CHAPTER 18

How to Get the Most Out of Science

> What a field have we at our doors to signalize our-
> selves in! . . . [Science] is the work to which the
> young men . . . should lay their hands. We have
> spent the prime of our lives in procuring them the
> precious blessing of liberty. Let them spend theirs
> in showing that it is the great parent of science
> and virtue; and that a nation will be great in both
> always in proportion as it is free.
> — THOMAS JEFFERSON (1789)

THE LAY administrator, the citizen who will be called on to support
the scientific enterprise in the future and who will determine the
way in which his money will be spent, needs general principles as
guides to action; it is the purpose of this final chapter to make such
principles explicit and to see how they are illustrated and illuminated
by the case histories we have studied in the preceding chapters. I
offer here no program by means of which our support of science and
its applications can be made most effective; the general aspects of
such programs have been discussed during the last several years by
scientists, administrators, newspapermen, radio commentators, and
our elected representatives in Washington, and in the end will be
shaped by such democratic friction. The details must be worked
out slowly by trial and error, and by those who are engaged in the
business of scientific research and its administration. Meanwhile, we
as citizens will lend an interested ear to all proposals, but we must
judge them in terms of such understanding of the scientific enterprise as a whole as this book has attempted to provide.

The purpose of this book has been to give the layman, who ordi-
narily has no valid basis for judgment of the scientific enterprise,
a share in the experience of the scientists themselves: both those who
advance fundamental scientific knowledge and those who put science to work for whatever purposes our society values. You, the

reader, can now appreciate some of the characteristics of the nature of science which are part and parcel of the experience of all scientists. You can see what the scientist means when he says that, in general, the future progress in any area of science is largely unpredictable; what he means by the total scientific situation; recognize, as he does, the necessity for genius and individual effort, but also the way in which the achievement of any scientist, however great, is limited by the general conditions of science at the time he does his work; the role of chance or the "happy accident"; the manner in which a given research may bear its fruits slowly and only after many years that appear to have been barren, in which a discovery, if it is to affect either science itself or society at large, must fit the times in its own special way; and, above all, see the continuous spectrum of scientific activity from applied research and development at one end to the systematic search for abstract truths at the other.

With the understanding derived from studying the case histories of this book and their analysis, the lay administrator may face the general problem of the relation of science to his life with sensitivity to its nature and sympathy for its values, that will inform his judgment; and, I hope, with a sense of having participated in its experiences, however vicariously.

Keeping in mind that the uses to which scientific discoveries are put depend on the goals which we, as members of society, set, let us now face the problem at the very heart of our aspirations: How can we get the most out of science in the years ahead? How can our investment in the scientific enterprise best yield us a profitable return in practical dividends, and advance the cause of truth, or fundamental knowledge? Now we grasp the full significance of the late President Roosevelt's letter to Vannevar Bush, director of OSRD, in which he declared, "New frontiers of the mind are before us, and if they are pioneered with the same vision, boldness, and drive with which we have waged this war, we can create fuller and more fruitful lives."

Two quite different schools of thought exist today concerning the method of obtaining the greatest return from the scientific enterprise. One of these believes that the reason we have not made even more of science than we have is that we do not plan "theoretical research" and carry it out "more systematically." We have not, many writers tell us, accomplished the great things possible to science because the scientists have never admitted "the social responsibility of science," and this is the reason we have not had more planning. The leaders of this school are largely a group of brilliant young Englishmen,[1] but they have many followers in this country who make the charge that only during periods of war has science been given an "over-all purpose and direction."

The other school, at the opposite extreme, has banded together in England into an organization called The Society for Freedom in Science.[2] In America, a large group of leading scientists and administrators, equally anxious to have the people and the government support scientific research, want our science to be as well equipped as possible for what Harlow Shapley eloquently describes as warfare against the tyranny of the unknown. These people, however, hold that an essential condition for scientific progress, to quote from Dr. Shapley's preface to this book, is "the need of freedom for the investigator in choosing his field of study and following his own inspiration."

Now both "planning" and "freedom" are of the type sometimes called "loaded" words. If you are an ardent New Dealer, "planning" implies an easy path to the millennium; if you are a Republican, the very mention of the word is like waving a red flag before the proverbial bull. Any attempt at an impartial discussion of planning in science may, therefore, reflect not the merits of the subjects so much as the general social and political philosophy of the arguer.

Even so, let us try to assess — with what I hope is the objectivity that examines theory in the light of repeated case histories — the workability of the two opinions. But I admit that my own conclusions must necessarily, if unwittingly, reflect my own political and social outlook.

Whoever really wants to understand the problem of over-all planning in science, or who wishes to know what general course of action should be recommended in the future for American science, must consider his discussion on three distinct planes. The first entails the great problem of how we may extend the scope of fundamental research: scientific inquiry which adds significantly to the foundations of knowledge. The second is the related problem of pioneering the applications of that knowledge to specific useful ends, in order to better and enrich our lives. Lastly, there is a general problem of how these applications, once they have been worked out, are to be made available most effectively and generously to the entire public. We will examine into these three planes of discussion in reverse order.

          ~   ~   ~

Every member of society must be concerned with the state of his community: town or city, county, state, nation. Good Government classes teach that *we* (each of us) perpetually carry the responsibility of seeing to it that our laws are both wise and well administered. How does this affect the application of science?

Consider the case of the pasteurization of milk. There is no question about the value of pasteurization for better health; for one half of a century this has been consistently demonstrated. Yet many states in our country still have laws which permit the public sale of unpasteurized milk. An unwary citizen, traveling from a state with strict pasteurization laws to another that does not afford such protection, may not even be aware of the fact that the milk he drinks in the latter is not pasteurized. Many diseases are transmitted by unpasteurized milk, among them brucellosis. I know of a man working on medical research, who summers in a state in which there are no laws requiring pasteurization. He and his wife unwittingly drank unpasteurized milk, and his poor wife contracted brucellosis, a chronic disease for which there is no cure.

As another example, we may cite vaccination for smallpox, which was discovered in the 1790's by Edward Jenner, and whose efficacy in preventing smallpox has been known for about a century and a half. Yet a great many states in our country do not have any vaccination laws at all! Others expressly prohibit compulsory vaccination, and still others leave the question to local option. During the period 1918–1928, only *ten* states required compulsory vaccination. Now look at the following table.[3] These figures indicate the relation of smallpox morbidity to vaccination laws in the United States during the period 1919–1928:

RELATION OF SMALLPOX MORBIDITY TO VACCINATION LAWS IN THE UNITED STATES, 1919–1928

Vaccination laws	Number of states *	Population	Number of cases	Incidence per 100,000
Compulsory vaccination	10	32,434,954	21,543	6.6
Local option	6	17,930,882	91,981	51.3
No vaccination laws	29	59,923,117	393,924	66.7
Compulsory vaccination prohibited	4	4,002,888	46,110	115.2

* Including the District of Columbia.

This table tells its tale more graphically than any polemic. The incidence per 100,000 of the population is in direct proportion to the kind of law operating.

These two examples, pasteurization and vaccination laws, show very clearly that what would seem to most readers to be obviously time-tested practical results of scientific research are not universally applied. Faced with such a grievous wrong, we ask: What should we do about it?

There can not be much argument that in the "ideal" totalitarian state, by the very nature of its *totality!,* once the government recognized the value of pasteurization or vaccination, the benefits of these practices would be universal. Those who argue for a planned state point out that there would be no inequalities of the possible benefits, such as may be found in our federated democracy. Nevertheless, serious as our failures may be (and as a scientist-citizen I will get up on the soapbox every time I learn of such a case!), I still prefer the system under which, to our bitter shame, such tragic inequalities are able to exist, to the *complete* uniformity with which *both good and evil* are applied in a totalitarian state! Our form of government, with the very human quality of its occasional blundering, leaves room for checks and balances, for the reconsideration of mistakes, for changes of policy, and, above all, for the exercise of my right as a citizen to stand up on my own two feet and express myself freely without fear of recrimination.

In any case, I do not believe that *only* under totalitarianism can the benefits of science be made universally available to all men. The very flexibility of our democratic form of government, in being able to adapt itself, with the consent of the governed, to new situations as they arise, represents the greatest single factor of our strength.

Over and over again we have made basic changes: abolishing slavery, or extending the franchise to women. Surely there is no reason why we cannot by our own laws ensure to all the community the benefits of good health deriving from vaccination and pasteurization.

∾   ∾   ∾

On this level, that is, the availability of the applications of scientific knowledge, the scientist has his responsibility as a citizen, with an additional burden deriving from his special competence. The scientist, finding that the applications of his discoveries are not equally shared by all, must bring the facts to light. In this way the scientist acts as the conscience of humanity.

But I would re-emphasize that he must not give up being a scientist to do it. The number of men who can make first-class contributions to science is limited by nature's endowment. Their training is long and arduous, requiring a schooling of a minimum of about 21 years (8 in elementary school, 4 in high school or preparatory school, 4 in college, and about 5 years in graduate and postgraduate training). They serve their prime purpose in the civic community as scientists.

It is frequently pointed out that when a scientific discovery is applied to technology, the effects may benefit a majority of the people upon our earth, at dreadful cost to a minority thereby rendered helpless. For example, during the nineteenth century, chemists learned how to produce dyes synthetically from coal tar; almost overnight, huge areas in Europe and Asia, formerly devoted exclusively to the cultivation of plants from which dyes were extracted (such as madder), were desolated, and unemployment was widespread. Should such unemployment be laid at the feet of science? It seems to me that if blame should be attached to any group, it should be attached to the whole of society. A society that had given thought to the welfare of *all* of its citizens might well have seen to it that the introduction of the coal-tar dyes would not have resulted in widespread unemployment; it could have advised people living in the area where dye plants were grown to cultivate some other form of plant. This is "planning" if you wish; the foresight and planning that should be the care of all good government. The scientists had discovered how to produce the dyes from coal tar. Our society found this discovery valuable in a variety of ways: not only in establishing a synthetic dye industry, but also because our knowledge of dyes has had important repercussions in medicine, in which Ehrlich's Salvarsan and the more recent discovery of the sulfa drugs are but two of many examples.

The fallacy in blaming science for what society does with its discoveries may be illustrated best perhaps by a somewhat parallel situation from technology. Could you say offhand whether the development of labor-saving machinery was conducive to an *increase* in human slavery, or a *decrease* in that vile practice?

Depending on the circumstances and the nature of the society, somewhat similar inventions may produce wholly different effects. We have referred in an earlier chapter (5) to the importance of the mechanical inventions and technological advances made in the Middle Ages. We saw that such a simple innovation as the wheelbarrow reduced the element of human labor by one half in transporting materials, and that the invention of the horse collar and iron horseshoe enabled man for the first time effectively to harness rapidly moving beasts of burden such as the horse. These innovations had the effect, in Catholic medieval Europe, of reducing human slavery by vast proportions, since a horse became a cheaper and more efficient prime mover than a large number of human beings.[4]

But many centuries later another labor-saving device in a different form of society had just the opposite effect. The cotton gin, invented by Eli Whitney as a labor-saving device, prolonged slavery in the United States at a time when it was rapidly on the decline. The reason was that the cotton gin made slave labor more efficient, made cotton growing economically profitable, and provided slave owners with additional capital with which to purchase more slaves, farm an even larger terrain, and thereby extend their enterprise.[5] Should Eli Whitney therefore have been execrated rather than honored by posterity? Should we tear his picture out of our schoolbooks?

These examples indicate that the answers to even the simplest questions about the effect of innovations on society may depend to a large degree on the circumstances in which they occurred. We should be warned of the inherent fallacy of too simple an answer.

∾   ∾   ∾

Let us now turn to the second plane of discourse: pioneering the application of known scientific principles. The greater part of industrial research, as we saw in Chapter 4, is devoted to this task. The success of our industrial laboratories in the United States leads many votaries of "planned science" to the belief that here is case proof of their thesis on the value of planning. In the table printed on page 58, it is evident that by far the greatest amount of money spent for scientific research and development (except during the war years) was spent by the industrial laboratories. This figure increased from $115 million in 1930 to $234 million in 1940, as contrasted to some $30 million spent on research by our universities. In the latter year, there were approximately 2200 laboratories maintained by industrial organizations, constituting a very significant sector of our total scientific facilities.

Most of the scientific activity of the United States, carried on in industrial laboratories, is subject to some sort of planning by the industry in question. The reason why this is possible is that, to a very large degree, industry is concerned much more with research at the applied end of the spectrum of scientific activity than with fundamental research, or pure science. In other words, the laboratories maintained by industry devote their attention largely to the development of *existing* ideas rather than to the discovery of new and fundamental knowledge.

But let us here remind the reader of the nature of the spectrum. If you recall Chapter 4 you will remember that "applied" research is an occupation that differs from the search for truth. The difference between those who work at fundamental research and those who work at applied research is in the point of view with which they face the problem and the goals they have in mind. The man working at the "pure science" end of the spectrum, whether in a university or in an industrial laboratory, pursues a problem because it is interesting or because it appears to have a certain relevance to fundamental knowledge. By contrast, the man working at the "applied science" end of the spectrum pursues a problem because it has a relevance to a particular practical goal. Frequently such research is concerned only with problems of a purely economic kind, such as how to manufacture a given product using materials that at that particular time are cheaper or more available than others. A great part of the applied research prosecuted by industry is far removed from the search for truth and, as we pointed out in Chapter 4, it is often classified by industry itself as "development" (improving certain steps in the manufacturing process) or pilot plant operation.

Let us keep in mind, however, that the spectrum of scientific activity is a continuous one; there are no sharp gradations. While a vast difference exists between the fundamental research of the type carried on in our universities and the development of manufacturing processes in industrial laboratories, in between there is a considerable activity which is joined continuously to these two extremes, and which partakes almost simultaneously of the nature of both. Carothers's work on linear super-polymers affords an excellent example of what I have in mind. It began with an unrestricted foray into the unknown (but in a field of chemistry which the Du Pont Company thought it profitable to study); after a considerable amount of research had indicated an economic possibility, the whole research activity was given an applied direction. Then the same attention which had previously been focused on the goal of adding to knowledge was refocused on a new goal, the production of a new fiber.

The only planning of Carothers's work, at the stage when he was studying the new field of chemistry, was that of Carothers himself; it was indistinguishable from the self-imposed planning of any scientist who is attacking a new problem. Yet once the knowledge obtained by Carothers appeared to be related to the possibility of making a synthetic fiber, he was "encouraged" — to use the Du Pont expression — to devote his attention to the production of a practical fiber and to develop the applied aspects already immanent in his fundamental findings.

(Before we generalize too broadly on the basis of this case history, let us remember that the directors of industrial laboratories constantly tell us that, in the future, they expect most of the fundamental discoveries which their own scientists will apply to be made in universities rather than in their own industrial laboratories.)

On the pilot plant level of applied research in industry, there can be no question but that there is complete planning. In the systematic search for applications of existing knowledge, a considerable amount of planning is employed. But, however successful this type of planning may be, we must not for a moment forget that any plans that are made must be formulated in terms of today's knowledge and yesterday's. The discoveries of tomorrow on the fundamental level may make such plans futile.

Even then, the leaders of industrial research warn us against too rigid an interpretation of *how,* and the *extent* to which, industrial research may be planned. For example, Dr. Oliver E. Buckley, president of the Bell Telephone Laboratories, admonishes: "One sure way to defeat the scientific spirit is to attempt to direct inquiry from above. All successful industrial directors know this, and have learned by experience that one thing a 'director of research' must never do is to direct research, nor can he permit direction of research by any supervisory board. Successful research goes in the direction in which some inquiring mind finds itself impelled." Dr. Buckley points out that goals are set; in the case of applied research the goals are those of "practical accomplishment." The effectiveness with which such goals are attained is increased by teamwork, and the director of research has the job of building teams and seeing to it that "they are supplied with facilities and given freedom to pursue their inquiry. He also insures for them contacts essential to their work, but at the same time protects them from interference or diversion arising from demands of immediate operating need. He assigns fields of research and broad objectives to the different groups working under his direction, but he must depend largely on those doing the work to find the gaps in knowledge and the opportunities for practical improvements."[6]

Another experienced director of research, Dr. C. E. Kenneth Mees, Vice-President in Charge of Research of Eastman Kodak Company, has written two interesting books: one *Organization of Industrial Scientific Research,* the other *The Path of Science.* The first of these, published in 1920, assumed that the organization of a research institution might be similar to that of a factory or an army. Twenty-five years later, in the second one, the same writer has become convinced that this does not correspond to the realities of the situation:

Scientific research cannot really be organized under department heads, who are themselves working scientists carrying out research work. The fact is that the unit of scientific research is a *scientist* with a group of assistants and he is, by definition, capable of directing his own work by his own methods. In the operation of his work, he must be independent of all control and free to do whatever he wishes. The function of his superior in the organization is not to control the operation of the work; it is to direct the work toward the problems that seem most desirable, to insure and assist co-operation between the individual research units, to provide the necessary working conditions and environment, and, in an industrial laboratory, to see that any results obtained are applied in practice.[7]

               ◆   ◆   ◆

What about the last of our three levels of discussion: Will the research aimed at increasing knowledge profit by planning?

One reason that many people today advocate the planning of scientific research is the very obvious success of the Office of Scientific Research and Development during World War II. "It" worked during the war, the planners declare, why should we not make "it" work in peacetime? The answer is given by President James B. Conant: During the war, direction and planning in the research operated by our federal government was highly successful because targets could be chosen with a reasonable degree of certainty.[8] Those engaged in wartime research attempted no over-all search for unsuspected truths, nor were they concerned with fields of research that might possibly lead to something of military value or a means of saving lives only after a long period, say, ten or fifteen years. By that time the war would surely be over. The only research carried out was in fields of activity that seemed likely to yield immediate results. Our scientists explored the limits of the total scientific situation as it then existed, without any concern for possible new conditions that would change that situation. Theirs was primarily a job of applied research and development.

President Conant points out that those who make too close an analogy between the wartime research conducted by OSRD and a program for peacetime commit a serious error; such an analogy presupposes that no difference exists between fundamental and applied research. The Russians, and those who agree with the Russians' point of view with regard to science, argue for planning on both the pure or fundamental level *and* the applied; in fact they refuse to admit any distinction between the two. Even those who talk of planning under the disguise of "supervision and direction," under our own free enterprise system, usually will not allow a distinction between the search for fundamental truths of nature and the process of applying that knowledge for practical purposes. Because in some measure applied science can be, and is, successfully planned, those who claim that pure and applied science are absolutely identical say that *all* research should be planned.

President Conant tells us, "There is only one proved method of assisting the advancement of pure science — that of picking men of genius, backing them heavily, and leaving them to direct themselves. There is only one proved method of getting results in applied science — picking men of genius, backing them heavily, and keeping their aim on the target chosen." [9]

The success of the research organized, planned, and directed during the war by OSRD was owing to the fact that "its objective was not to advance science but to devise and improve instrumentalities of war. Any advancement of science was a pure by-product, and it was the task of those in control to keep such by-products to a minimum. We owed it to the men who were risking their lives in combat," President Conant concludes, "to see to it that every dollar and every man-hour was expended for just one purpose, namely, to hasten the day of victory."

Because almost all the work done by OSRD during the war occurred at the applied end of the spectrum, its success was very great; but when we come to fundamental research or pure science, the situation is obviously different. Even the most ardent advocate of planning, J. D. Bernal, admits that one can never foresee "the possibilities of fundamental, new discoveries and their effect in revolutionizing the whole progress of science." [10]

◆◆◆   ◆◆◆   ◆◆◆

Let us return to the case histories of our book in order to see wherein the arguments for planning of all scientific research are misinformed. As an example of the "failure" of an unplanned system of research, we are told to look at the decade that elapsed between the time that Fleming "discovered" penicillin and its application by Florey, Chain, and their associates.

Now if it be true that the present organization of scientific research in democratic countries has certain features inimical to our best interests, then by all means we should see to it that a remedy is proposed and adopted. Yet readers of this book will know that the often used example of penicillin betrays a fundamental ignorance of the way in which science develops. To say that Fleming discovered penicillin and that its applications were not found until some ten years later is far from the truth. We know that the so-called ten-year time lag was occasioned by what we have denoted the total scientific situation. As it obtained in the late '20s, the total scientific situation practically precluded any further work on penicillin until some years had passed. (See Chapter 2.) Furthermore, another factor was Fleming's initial observation that penicillin was "unstable."[11] Because of this instability of penicillin, Florey and Chain, although interested in the problem of supressing bacterial growth by various agents obtained from the plant and animal kingdom, tried other substances before they turned to penicillin.

Considering the state of the total scientific situation, as well as the fact that the original discoverer of penicillin had declared it unstable, I personally very much doubt whether any kind of direction or planning could have forced scientists to complete the discovery of penicillin one or two years after Fleming's observation rather than waiting out the full time.

It is very easy in science to indulge in what President Conant calls "Monday morning quarterbacking."[12] Or, to use the expression of Michael Polanyi, to read the history of science backwards.[13] From our vantage point of 1948 we may say that, had such a group as the one assembled by Florey and Chain undertaken their work of 1939 in 1929, we would have had penicillin ten years earlier. Yet I find it hard to conceive of any committee, even if composed of the most eminent scientists, recommending in 1929 that this be done. Such a group, if empowered with funds, and if able to issue the necessary directives, would have acted in terms of the contemporary climate of opinion and surely would have caused attention to be concentrated on vaccines, toxins, and antitoxins, rather than on microbial antagonism.

This is the very reason why planning in science must always be limited, and why the future scientific discoveries will remain unpredictable. Every scientist is a product of his environment; and his thinking, even in science, is limited by the scientific situation in which he lives and works.

It may very well be, for example, that the fundamental key to the cancer problem has already been found and now slumbers peacefully in some scientific journal. (We should not really say "found" because a discovery is not completed until the facts have been incorporated into the main body of scientific knowledge to serve as the cornerstone of further developments.) Perhaps at some future time, either a few years or many years from now, the total scientific situation will change, and then in the new environment the slumbering observation will be newly interpreted. It will become clear to one or more research workers that so-and-so, who published a paper years ago, had made the beginnings of what would certainly be one of the most significant achievements in medicine in the twentieth century.

Most of us are willing to support the advance of science largely in order to profit by its useful return. But let us never forget that the ideas whose implementation in the form of practical innovations have most altered the conditions of the material world came from discoveries of unknown and unsuspected phenomena. From the time of Hippocrates onward, physicians have been anxious to know the state of things inside the human body. Since it is not possible to look directly into the patient, various ways of obtaining such information were developed. One was the method of auscultation, in which the physician taps the patient on his chest and back in order to find out about conditions inside. Another is the use of a stethoscope, which enables the physician to listen to the internal organs, notably those of the circulatory system. But no physician in the latter part of the nineteenth century, however interested he might have been in this general problem, would have thought of, or ever have *discovered,* x-rays — because before their discovery, who had any idea that x-rays existed, or could have guessed that they might have the properties we now associate with them?

(This example also illustrates that advances in fundamental science of all kinds have practical implications in biology and medicine. Indeed, many important practical innovations in medical practice have been the result, not so much of the strivings of physicians, as of those who were pursuing fundamental research for new truths in other fields.) Had there been a concerted effort to find new methods of fighting disease in 1932 those who made the plans would, by necessity, have been limited to directions determined by the total scientific situation which then obtained. They would have sought for new and better vaccines, toxins and antitoxins, and new modes of treatment, but they would never have devoted an all-out effort to following Fleming's discovery through to its logical conclusions, because the environment necessary to engender such a point of view would not yet have existed. Dubos would have stopped his apparently "useless" work on microbial antagonism and Domagk his studies on coal-tar dyes. The result would have been to deprive the world of sulfa drugs, of gramicidin, and of tyrocidine. The total scientific situation would not have changed in the way it did and when it did. We would not only have lost sulfa drugs and the antibiotics of Dubos, but we would never have had penicillin at all!

In any case, before a discovery can be applied, it must be completed and fully understood. The history of penicillin, as Dr. John F. Fulton observes, falls into three phases: (1) Fleming's initial observation; (2) the successful extraction and purification of penicillin and the demonstrations of its therapeutic properties; and (3) the remarkable feat of its commercial production. Phases one and two, though separated by a period of ten years, together make up "the discovery." Had nothing more been done than to make Fleming's initial observations, we would today be far from the practical therapeutic application. The discovery begun by Fleming was completed by Florey, Chain, and their associates.[14]

We have seen that Abbot Mendel announced the fundamental laws of heredity long before the total scientific situation was ready for their acceptance, so that they could be incorporated into the body of scientific knowledge. The continuous development and history of genetics dates not from the middle of the nineteenth century, therefore, but rather from the beginning of the twentieth. No directives can alter the fundamental condition for the acceptance of an unusual idea which, in the very special sense we have used in this book, may be "ahead of the times." Successful planning necessitates some foreknowledge of the eventual result — a meta-science, transcending human limitations.

❧   ❧   ❧

Throughout this book (Part Four especially), we have exhibited scientific discoveries which, although they provided important applications at a later date, seemed to be in the "useless" category for a considerable period. This situation was not due to any lack of vision or of social consciousness on the part of the discoverer, nor necessarily to purely economic considerations. As an outstanding example of what I have in mind, let us recall the story of the foraminifera, the microfossils now used so extensively in oil prospecting. The reason that the foraminifera have become so important is that, owing to the advent of the automobile and the extensive use of the internal-combustion engine, the demand for gasoline and hence petroleum has been considerably greater during the last thirty years than it ever was before. This demand had grown to such proportions by the end of the First World War that the search for oil on a world-wide scale never before conceived took place. It then became necessary to use whatever methods might be devised to make this search more effective. As we saw in Chapter 15, knowledge of the microscopic fossils was then at hand and ready to be put to use.

But quite clearly, since the only practical application of microfossils has so far been in oil prospecting, the application could not be made at all until there occurred a large-scale demand for oil. No matter how great a social consciousness any of the investigators in this field might have had, he would not have found an application for his work in the late years of the nineteenth century or earliest years of the twentieth. Conversely, had those who studied the foraminifera been limited only to research on "useful" subjects, their studies would never have been made at all. At the time that we needed their knowledge, it would not have been at hand ready to be used. We should have been deprived of the very kind of discovery that both planners and non-planners hope to have available when needed.

Applied scientific research, that is, the systematic development of existing knowledge, is an activity that may be better for planning. We are certainly committed to planned development in the case of atomic energy. But we have seen throughout this book that many practical innovations, affecting all aspects of our life, come from fundamental research, the planning of which appears to be inimical to its very progress. How can one tell which area of science to pursue in order to solve a given practical problem? What seems so abstract as to be unrelated to the needs of today may swiftly change and become the very cornerstone of tomorrow's technology. Why should this be so?

As we have seen by the examples in this book, this question has two separate aspects. In the first place, as in the case of the foraminifera, and also in the case of magnetostriction, the piezoelectric effect, and much of the work of organic chemistry, the reason may be that the need for a particular scientific result may as yet not have arisen in our society or our technology. On the other hand, we have examples, such as the method of electron diffraction and others, in which the need for studying the surfaces of metals may be present and even pressing, but no one can tell *before the work is completed* that one particular avenue of research, rather than another, will provide an instrument or a method for solving the problem at hand.

J. G. Crowther would condemn the pursuit of science of the last three centuries for "piling up discoveries in regions artificially isolated from the general body of knowledge and social welfare." [15] If scientists had a grain of social conscience, they would abandon such pursuits because they are "a little cold, mean and selfish." [16] In any case, says J. D. Bernal, scientists cannot expect society to pay them "merely to amuse themselves." [17]

At this point I hope my readers will simply sigh, as I do, at the blindness of men who can make such statements, and, to refresh their souls and senses, will turn to the glorious pages of the history of science.

Because of the very unpredictable nature of scientific progress, we must be careful not to limit, restrict, or attempt to direct, the fundamental research from which we expect our future benefits. No field of work, however abstract or remote it may seem, can be said with any degree of certainty to be absolutely "useless," even from the most hardheaded and practical point of view. But even if there may be fields of work which appear not to yield us a practical return for many years to come, and perhaps never at all, let us encourage and support them! I most earnestly recommend to the lay administrator of science a program of research on *every* frontier of the unknown. The *discovery of a fundamental truth is an inspiring thing in itself,* even if it may not lead to a better dentifrice, a cure for a disease, or a new mode of attacking the weed problem. Who is there amongst us whose imagination is not stirred by such a discovery as that of

Dr. Harlow Shapley and Miss Levitt on the Cepheid variables, which enables the scientist to tell us the size of the universe? And shall we deny the means of making discovery to the scientist who may tell us the secret of life itself, even if it yield no immediate practical dividend? When all is said and done, science, the endless adventure into the unknown, is at bottom a means of exploring the universe. Incidentally, but only incidentally, it supplies us with the tangible aspects of advance that make it worth our while to support it were we too dull to care why we live and breathe, why the sun rises and sets, or why the particles of matter hold together.

Even if we believe that rigid over-all planning is dangerous to the best interests of science, those who direct the expenditure of public moneys for the support of research may be well advised to take some steps toward filling in gaps of knowledge. For example, nowhere in the United States is the subject of low temperature physics prosecuted widely or thoroughly as it was before the war in Holland. Since this is an important area, and one in which we are making no contributions to knowledge, a National Science Foundation might well wish to encourage the study of low temperature physics in the United States. One simple way in which this can be done, consistent with the full freedom of science, is for the board of such a foundation to announce that it would like to have the subject investigated and stands ready to back the establishment of an institute for investigation in this field by any responsible group. The result of such an announcement would probably be that groups of physicists in several of our universities would draw up programs and submit them to the foundation. Depending on the size and scope of the several proposals, the foundation might then give funds to one, two, or even more, such groups to enable them to prosecute that part of the field which the group in question had decided would interest it.

Another such function might be to establish, in very much the same way, more seismographic stations for the recording of earthquakes. Two of the best stations in the United States are both located in Massachusetts, one in Weston belonging to the Jesuit Weston College, and the other at Oak Ridge (Massachusetts), maintained by Harvard University. It would be most valuable to have other stations located in far-flung regions of the United States. The procedure just described for low temperature laboratories could be followed.

Some scientists have envisioned that a function of the National Science Foundation might be to draw up a catalogue, to which all scientists would be invited to contribute, which would list what might be considered the outstanding unsolved problems in the whole range of fundamental science. Yet such a list must be used with caution. Many problems remaining to be solved would be of a very general kind, dealing, for example, with the over-all problem of the mechanics of the nucleus. This would not be entirely helpful because almost every physicist knows that in this area of knowledge much information is desired and precious little known. Likewise, it is commonly the case in science that once a question is formulated exactly, then the solution is almost at hand. My late tutor, G. D. Birkhoff, used to say with great wisdom that the man who could formulate a problem in exact terms so that it could be solved was a much rarer genius than the man who could then solve the problem.

There is one "master plan" for scientific research in the postwar world that I should like to recommend to the lay administrator of science. Proposed by President James B. Conant, himself both a distinguished scientist and a gifted administrator, it has five features. The first is *to provide an educational system which offers equality of opportunity* so that those with talent may be educated no matter what their financial background; second, *to find the superior men among those given this opportunity* while they are still in training; third, *to give these men every advantage and facility possible* in the way of machines, materials, and helping hands; fourth, *to be certain that there are many rival and independent groups* competing for scientific and technical achievement and that no group can long perpetuate itself; and, fifth, *to beware in times of peace of coordinating agencies with dictatorial powers* — that is, of a peacetime general staff.[18]

Bibliography and Guide to Further Reading, and Notes

IN THE LIST of books which follows, some are distinguished from others by one of two special symbols. Books which are marked off by the symbol ➤ are those to which the lay reader may turn with profit if he or she wishes to read more about the subject and those which have proved particularly useful to me in writing the chapter in question; while those marked off by the symbol ★ are either fundamental works or those which have been of special help to me in writing the chapter, but may, perhaps, be too technical or too difficult for the lay reader with no scientific background in the subject.

For each chapter of the book, there is a combined Bibliography and Guide to Further Reading. There is also a section of Notes which refer in each case to the bibliography for that chapter.

The bibliographical entries have been made in accordance with the suggestions of DR. JOHN F. FULTON, eminent neurologist, historian of science, and bibliographer and bibliophile, in his article: The Principles of Bibliographical Citation, *Bulletin of the Medical Library Association* (1934), vol. 22, pp. 183–197.

The greater portion of the bibliographical cards were made by MR. DAVID FEIGENBAUM, whose knowledge of bibliographical techniques and whose care and accuracy in such matters were of invaluable assistance to me. The typed bibliographies were checked against the originals by my mother, MRS. BLANCHE B. COHEN, to whom my debt is equally considerable; she also read the galley proofs of the bibliographies.

CHAPTER 1: THE SCIENTIFIC EDUCATION OF THE LAYMAN

Bibliography and Guide to Further Reading

→ BECKER, CARL. (1940) The Declaration of Independence, a study in the history of political ideas. New York: Peter Smith, 286 pp.
    Especially pp. 39–52, on the eighteenth-century concept of nature.
BLAKESLEE, ALBERT FRANCIS. (1940) Ideals of science. Science, vol. 92, pp. 589–592.
★ BUSH, VANNEVAR. (1945) Science the endless frontier, a report to the president. Washington: United States Government Printing Office, ix + 184 pp.
CAJORI, FLORIAN. See NEWTON (1943).
→ CANNON, WALTER BRADFORD. (1945) The way of an investigator, a scientist's experiences in medical research. New York: W. W. Norton and Company, Inc., 229 pp.
COHEN, I. BERNARD. (1942) Newton and the modern world. American Scholar, vol. 11, pp. 328–338.
COHEN, I. BERNARD. (1943 [1]) Isaac Newton (1643–1727). Sky and Telescope, vol. 2 (January), pp. 3–5.
COHEN, I. BERNARD. (1943 [2]) Benjamin Franklin and the mysterious Dr. Spence: the source and date of Franklin's interest in electricity. Journal of the Franklin Institute, vol. 235, pp. 1–25.
COHEN, I. BERNARD. (1947) For the education of the layman. The New York Times Book Review, 7 Sept. 1947, pp. 30, 32.
COHEN, I. BERNARD. See FRANKLIN (1941).
→ CONANT, JAMES B. (1947) On understanding science: an historical approach. New Haven: Yale University Press, xv + 146 pp.
    The Terry Lectures.
COOLIDGE, WILLIAM D. (1942) The role of science institutions in our civilization. Science, vol. 96, pp. 411–417.
DIETZ, DAVID. (1942) Science and the future. American Scholar, vol. 11, pp. 292–303.
ENESTRÖM, GUSTAF. (1910, 1913) Verzeichnis der Schriften Leonhard Eulers. Jahresbericht d. Deutschen Mathematiker-Vereinigung, d. Ergänzungsbände IV. Bd., 1. Lieferung, pp. 1–208; 2. Lieferung, pp. 209–388.
FORD, GUY STANTON. (1933) Science and civilization. Minneapolis: The University of Minnesota Press (The Day and Hour Series, no. 1), 29 pp.
[FRANKLIN, BENJAMIN]. (1941) Benjamin Franklin's experiments: a new edition of Franklin's "Experiments and observations on electricity." Edited with a critical and historical introduction by I. Bernard Cohen. Cambridge: Harvard University Press, xxviii + 453 pp.
GRAY, GEORGE J. (1907) A bibliography of the works of Sir Isaac Newton, together with a list of books illustrating his works. Second edition, revised and enlarged. Cambridge: Bowes and Bowes, vi + 80 pp.
GRUNDFEST, HARRY. See MATHER, GRUNDFEST, PHILLIPS. (1944).
KOENIG, FREDERICK O. (1943) Science and the humanities. The Humanities Look Ahead; Report of the First Annual Conference held by the Stanford School of Humanities May 7 and 8, 1943, pp. 15–24.
KRIEGHBAUM, HILLIER. (1941) American newspaper reporting of science news. Kansas State College Bulletin (Industrial Journalism Series, 16), vol. 25, no. 5. 73 pp.
LINDSAY, R. B. (1942) The impact of science on contemporary civilization. Sigma Xi Quarterly, vol. 30, pp. 51–65.
LODGE, SIR OLIVER. (1927) Science and human progress. London: George Allen & Unwin, Ltd. (Halley Stewart Lectures 1926.) 187 pp.
LUCKIESH, M. (1929) Science as a source of ideas. Scientific Monthly, vol. 29, pp. 236–242.
MACLAURIN, W. RUPERT. (1947) Federal support for scientific research. Harvard Business Review, vol. 25, pp. 385–396.
MATHER, COTTON. (1721) The Christian philosopher: a collection of the best discoveries in nature, with religious improvements. London: Eman. Matthews, viii + 304 pp.
MATHER, KIRTLEY F.; GRUNDFEST, HARRY; PHILLIPS, MELBER. (1944) The Future of American science. New

York: United Office and Professional Workers of America, CIO, 19 pp.

MERTON, ROBERT K. (1942) A note on science and democracy. *Journal of Legal and Political Sociology*, vol. 1, pp. 115–126.

MITCHELL, WESLEY C. (1939) The public relations of science. *Science*, vol. 90, pp. 599–607.

NEWTON, ISAAC. (1931) *Opticks, or a treatise of the reflections, refractions, inflections & colours of light*. Reprinted from the fourth edition (London, 1730) with a foreword by Albert Einstein and an introduction by E. T. Whittaker. London: G. Bell & Sons, Ltd., xxx + 414 pp.

NEWTON, ISAAC. (1934) *Mathematical principles of natural philosophy*. Translated into English by Andrew Motte in 1729. Revised, and supplied with an historical and explanatory appendix, by Florian Cajori. Editor's note by R. T. Crawford. Berkeley: University of California Press, xxxv + 680 pp.

NICOLSON, MARJORIE HOPE. (1946) *Newton demands the muse: Newton's "Opticks" and the eighteenth century poets*. Princeton: Princeton University Press, xi + 177 pp.

PHILLIPS, MELBER. *See* MATHER, GRUNDFEST, PHILLIPS. (1944)

RANDALL, JOHN HERMAN, JR. (1940) *The making of the modern mind, a survey of the intellectual background of the present age*. Revised edition. Boston: Houghton Mifflin Company, xii + 696 pp.
Especially Book III, on the effects of Newtonianism.

SARTON, GEORGE. (1921) Herbert Spencer. *Isis*, vol. 3, pp. 375–390.

SARTON, GEORGE. (1936) *The study of the history of science*. Cambridge: Harvard University Press, 75 pp.

SARTON, GEORGE. (1937) *The history of science and the new humanism*. Cambridge: Harvard University Press, xx + 196 pp.

SCHRECKER, PAUL. (1946) Descartes and Leibniz in 1946, on their 350th and 300th birthdays. *Philosophy, Journal of the British Institute of Philosophy*, vol. 21, pp. 205–233.

[SCIENTIFIC RESEARCH]. (1944) *Scientific research and development; pre-sented by the Lord President of the Council to Parliament by command of His Majesty, April, 1944*. London: Printed and Published by His Majesty's Stationery Office, 12 pp.

SIGERIST, HENRY E. (1944) The history of science in postwar education. *Science*, vol. 100, pp. 415–420.

★ SMITH, PRESERVED. (1934) *A history of modern culture*, vol. 2, The enlightenment. New York: Henry Holt and Company, vii + 703 pp.
Especially ch. iv, "The place of science in eighteenth-century thought."

★ STEELMAN, JOHN R. (1947) *Science and public policy*. Vol. 1, A program for the nation. Washington, D. C.: U. S. Government Printing Office, x + 73 pp. Report of the President's Scientific Research Board; the first of 5 vols. See comments by Robert W. King in *Science*, 31 Oct. 1947, p. 415.

TANSLEY, A. G. (1942) *The values of science to humanity: The Herbert Spencer Lecture, Oxford University, 2 June, 1942*. London: George Allen & Unwin, Ltd., 31 pp.

WADDINGTON, C. H. (1941) *The scientific attitude*. Harmondsworth, Eng.: Penguin Books, Ltd. (Pelican Books, A84), 128 pp.

WATSON, D. M. S. (1942) *Science and government, being the twenty-fourth Earl Grey Memorial Lecture delivered at King's College, Newcastle upon Tyne, 1st May, 1942*. Newcastle upon Tyne: King's College, 26 pp.

WEAVER, WARREN. (1929) Science and imagination. *The Scientific Monthly*, vol. 29, pp. 425–434.

→ WOLF, A. (1935) *A history of science, technology, and philosophy in the 16th & 17th centuries*. New York: The Macmillan Company (History of Science Library), xxvii + 692 pp.

→ WOLF, A. (1939) *A history of science, technology, and philosophy in the eighteenth century*. New York: The Macmillan Company (History of Science Library), 814 pp.

Chapter 1: Notes

1 Quoted in *Bush* (1945), p. 7.
2 *Steelman* (1947), pp. 30–31.

3 This idea has been developed in *Cohen* (1947).

4 *Eneström* (1910, 1913), pp. 80–94.

5 *Gray* (1907), pp. 41–42.

6 *Ibid.*, p. 33.

7 *Ibid.*, p. 31.

8 Quoted in *Nicolson* (1946), pp. 15–16.

9 On this point, see *Cohen* (1943 [1]).

10 See *Becker* (1940), pp. 43 ff.

11 *Cohen* (1943 [2]).

12 Quoted in *Franklin* (1941), preface, p. x.

13 See *Schrecker* (1946), pp. 217 ff.

14 *Newton* (1931), p. 1.

15 *Cannon* (1945), p. 34.

16 See *Sarton* (1921).

17 *Conant* (1947), p. 11.

18 *Ibid.*, p. 19.

19 *Ibid.*, p. 18.

CHAPTER 2: CONDITIONS OF SCIENTIFIC DISCOVERY

Bibliography and Guide to Further Reading

CARLSON, ANTON J. (1940) The role of the fundamental sciences in medical progress. *Scientific Monthly*, vol. 50, pp. 59–64.

→ CHAIN, E., and FLOREY, H. W. (1944) Penicillin. *Endeavour*, vol. 3, pp. 3–14.

CHAIN, E. *See* FLOREY and CHAIN (1944).

CHANDLER, ASA CRAWFORD. (1944) Biology and medicine. *Annual Report of the Board of Regents of the Smithsonian Institution*, pp. 317–330. ". . . Reprinted by permission from *The Rice Institute Pamphlet*, vol. 30, no. 4, October, 1943."

★ CREW, HENRY. (1935) *The rise of modern physics*. Second edition. Baltimore: The Williams and Wilkins Company, xix + 434 pp.

CUSHING, HARVEY. *See* FULTON and CUSHING (1936).

DALE, H. H. (1924) Progress and prospects in chemotherapy. *Science*, vol. 60, pp. 185–191.

DALE, SIR HENRY H. (1933) Academic and industrial research in the field of therapeutics. *Science*, vol. 77, pp. 521–527.

An address delivered at the opening ceremony of the Research Laboratories of Merck and Company, Inc., Rahway, New Jersey, April 25, 1933.

→ DE KRUIF, PAUL. (1943) *Microbe hunters*. New York: Pocket Books, Inc. (Pocket Book no. 49), 400 pp.

★ DUBOS, RENÉ J. and HOTCHKISS, ROLLIN D. (1942) Origin, nature and properties of gramicidin and tyrocidine. *Transactions & Studies of the College of Physicians of Philadelphia*, vol. 10, fourth series, pp. 11–19.

★ DUBOS, RENÉ J. (1944) Trends in the study and control of infectious diseases. *Proceedings of the American Philosophical Society*, vol. 88, pp. 208–213.

★ DUBOS, RENÉ J. (1945) *The bacterial cell in its relation to problems of virulence, immunity and chemotherapy*. With an addendum by C. F. Robinow. Cambridge: Harvard University Press (Harvard University Monographs in Medicine and Public Health), xix + 460 pp.

→ EPSTEIN, SAMUEL, and WILLIAMS, BERYL (1946) *Miracles from microbes, the road to streptomycin*. With an introduction by Maj. Gen. Norman T. Kirk. New Brunswick: Rutgers University Press, xii + 155 pp.

★ FLOREY, H. W., and CHAIN, E. (1944) The development of penicillin in medicine. *Annual Report of the Board of Regents of the Smithsonian Institution*, pp. 461–466. "Reprinted by permission from *Hygeia*, vol. 22, no. 4, April, 1944."

FLOREY, H. W. *See* CHAIN and FLOREY (1944).

★ FULTON, JOHN F., and CUSHING, HARVEY (1936) A bibliographical study of the Galvani and the Aldini writings on animal electricity. *Annals of Science*, vol. 1, pp. 239–268.

→ FULTON, JOHN F. (1937) *Sir Kenelm Digby, writer, bibliophile, and protagonist of William Harvey*. New York: Peter & Katharine Oliver, 75 pp.

→ FULTON, JOHN F. (1945) Penicillin, plasma, plasma fractionation, and the physician. *Atlantic Monthly*, vol. 1, September, pp. 107–114.

★ GALDSTON, IAGO. (1939) The ideological basis of discovery. *Bulletin of the History of Medicine*, vol. 7, pp. 729–7

GALDSTON, IAGO. (1940 [1]) Some notes on the early history of chemotherapy. *Bulletin of the History of Medicine,* vol. 8, pp. 806–818.

GALDSTON, IAGO. (1940 [2]) *Progress in medicine, a critical review of the last hundred years.* With a foreword by Henry E. Sigerist. New York, London: Alfred A. Knopf, ix + 347 + xiv pp.

GALDSTON, IAGO. (1943) *Behind the sulfa drugs, a short history of chemotherapy.* With a preface by Perrin H. Long. New York, London: D. Appleton-Century Company, Incorporated, xx + 174 pp.

GARROD, L. P. (1942) Progress in bacterial chemotherapy. *Endeavour,* vol. 1, pp. 122–125.

GREGG, ALAN. (1941) *The furtherance of medical research.* New Haven: Yale University Press, ix + 129 pp. The Terry Lectures.

HENDERSON, LAWRENCE J. (1935) The relation of medicine to the fundamental sciences. *Science,* vol. 82, pp. 477–481.

HOTCHKISS, ROLLIN D. *See* DUBOS and HOTCHKISS (1942).

KEEFER, CHESTER S. (1944) The present status of penicillin in the treatment of infections. *Proceedings of the American Philosophical Society,* vol. 88, pp. 174–176.

[MERCK & CO., INC.]. (1945) *Penicillin: brochure with annotated bibliography.* Rahway, N. J.: Merck & Co., Inc., 191 pp.

[MERCK & CO., INC.]. (1946) *Penicillin: brochure with bibliography, supplement 1946.* Rahway, N. J.: Merck & Co., Inc., 73 pp.

NORTHROP, F. S. C. (1938) The history of modern physics in its bearing upon biology and medicine. *Yale Journal of Biology and Medicine,* vol. 10, pp. 209–232.

[PENICILLIN]. (1944) Penicillin number. *MSN: Monthly Science News,* No. 41, pp. 1–12.

POTAMIAN, Brother, and WALSH, JAMES J. (1909) *Makers of electricity.* New York: Fordham University Press, vi + 404 pp. Contains a chapter on Galvani and one on Volta.

RATCLIFF, J. D. (1945) *Yellow magic, the story of penicillin.* With a foreword by Chester Keefer. New York: Random House, xvi + 173 pp.

★ SARTON, GEORGE. (1931) The discovery of the electric cell (1800). *Isis,* vol. 15, pp. 124–157. Contains a facsimile reprint of Volta's paper, with comments.

→ SIGERIST, HENRY E. (1941) *Medicine and Human welfare.* New Haven: Yale University Press, ix + 148 pp.

→ SOKOLOFF, BORIS. (1945) *The story of penicillin.* Chicago, New York: Ziff-Davis Publishing Company, xii + 167 pp.

SPINK, WESLEY W. (1940) Sulfanilamide and related chemicals in the treatment of infectious diseases. *Annual Report of the Board of Regents of the Smithsonian Institution,* pp. 479–488.

→ VALLERY-RADOT, RENÉ. (1926) *The Life of Pasteur.* Translated from the French by Mrs. R. L. Devonshire, with an introduction by Sir William Osler. Garden City, N. Y.: Garden City Publishing Co., Inc., xxi + 484 pp.

★ VOLTA, ALESSANDRO. (1800) On the electricity excited by the mere contact of conducting substances of different kinds. *Philosophical Transactions,* vol. 90, pp. 403–431.

★ WAKSMAN, SELMAN A. (1945) Soil microbiology as a field of science. *Science,* vol. 102, pp. 339–344.

→ WHEWELL, WILLIAM. (1860) *On the philosophy of discovery, chapters historical and critical; including the completion of the third edition of the philosophy of the inductive sciences.* London: John W. Parker and Son, xvi + 531 pp.

WILLIAMS, BERYL. *See* EPSTEIN AND WILLIAMS (1946).

Chapter 2: Notes

1 *Fulton* (1937), pp. 28, 33–35.
2 *Ratcliff* (1945), pp. 16, 17.
3 *Ibid.,* p. 19.
4 *Merck* (1945), p. 3.
5 Quoted *ibid.*
6 *Galdston* (1943), p. 48.
7 Quoted *ibid.,* p. 128.
8 R. Hilgermann, quoted *ibid.,* p. 140.
9 *Vallery-Radot* (1926), p. 299.
10 *Epstein and Williams* (1946), pp. 80 ff.

11 *Ibid.*, pp. 81–82.
12 *Ibid.*, p. 82.
13 *Dubos and Hotchkiss* (1942).
14 *Epstein and Williams* (1946), p. 97.
15 *Ibid.*
16 *Chain and Florey* (1944), p. 4.
17 *Ibid.*; cf. *Florey and Chain* (1944).
18 *Fulton and Cushing* (1936).
19 *Crew* (1935), pp. 192–193.

Chapter 3: The "Happy Accident" and Its Consequences

Bibliography and Guide to Further Reading

→ ARTHUS, MAURICE. (1943) *Philosophy of scientific investigation.* Preface to *De l'anaphylaxie à l'immunité*, Paris, 1921. Translated from the French, with an introduction by Henry E. Sigerist. Foreword by Warfield T. Longcope. Baltimore: The Johns Hopkins Press, ii + 26 pp.
   Reprinted from *Bulletin of the History of Medicine*, vol. 14 (1943), pp. 366–390.

BARKER, GEORGE F. *See* RÖNTGEN (1899).

BEAUMONT, WILLIAM. (1941) *Experiments and observations on the gastric juice and the physiology of digestion.* Facsimile of the original edition of 1883, together with a biographical essay, "A pioneer American physiologist," by Sir William Osler. New York: Peter Smith, xl + 280 pp.

BOVERI, MARGARET. *See* GLASSER (1934).

→ CANNON, W. B. (1940) The role of chance in discovery. *Scientific Monthly,* vol. 50, pp. 204–209.

→ CANNON, WALTER BRADFORD. (1945) *The way of an investigator, a scientist's experiences in medical research.* New York: W. W. Norton and Company, Inc., 299 pp.

COHEN, I. BERNARD. (1946) Authenticity of scientific anecdotes. *Nature,* vol. 157, pp. 196–197.
   Discusses the authenticity of the anecdote concerning Newton and the apple.

→ COMPTON, KARL T. (1938) Universities and the public welfare. *Addresses:*

Dedication of the Research Building, Abbott Laboratories, North Chicago, Illinois. North Chicago: Abbott Laboratories, pp. 9–16.

→ DICKINSON, H. W., and VOWLES, H. P. (1944) *James Watt and the industrial revolution.* London: Published for the British Council by Longmans Green & Company (Science in Britain), 59 pp.

★ GLASSER, OTTO. (1934) *Wilhelm Conrad Röntgen and the early history of the roentgen rays.* With a chapter, "Personal reminiscences of W. C Röntgen," by Margaret Boveri. Springfield, Illinois: Charles C. Thomas, xi + 494 pp.

HICKEY, PRESTON M. (1931) The progress of roentgenology and its contribution to medical science. *Science* vol. 73, pp. 627–632.

JAUNCEY, G. E. M. (1945) The birth and early infancy of x-rays. *American Journal of Physics,* vol. 13, pp. 362 379.

LONGCOPE, WARFIELD T. *See* ARTHU (1943).

→ McLEAN, FRANKLIN C. (1941) Th happy accident. *Scientific Monthl* vol. 53, pp. 61–70.

RICHET, CHARLES. (1923) *Le savar* Paris: Librairie Hachette, 126 pp.

→ RAYLEIGH, LORD. (1936) Some reminiscences of scientific workers of the p generation, and their surroundin, *Proceedings of the Physical Socie* London, vol. 48, pp. 217–246.

★ RÖNTGEN, W. C. (1899) *Röntgen ra memoirs by Röntgen, Stokes a J. J. Thomson.* Translated and edi by George F. Barker. New York a London: Harper & Brothers P lishers (Harper's Scientific Memo edited by J. S. Ames), vi + 76 pp.

★ SARTON, GEORGE. (1937) The discov of x-rays. *Isis,* vol. 26, pp. 349–369.
   Contains a facsimile of Roentg original publication of 1896.

→ SARTON, GEORGE. (1936). *The study the history of science.* Cambri Harvard University Press, 75 pp.

SIGERIST, HENRY E. *See* ARTHUS (19

STOKES, G. G. *See* RÖNTGEN (1899)

THOMSON, J. J. *See* RÖNTGEN (1899)

★ THURSTON, ROBERT H. (1878) *A hi of the growth of the steam-eng* New York: D. Appleton and Com

(The International Scientific Series),
xviii + 490 pp.

VOWLES, H. P. *See* DICKINSON (1947).

Chapter 3: Notes

1 *Cannon* (1945), p. 71.
2 *Ibid.*, pp. 71–72; cf. *Richet* (1923).
3 *Arthus* (1943), pp. 18–19.
4 *Cohen* (1946).
5 *Sarton* (1936), p. 51.
6 *Rayleigh* (1936).
7 *Glasser* (1934), pp. 222–223, 279.
8 Cf. *Jauncey* (1945); *Sarton* (1937);
   Röntgen (1899); *Glasser* (1934).
9 Quoted in *Cannon* (1945), p. 76.
10 *Rayleigh* (1936).
11 Probably a common experience!
12 *Beaumont* (1941).
13 *Dickinson and Vowles* (1944), p. 31.
14 *Ibid.*
15 *Thurston* (1878), p. 101.
16 From *Compton* (1938).
17 *Cohen* (1946).
18 *Ibid.*
19 *Ibid.*

CHAPTER 4: THE SPECTRUM OF SCIENTIFIC ACTIVITY

Bibliography and Guide to Further Reading

ADAMS, CHARLES C. (1940) Selected references on the relation of science to modern life. *New York State Museum Bulletin 322: One Hundred Second Report of the New York State Museum*, pp. 79–96.

BABBAGE, CHARLES. (1832) *On the economy of machinery and manufactures.* Philadelphia: Carey & Lea, xix + 282 pp.

BAKER, JOHN R. (1945) The threat to pure science. *Science*, vol. 101, pp. 300–301.

BIRKHOFF, GEORGE D. (1938) Intuition, reason and faith in science. *Science*, vol. 88, pp. 601–609.

BLACKWELDER, ELIOT. (1941) Science and human prospects. *Science*, vol. 93, pp. 359–366.

BOGGS, S. W. (1945) Mapping some of the effects of science and technology on human relations. *The Department of State Bulletin*, vol. 12, pp. 183–188.

➤ BOYD, T. A. (1935) *Research, the pathfinder of science and industry.* New York: D. Appleton-Century Company, xv + 319 pp.

➤ BRIDGMAN, P. W. (1945) The prospect for intelligence. *The Yale Review*, vol. 34, pp. 444–461.

BUTT, NEWBERN I. *See* HARRIS (1924).

★ CARTY, JOHN J. (1916) The relation of pure science to industrial research. *Science*, vol. 44, n.s., pp. 511–518.

COLBY, CHARLES W. (1939) *The historical background of applied science.* New York: The Newcomen Society, American Branch, 36 pp.

COMPTON, KARL T. (1933 [1]) The battle of the alchemists. *Annual Report of the Board of Regents of the Smithsonian Institution*, pp. 269–282.
   ". . . Reprinted by permission from *The Technology Review*, vol. 35, no. 5, February, 1933."

COMPTON, KARL T. (1933 [2]) High voltage. *Science*, vol. 78, pp. 19–24, 48–52.

➤ COMPTON, KARL T. (1938) *The social implications of scientific discovery; delivered at the American Philosophical Society, Independence Square, Philadelphia, March 15, 1938.* Philadelphia: American Philosophical Society, 33 pp. Jayne Memorial Lecture.

★ COMPTON, KARL T. (1941) Industrial research expenditures. *Research — a national resource. II. Industrial research. Report of the National Research Council to the National Resources Planning Board.* Washington: United States Government Printing Office, pp. 124–125.

➤ CONANT, JAMES B. (1944) The advancement of learning in the United States in the postwar world. *Proceedings of the American Philosophical Society*, vol. 87, pp. 291–298.

★ CONANT, JAMES BRYANT. (1945) National research argued. [A letter to the editor of *The New York Times*, dated 10 August 1945].

★ CONANT, JAMES B. (1947) Science and the practical arts. *Harvard Business Review*, vol. 25, pp. 545–553.

COOLIDGE, WILLIAM D. (1937) Research in a large industry. *Armour Engineer and Alumnus*, vol. 3, pp. 9–11, 38.

★ COOLIDGE, WILLIAM D. (1940) *Research and invention: statement . . . before the Temporary National Economic Committee.* Schenectady: General Electric Company, 14 pp.

COOLIDGE, WILLIAM D. (1940) The Research Laboratory of the General Electric Company. *Science*, vol. 92, pp. 594–595.

★ COOPER UNION LIBRARY, THE. (1946) A guide to the literature on the history of engineering available in the Cooper Union Library. *Cooper Union Bulletin*, Engineering and Science Series, Number 28, ix + 46 pp.

DANFORTH, RALPH E. (1929) Tools of progress. *The Scientific Monthly*, vol. 29, pp. 83–86.

★ DARROW, KARL K. (1944) Discussion on the symposium "Organization, direction, and support of research." *Proceedings of the American Philosophical Society*, vol. 87, pp. 321–322.

★ DESCH, CECIL H. (1931) Pure and applied science. *Science*, vol. 74, pp. 495–502.

DOWNES, ROBERT B. (1946) Where are America's research resources? *Scientific Monthly*, vol. 62, pp. 511–516.

→ EVANS, HERBERT M. (1938) The spirit and task of research. *Addresses. Dedication of Research Building, Abbott Laboratories, North Chicago, Illinois.* North Chicago: Abbott Laboratories, pp. 17–26.

★ FARNHAM, DWIGHT T., et al. (1925) *Profitable science in industry.* Foreword by S. W. Stratton. New York: The Macmillan Company, x + 291 pp.

Contains contributions by James A. Hall, R. W. King, and H. E. Howe.

FIELD, PHILIP M. *See* PERAZICH and FIELD (1940).

[FRANKLIN, BENJAMIN]. (1941) *Benjamin Franklin's experiments: a new edition of Franklin's "Experiments and observations on electricity."* Edited with a critical and historical introduction by I. Bernard Cohen. Cambridge: Harvard University Press, xxviii + 453 pp.

→ GALDSTON, IAGO. (1946) The history of research, with particular regard to medical research. *Ciba Symposia*, vol. 8, pp. 338–372.

GERARD, RALPH W. (1938) The role of pure science. *Science*, vol. 88, pp. 361–368.

[GOLDWATER MEMORIAL HOSPITAL]. (1945) *Research; an experiment in municipal organization.* New York: Department of Hospitals, 74 pp.

→ GREGG, ALAN. (1945) The essential need of fundamental research for social progress. *Science*, vol. 101, pp. 257–259.

HAMOR, WILLIAM A. (1945) Human aspects of scientific research. *Science*, vol. 102, pp. 237–241.

★ HARRIS, FRANKLIN STEWART, and BUTT, NEWBERN I. (1924) *Scientific research and human welfare.* New York: The Macmillan Company, ix + 406 pp.

★ HIRSHFELD, C. F. (1938) *Industrial research; an address delivered before Princeton University on November 10 1936, in the Cyrus Fogg Brackett Lectureship in applied engineering and technology.* With a foreword by Arthur M. Greene, Jr. Princeton: The Guild of Brackett Lectures, 27 pp.

HOLLAND, MAURICE. (1931) Industrial science — a gilt edge security. *Science*, vol. 74, pp. 279–282.

★ HUGHES, RAYMOND H. (1938) Research in American universities and colleges. *Research — a natural resource. I. — Relation of the federal government to research. Report of the Science Committee to the National Resources Committee.* Washington: United States Government Printing Office, pp. 167–193.

JAMES, F. CYRIL. (1941) Science and society. *Scientific Monthly*, vol. 53, pp. 51–60.

JEWETT, F. B. (1932) The social effects of modern science. *Science*, vol. 76, pp. 23–26.

JEWETT, FRANK B. (1932) Problems of the engineer. *Science*, vol. 75, pp. 255–256.

→ JEWETT, FRANK B. (1939) Research in industry. *Scientific Monthly*, vol. 48, pp. 195–202.

JOHNSTON, JOHN. (1939) Applications of science to the metallurgical industry. *Scientific Monthly*, vol. 48, pp. 495–503.

LANGMUIR, IRVING. (1935) Fundamental industrial research. *General Electric Review*, vol. 38, pp. 324–333.

LANGMUIR, IRVING. (1937) Fundamental research and its human value. *General Electric Review*, vol. 40, pp. 569–573.

LINDSAY, R. B. (1942) The impact of science on contemporary civilization. *Sigma Xi Quarterly*, vol. 30, pp. 51–65.

LOVELL, BERNARD. (1939) *Science and civilization*. London: Thomas Nelson and Sons, Ltd., x + 150 pp.
". . . a plea for the interpretation of science to the public in its social context." In addition to much interpretive material, it contains many statistical data on the universities and "the existing structure of research," chiefly in Great Britain.

LOW, A. M. (1939) *Science in industry*. London: Oxford University Press, 160 pp.

[MAXWELL, JAMES CLERK.] (   ) *The scientific papers* of James Clerk Maxwell. Edited by W. D. Niven. Vol. 2. Paris, Librairie Scientifique J. Hermann, viii + 806 pp. (A reprint of the 1890 edition published by Cambridge University Press.)
Especially the Rede Lecture on the telephone, pp. 743–755.

MERTON, ROBERT K. (1938) Science, technology and society in seventeenth-century England. *Osiris*, vol. 4, pp. 360–632.

MEES, C. E. KENNETH. (1920) *The organization of industrial scientific research*. New York: McGraw-Hill Book Company, Inc., ix + 175 pp.

MERRIAM, JOHN C. (1920) The research spirit in everyday life of the average man. *Science*, vol. 52, pp. 473–478.

MITCHELL, WESLEY C. (1939) The public relations of science. *Science*, vol. 90, pp. 599–607.

MUMFORD, LEWIS. (1934) *Technics and civilization*. New York: Harcourt Brace and Company, xi + 495 pp.

PASTEUR, LOUIS. (1871) Pourquoi la France n'a pas trouvé d'hommes supérieurs au moment du péril. *Revue scientifique*, 2ᵉ Sér., vol. 1, pp. 73–77.

PERAZICH, GEORGE, and FIELD, PHILIP M. (1940) *Industrial research and changing technology*. Philadelphia: Works Progress Administration, National Research Project (Studies in Equipment Changes and Industrial Techniques), xii + 81 pp.
"Report No. M-4."

★ PLEDGE, H. T. (1939) *Science since 1500, a short history of mathematics, physics, chemistry, biology*. London: His Majesty's Stationery Office, 357 pp.
By all odds, the best one-volume history of modern science. Points out applications of discoveries and discusses backgrounds of both discoverers and their work.

PORTERFIELD, AUSTIN L. (1941) *Creative factors in scientific research. A social psychology of scientific knowledge studying the interplay of psychological and cultural factors in science with emphasis upon imagination*. Durham, North Carolina: Duke University Press, xi + 282 pp.

→ QUINE, W. V. (1939) Relations and reason: how mathematical logic throws switches for Institute engineers, outlines clauses for actuaries, and provides amusement for the puzzle-minded. *The Technology Review*, vol. 41, pp. 299–301, 324–327.

★ ROWLAND, HENRY AUGUSTUS. (1883) A plea for pure science. *Proceedings of the American Association for the Advancement of Science* (August, 1883), pp. 105–126.

SODDY, FREDERICK. (1920) *Science and Life, Aberdeen Addresses*. New York: E. P. Dutton and Company, xii + 229 pp.
Especially "Physical force — man's servant or his master?", pp. 25–42; "Chemistry and national prosperity," pp. 43–48; "Science and the state," pp. 49–64; "The future of science, and what bars the way," pp. 65–84; "The ideals of a science school," pp. 181–206.

★ STANDARD OIL DEVELOPMENT CO. (1945) *The future of industrial research: papers and discussion*. New York: Standard Oil Development Co., viii + 173 pp.
A most valuable and interesting symposium, by leaders of business and of military, industrial, and academic scientific research.

STEELMAN, JOHN R. (1947) *Science and public policy*. Vol. 1, a program for the nation. Washington, D. C.: U. S.

Government Printing Office, x + 73 pp.

Report of the President's Scientific Research Board.

★ STINE, CHARLES M. A. (1941) Fundamental research in industry. *Research — a national resource. II. — Industrial research. Report of the National Research Council to the National Resources Planning Board.* Washington: United States Government Printing Office, pp. 98–107.

See, also, other titles by Dr. Stine, listed under Chapter 8, "Synthetic Rubber and Nylon."

SWENSON, T. L. (1946) Research on agricultural products. *The Scientific Monthly,* vol. 62, pp. 525–537.

★ TAYLOR, HUGH S. (1944) The organization, direction, and support of research in the physical sciences. *Proceedings of the American Philosophical Society,* vol. 87, pp. 299–306.

WALLACE, R. C. (1938) The changing values of science. *Science,* vol. 88, pp. 265–271.

WARREN, BERTRAM E. (1941) Glassy geometry: how the properties of glass depend on atomic arrangement; research finds ways to correlate the two. *The Technology Review,* vol. 43, pp. 253–255, 273–274.

WEIDLEIN, EDWARD R. (1926) The administration of industrial research. *Industrial and Engineering Chemistry,* vol. 18, pp. 98–101

★ WHITNEY, WILLIS R. (1931) Technology and material progress. *Proceedings of the American Philosophical Society,* vol. 70, pp. 255–262.

★ WHITNEY, WILLIS R. (1933) The relation of science to industry. *Harvard Business Review,* vol. 11, pp. 445–456.

WILLIAMS, C. C. (1940) Decisive inventions versus decisive battles. [New York]: The Newcomen Society, American Branch, 36 pp.

Chapter 4: Notes

1 *Bridgman* (1945).
2 *O. E. D.*
3 *Ibid.*
4 *Ibid.*
5 *Ibid.*
6 *Babbage* (1832).
7 *Pasteur* (1871).
8 *Conant* (1945).
9 From *Steelman* (1947).
10 Quotation from *Stine* (1941).
11 Taken from *Stine* (1941).
12 *Ibid.*
13 *Maxwell* (   ), vol. 2, p. 743.
14 *Rowland* (1883).

CHAPTER 5: PRACTICAL APPLICATIONS OF FUNDAMENTAL RESEARCH

Bibliography and Guide to Further Reading

★ AGRICOLA, GEORGIUS. (1912) *De re metallica.* Translated from the first Latin edition of 1556, with biographical introduction, annotations and appendices upon the development of mining methods, metallurgical processes, geology, mineralogy and mining law from the earliest times to the 16th century. By Herbert Clark Hoover and Lou Henry Hoover. London: The Mining Magazine, xxxi + 640 pp.

ADAM, NEIL KENSINGTON. (1938) *The physics and chemistry of surfaces.* Second edition. Oxford: at the Clarendon Press, x + 402 pp.

→ ALLEN, H. STANLEY. (1932) *Electrons and waves; an introduction to atomic physics.* London: Macmillan and Co. Limited, vii + 336 pp.

AUSTIN, ÉLAINE. *See* SHAW (1936).

★ BEECHING, R. (1936) *Electron diffraction.* With a preface by G. P. Thomson. London: Methuen and Co., I (Methuen's Monographs on Physical Subjects), viii + 107 pp.

→ CASTIGLIONI, ARTURO. (1946) *A history of medicine.* Translated from the Italian and edited by E. B. Krumbhaar. New York: Alfred A. Knopf, xxv + 1013 + xl pp.

★ CLARK, GEORGE L. (1944) Electron diffraction. *Medical physics,* edited by Otto Glasser. Chicago: The Year Book Publishers, Inc., pp. 379–387.

COCHRANE, W. *See* THOMSON & COCHRANE (1939).

COHEN, I. BERNARD. (1942) The astronomical work of Galileo Galilei (1564–1642). *Sky and Telescope,* 1, pp. 3–5.

COHEN, I. BERNARD. (1945) How practical was Benjamin Franklin's science? *Pennsylvania Magazine of History and Biography,* vol. 69, pp. 284–293.

→ CONANT, JAMES B. (1947) *On understanding science, an historical approach.* New Haven: Yale University Press, xv + 145 pp. The Terry Lectures.

CREW, HENRY. *See* GALILEO (1914).

→ DARROW, KARL K. (1937) *The renaissance of physics.* New York: The Macmillan Company, ix + 306 pp.

★ DAVISSON, C. J., and GERMER, L. H. (1927) Diffraction of electrons by a crystal of nickel. *The Physical Review,* vol. 30, second series, pp. 705–740.

DAVISSON, C. J. (1929) Electrons and quanta. *Journal of the Optical Society of America and Review of Scientific Instruments,* vol. 18, pp. 193–201.

DAVISSON, C. J. (1929) The scattering of electrons by crystals. *Scientific Monthly,* vol. 28, pp. 41–51.

★ DAVISSON, C. J. (1932) The conception and demonstration of electron waves. *Bell System Technical Journal,* vol. 11, pp. 546–562.

DAVISSON, C. J. (1937) What electrons can tell us about metals. *Journal of Applied Physics,* vol. 8, pp. 391–397.

— DE BROGLIE, LOUIS. (1937) *La physique nouvelle et les quanta.* Paris: Ernest Flammarion, Editeur (Bibliotheque de philosophie scientifique), 307 pp.

— DE BROGLIE, LOUIS. (1939) *Matter and light; the new physics.* Translated by W. H. Johnston. New York: W. W. Norton and Co., Inc., Publishers, 300 pp.

DE SALVIO, ALFONSO. *See* GALILEO (1914).

FAVARO, ANTONIO. *See* GALILEO (1914).

[FRANKLIN, BENJAMIN]. (1941) *Benjamin Franklin's experiments: a new edition of Franklin's "Experiments and observations on electricity."* Edited with a critical and historical introduction by I. Bernard Cohen. Cambridge: Harvard University Press, xxviii + 453 pp.

GALILEO, GALILEI. (1914) *Dialogues concerning two new sciences.* Translated from the Italian and Latin by Henry Crew and Alfonso de Salvio, with an introduction by Antonio Favaro. New York: The Macmillan Company, xxiii + 300 pp.

Reissued by Macmillan 1933; by the Editorial Board of Northwestern University Studies, Evanston and Chicago, Ill., 1939; reissued 1946.

★ GERMER, L. H. (1928) Optical experiments with electrons. *Journal of Chemical Education,* vol. 5, pp. 1041–1055, 1255–1271.

GERMER, L. H. *See* DAVISSON & GERMER (1927).

→ HOLLAND, MAURICE. (1928) Research, science, and invention. *A century of industrial progress,* edited by Frederic William Wile. Garden City, New York: Doubleday Doran & Company, Inc. (For the American Institute of the City of New York), pp. 312–334.

HOOVER, HERBERT CLARK. *See* AGRICOLA (1912).

HOOVER, LOU HENRY. *See* AGRICOLA (1912).

KRUMBHAAR, E. B. *See* CASTIGLIONI (1946).

★ MARTIN, THOMAS HENRI. (1928) Optical instruments erroneously attributed to the ancients. *Origin and development of the microscope,* edited by Alfred N. Disney in collaboration with Cyril F. Hill and Wilfred E. Watson Baker. London: The Royal Microscopical Society, pp. 44–65.

→ MILHAM, WILLIS I. (1941) *Time & timekeepers, including the history, construction, care, and accuracy of clocks and watches.* New York: The Macmillan Company, xix + 616 pp.

★ PASCAL, BLAISE. (1937) *The physical treatises of Pascal: the equilibrium of liquids, and the weight of the mass of the air.* Translated by I. H. B. and A. G. H. Spiers, with introduction and notes by Frederick Barry. New York: Columbia University Press (Records of Civilization, no. 28), xxviii + 181 pp. Contains selections from Galileo, and also Torricelli's letters in English translation.

ROSEN, EDWARD. (1947) *The naming of the telescope.* Foreword by Harlow Shapley. New York: Henry Schuman, xvi + 110 pp.

→ SHAW, Sir NAPIER. (1936) *Manual of Meteorology.* Vol. 1, Meteorology in history. (With the assistance of Elaine Austin.) Cambridge: At the University Press, xx + 339 pp.

SPIERS, I. B. H. *See* PASCAL (1937).

★ Thomson, G. P., and Cochrane, W. (1939) *Theory and practice of electron diffraction.* London: Macmillan and Co., Limited, xi + 334 pp.

→ Thomson, Sir J. J. (1928) *Beyond the electron.* Cambridge: at the University Press, 43 pp.
"A lecture given at Girton College on 3 Mar. 1928."

★ Usher, Abbott Payson. (1929) *A history of mechanical inventions.* New York: The McGraw-Hill Book Co.; xi + 401 pp.

→ White, Lynn, Jr. (1940) Technology and invention in the Middle Ages. *Speculum: a Journal of Mediaeval Studies,* vol. 15, pp. 141–159.

Chapter 5: Notes

1 *Galileo* (1914), p. 16.
2 See *Pascal* (1937), pp. 163–170.
3 *Pascal* (1937).
4 *Shaw* (1936), pp. 147–149.
5 *Franklin* (1941).
6 *Cohen* (1945).
7 E. B. Krumbhaar in *Castiglioni* (1946), pp. 591–592.
8 *Ibid.*
9 *White* (1940).
10 *Milham* (1941), pp. 473–474.
11 *Darrow* (1937).
12 *Clark* (1944).
13 *Ibid.*
14 *Holland* (1928), p. 318.
15 *Martin* (1928).
16 *Rosen* (1947).
17 *Cohen* (1942).
18 Personal communication from P. W. Bridgman.
19 *Conant* (1947), p. 23.
20 *Ibid.*

Chapter 6: Auxins and Agriculture

Bibliography and Guide to Further Reading

Batjer, L. P.; Marth, P. C. (1945) New materials for delaying fruit abscission of apples. *Science,* vol. 101, pp. 363–364.

Batjer, L. P. *See* Gardner (1939).

Bonner, J. (1937) Vitamin B_1 a growth factor for higher plants. *Science,* vol. 85, pp. 183–184.

[British Council, The]. (1945) Chemical control of fruit development. *MSN: Monthly Science News,* no. 49, pp. 2–3.

Carlson, Robert F. *See* Smith (1946).

★ Gardner, F. E.; Marth, Paul C.; and Batjer, L. P. (1939) Spraying with plant growth substances for control of the pre-harvest drop of apples. *Proceedings of the American Society for Horticultural Science,* vol. 37, pp. 415–428.

Hamner, Charles L. *See* Smith (1946).

Hamner, C. L.; Moulton, J. E.; and Tukey, H. B. (1946) Treatment of muck and manure with 2,4-dichlorophenoxyacetic acid to inhibit germination of weed seeds. *Science,* vol. 103 pp. 476–477.

★ Hildebrand, E. M. (1946[1]) War on weeds. *Science,* vol. 103, pp. 465–468
A good general survey.

Hildebrand, E. M. (1946[2]) Herbicidal action of 2,4-dichlorophenoxyacetic acid on the water hyacinth, Eichornia crassipes. *Science,* vol. 103, pp. 477–479.

King, Joseph E., and Penfound, William T. (1946) Effects of new herbicides on fish. *Science,* vol. 103, p. 487.

→ Mangham, Sydney. (1939) *Earth's green mantle: plant science for the general reader.* Foreword by Sir Arthur W. Hill. New York: The Macmillan Company, 322 pp.

Marth, Paul C. *See* Gardner (1939).

Marth, P. C. *See* Batjer (1945).

★ Mitchell, John W.; and Rice, Ruby J. (1942) *Plant-growth regulators.* Washington, D. C.: United States Department of Agriculture (Miscellaneous Publication no. 495), 75 pp.

Mitchell, John W. *See* Stevens (1945).

Moulton, J. E. *See* Hamner (1946).

Offord, H. R. (1946) Rapid estimation of the phytocidal action of chemicals. *Science,* vol. 103, pp. 474–476.

Penfound, William T. *See* King (1946).

Robbins, W. J. (1922) Effect of autolized yeast and peptone on growth of e cised corn root tips in the dark. *Botanical Gazette*, vol. 74, pp. 59–79.

ROBBINS, W. J., and BARTLEY, M. A. (1937) Vitamin B_1 and the growth of excised tomato roots. *Science*, vol. 85, pp. 246–247.

ROBBINS, W. J. (1944) The importance of plants. *Science*, vol. 100, pp. 440–443.

SCHOPFER, W. H. (1943) *Plants and vitamins*. Authorized translation by N. L. Noecker. Foreword by W. J. Robbins. Waltham, Mass.: The Chronica Botanica Company, xiv + 293 pp.

SMITH, FREDERICK G.; HAMNER, CHARLES L.; and CARLSON, ROBERT F. (1946). Control of ragweed pollen production with 2,4-dichlorophenoxyacetic acid. *Science*, vol. 103, pp. 473–474.

SPECIAL PROJECTS DIVISION, CHEMICAL WARFARE SERVICE, Camp Detrick, Maryland. (1946) Plant growth regulators. *Science*, vol. 103, pp. 469–470.

STEVENSON, E. C., and MITCHELL, JOHN W. (1945) Bacteriostatic and bactericidal properties of 2,4-dichlorophenoxyacetic acid. *Science*, vol. 101, pp. 642–644.

TAYLOR, F. SHERWOOD. (1939) *Science front, 1939*. New York: The Macmillan Company, 301 pp.
Ch. 1, "Science and plant growth," pp. 11–37.

THIMANN, KENNETH V. *See* WENT (1937).

THIMANN, KENNETH V. (1941) Growth hormones in plants. *Annual Report of the Board of Regents of the Smithsonian Institution*, pp. 393–400.
". . . Reprinted by permission from the Journal of the Franklin Institute, vol. 229, no. 3, March, 1940."

THIMANN, KENNETH V. (1946[1]). *Growth hormones in plants.* 4 pp. [Planographed copy of paper read before "American Academy of Arts and Sciences, Regular Meeting, March 13, 1946."]

THIMANN, KENNETH V. (1946[2]) Plant hormones and the analysis of growth. *Currents in biochemical research*, edited by David E. Green. New York: Interscience Publishers, Inc., pp. 321–333.

TINCKER, M. A. H. (1941) Application of plant growth substances in practice. *Nature*, vol. 147, pp. 439–442.

TUKEY, H. B. *See* HAMNER (1946).

→ TUKEY, H. B. (1947) 2,4-D, a potent growth regulator of plants. *Scientific Monthly*, vol. 64, pp. 93–97.

★ VAN OVERBEEK, J. (1944) Growth-regulating substances in plants. *Annual Review of Biochemistry*, vol. 13, pp. 631–666.
Pp. 654 ff. are devoted to a summary of "practical aspects."

VAN OVERBEEK, J. (1945) Flower formation in the pineapple plant as controlled by 2,4-D and naphthaleneacetic acid. *Science*, vol. 102, p. 621.

VAN OVERBEEK, J., and VÉLEZ, ISMAEL. (1946) Use of 2,4-dichlorophenoxyacetic acid as a selective herbicide in the tropics. *Science*, vol. 103, pp. 472–473.

VÉLEZ, ISMAEL. *See* VAN OVERBEEK (1946).

★ WENT, F. W., and THIMANN, KENNETH V. (1937) *Phytohormones*. New York: The Macmillan Company (Experimental Biology Monographs), xi + 294 pp.
Although old, this is still a most useful work, especially for its excellent bibliography and for its generous historical material.

→ WENT, F. W. (1940) The regulation of plant growth. *Science in progress*, edited by George A. Baitsell, second series, pp. 33–54.
A splendid and eminently readable account.

→ WENT, F. W. (1943) The regulation of plant growth. *American Scientist*, vol. 31, pp. 189–210.

Chapter 6: Notes

1 *Hildebrand* (1946[1]), p. 465.
2 *Ibid.*
3 *Ibid.*
4 *Ibid.*
5 Quoted in *Went and Thimann* (1937), p. 10.
6 *Ibid.*
7 *Ibid.*, pp. 11–12.
8 *Thimann* (1946[1]), p. 1.
9 Quoted in *Went and Thimann* (1937), p. 3.
10 *Taylor* (1939), p. 19.

11 *Thimann* (1941), p. 397.
12 *Went and Thimann* (1937), ch. 11, "Root formation."
13 *Taylor* (1939), p. 21.
14 *Ibid.*, p. 24.
15 *Robbins* (1922); *Robbins and Bartley* (1937); *Bonner* (1937).
16 *Went* (1943), p. 192.
17 Personal communication from K. V. Thimann.
18 *Thimann* (1946), p. 3; *Van Overbeek* (1944), p. 654; *Gardner* et al. (1939).
19 *Hildebrand* (1946¹), p. 467; *Tukey* (1947), *Hamner* et al. (1946), *Van Overbeek and Vélez* (1946).
20 *Tukey* (1947).
21 Personal communication from K. V. Thimann.
22 Personal communication from Dr. Jas. K. Hunt of Du Pont.
23 Personal communication from F. W. Went.

CHAPTER 7: THE ELECTRIC CURRENT AND RADIO

Bibliography and Guide to Further Reading

→ APPLEYARD, ROLLO. (1931) *A tribute to Michael Faraday*. London: Constable & Co. Ltd., xiii + 203 pp.
A popular and readable account of Faraday and his discoveries.

ARCHER, GLEASON L. (1938) *History of radio to 1926*. New York: The American Historical Society, Inc., vi + 421 pp.

BRITISH COUNCIL, THE. (1945) Radar. *MSN: Monthly Science News*, no. 51, pp. 1–3.

→ CAMPBELL, LEWIS, and GARNETT, WILLIAM. (1882) *The life of James Clerk Maxwell, with a selection from his correspondence and occasional writings, and a sketch of his contributions to science*. London: Macmillan and Co., xvi + 662 pp.

COULTER, FRANCIS C. (1946) Sir Oliver Lodge, Lord Kelvin, and Hertzian waves. *Science*, vol. 104, p. 86.

★ FAHIE, J. J. (1901) *A history of wireless telegraphy, including some bare-wire proposals for subaqueous telegraphs*. Second edition, revised. Edinburgh

and London: William Blackwood a[nd] Sons, xxi + 348 pp.

★ FARADAY, MICHAEL. (1914) *Experimen[tal] researches in electricity*. London: J. [M.] Dent & Sons Ltd., New York: E. [P.] Dutton & Co., Inc. (Everyman's [Li-] brary), xix + 336 pp.

[FARADAY, M.] (1931) *A propos du ce[n-] tenaire des découvertes de Michel Fa[ra-] day, 1831–1931*. Paris: Société Fra[n-] çaise des Electriciens, 244 pp.

FIELD, HENRY M. (1866) *History of [the] Atlantic telegraph*. New York: Cha[rles] Scribner & Co., 364 pp.

GARNETT, WILLIAM. *See* CAMPBE[LL] (1882).

→ GLADSTONE, J. H. (1872) *Michael Fa[ra-] day*. London: Macmillan and C[o.,] vi + 176 pp.

HEADQUARTERS STAFF OF THE AMERIC[AN] RADIO RELAY LEAGUE. (1943) *T[he] radio amateur's handbook*. Twenti[eth] edition. West Hartford: The Americ[an] Radio Relay League, Incorpora[ted] 478 + 103 + 9 pp.

★ HERTZ, HEINRICH R. (1893) *Elec[tric] waves; being researches on the pro[pa-] gation of electric action with fi[nite] velocity through space*. Authori[zed] English translation by D. E. Jo[nes.] With a preface by Lord Kelvin. L[on-] don: Macmillan and Co., xv + 279 [pp.]

→ HIGGINS, THOMAS JAMES. (1945) Evo[lu-] tion of the three-phase 60-cycle al[ter-] nating-current system. *American Jo[ur-] nal of Physics*, vol. 13, pp. 32–36.

→ JOINT BOARD ON SCIENTIFIC INFORM[A-] TION POLICY. (1945) *Radar, a rep[ort] on science at war*. Washington: U. [S.] Government Printing Office, pp. iii [+] 53 pp.
"Released by the Joint Board on S[ci-] entific Information Policy for: [Of-] fice of Scientific Research and [De-] velopment, War Department, N[avy] Department."

★ JONES, BENCE. (1870) *The life and let[-] ters of Faraday*. 2 vols. London: Lo[ng-] mans, Green and Co., vol. 1, vi + [ ] pp.; vol. 2, 499 pp.
The standard biography.

KAEMPFFERT, WALDEMAR. (1924) [Sig-] nalling and talking by radio. *A Popu[-] lar History of American Invention,* [ed-] ited by Waldemar Kaempffert. N[ew] York: A. L. Burt Company, vol. [ ] pp. 351–378.

→ LODGE, SIR OLIVER. (1925) *Talks about radio with some pioneering history and some hints, and calculations for radio amateurs.* New York: George H. Doran Company, xiv + 265 pp.

★ MACLAREN, MALCOLM. (1943) *The rise of the electrical industry during the nineteenth century.* Princeton: Princeton University Press, xi + 225 pp.

MARTIN, T. COMMERFORD, (1924) The rise of electricity. *A Popular History of American Invention,* edited by Waldemar Kaempffert. New York: A. L. Burt Company, vol. 1, pp. 504–538.

→ MILLER, DAYTON CLARENCE. (1939) *Sparks, lightning, cosmic rays: an anecdotal history of electricity.* New York: The Macmillan Company, xvii + 192 pp.
"Christmas Week Lectures For Young People, 1937, The Franklin Institute."

NEILL, HUMPHREY B. (1940) *Forty-eight million horses.* Philadelphia, New York, London: J. B. Lippincott Company, xii + 241 pp.

OGILVIE, ALEXANDER. (1914) *Applications of electricity, for non-technical readers.* London: T. C. & E. C. Jack (The People's Books, no. 95), 94 pp.

★ PELSENEER, JEAN. (1944) *Zénobe Gramme, notice biobibliographique, suivie de la description de la dynamo par son inventeur et d'autres documents.* Deuxième édition. Bruxelles: Anc. Établiss. J. Lebèque & Cie, Éditeurs, 79 pp.

★ PIERCE, GEORGE W. (1910) *Principles of wireless telegraphy.* First edition, third impression, corrected. New York: McGraw-Hill Book Company, ix + 350 pp.

→ PUPIN, MICHAEL. (1923) *From immigrant to inventor.* New York, London: Charles Scribner's Sons, 396 pp.

[RADAR.] (1945) Radar secrets. *Science News Letter,* vol. 48, pp. 115–116.

★ RATCLIFFE, J. A. (1940) *The physical principles of wireless.* With a foreword by E. V. Appleton. Fourth edition, revised. London: Methuen & Co. Ltd. (Monographs on Physical Subjects), viii + 110 pp.

★ RIGHI, AUGUSTO, und DESSAU, BERNHARD. (1903) *Die Telegraphie ohne Draht.* Braunschweig, Druck und Verlag von Friedrich Vieweg und Sohn, xi + 481 pp.
The best source for the early history of radio.

★ SCHUSTER, SIR ARTHUR. (1911) *The progress of physics during 33 years (1875–1908): four lectures delivered to the University of Calcutta during March 1908.* Cambridge: at the University Press, x + 164 pp.
Contains a contemporary account of the discovery of radio and an excellent summary of Maxwell's electromagnetic theory.

SMITH, M. W. (1941) The role of science in the electrical industry. *Annual Report of the Board of Regents of the Smithsonian Institution.* pp. 199–209.
"Reprinted by permission from *Electrical Engineering,* vol. 59, no. 2, February, 1940.

SWOPE, HENRIETTA H. *See* WATSON (1945)

★ THOMPSON, SILVANUS P. (1896) *Dynamo-electric machinery; a manual for students of electrotechnics.* Fifth edition, revised. London: E. & F. N. Spon (Finsbury Technical Manuals), x + 835 pp.
Contains an excellent descriptive section on early generators and motors.

→ TURNER, D. M. (1927) *Makers of science; electricity & magnetism.* With an introduction by Charles Singer. London: Oxford University Press, xv + 184 pp.

→ TYNDALL, JOHN. (1870) *Faraday as a discoverer.* New edition. London: Longmans, Green, and Co., xii + 208 pp.
A classic — by a co-worker and friend.

→ VOWLES, HUGH P., and VOWLES, MARGARET W. (1931) *The quest for power from prehistoric times to the present day.* London: Chapman & Hall Ltd., xv + 354 pp.
An extraordinarily readable and reliable study — a masterpiece of popular exposition of a difficult subject.

VOWLES, MARGARET W. *See* VOWLES (1931).

★ VYVYAN, R. N. (1933) *Wireless over thirty years.* London: George Routledge & Sons, Ltd., xiv + 256 pp.
Reminiscences by one of Marconi's associates.

→ WATSON, FLETCHER G., and SWOPE, HENRIETTA H. (1945) Loran. *Sky and Telescope*, vol. 5, pp. 3–5.

★ WHITTAKER, E. T. (1910) *A history of the theories of aether and electricity from the age of Descartes to the close of the nineteenth century.* London: Longmans, Green, and Co., xvi + 475 pp.

> One of the *great* histories of a scientific subject — written for the scientist.

Chapter 7: Notes

1 *Vowles and Vowles* (1931), p. 213.
2 *Jones* (1870), vol. 2, pp. 395–396.
3 Quoted in *Jones* (1870), vol. 2, p. 415.
4 Quoted in *Tyndall* (1870).
5 *Gladstone* (1872), p. 145.
6 *Ibid.*
7 *Tyndall* (1870), p. 43.
8 *Appleyard* (1931), p. 92.
9 *Gladstone* (1872), p. 149.
10 Cf. *Pelseneer* (1944); *Thompson* (1896); *MacLaren* (1943).
11 Cf. *Whittaker* (1910).
12 Based, to a large extent, on *Schuster* (1911).
13 *Ibid.*
14 *Hertz* (1893).
15 *Joint Board . . .* (1945).
16 *Ibid.*

CHAPTER 8: SYNTHETIC RUBBER AND NYLON

Bibliography and Guide to Further Reading

★ ADAMS, ROGER. (1939) Biographical memoir of Wallace Hume Carothers. *National Academy of Sciences of the United States of America. Biographical Memoirs,* vol. 20, 12th memoir, pp. 293–309.

→ ASTBURY, W. T. (1944) Types of man-made fibers. *Endeavour,* vol. 3, pp. 98–103.

→ BALDWIN, A. W. (1944) Mercer and mercerization. *Endeavour,* vol. 3, pp. 138–143, 149.

BARUCH, BERNARD M. *See* CONANT, COMPTON & BARUCH (1942).

★ BOLTON, E. K. (1942 [1]) Nylon. *Chemical and Engineering News,* vol. 20, pp. 1365–1366.

★ BOLTON, E. K. (1942 [2]) Development of nylon. *Industrial and engineering chemistry,* Industrial edition, vol. 34, pp. 53–58.

→ BOLTON, E. K. (1945) Du Pont research. *Industrial and engineering chemistry,* vol. 37, pp. 107–115.

→ CARLISLE, NORMAN V. (1943) *Your career in chemistry.* With a preface by Dr. C. M. A. Stine. New York: E. P. Dutton and Co., Inc., xvi + 251 pp.

★ [CAROTHERS, WALLACE HUME]. (1940) *Collected papers of Wallace Hume Carothers on high polymeric substances.* Edited by H. Mark and G. Stafford Whitby. New York: Interscience Publishers, Inc., xix + 459 pp.

COMPTON, KARL T. *See* CONANT, COMPTON & BARUCH (1942).

CONANT, JAMES BRYANT. (1939) *The chemistry of organic compounds, a year's course in organic chemistry.* Revised with the assistance of Max Tishler. New York: The Macmillan Company, x + 658 pp.

★ CONANT, JAMES B.; COMPTON, KARL T.; BARUCH, BERNARD M., chairman. (1942) Report of the Rubber Survey Committees. [   ] [   ], 75 pp.

COOLIDGE, COLE. (1944) *Research makes jobs.* 4 pp.

> Mimeographed copy of "Speech . . . , *Herald Tribune* Forum, Monday night, October 16, 1944." Published *New York Herald Tribune,* 22 Oct. 1944, section VIII p. 3.

CRAMER, HOWARD I. (1942) Industrial progress in synthetic rubberlike polymers. *Journal of Industrial and Engineering Chemistry,* vol. 34, pp. 243–251.

→ CRAWFORD, M. D. C. (1941) *The heritage of cotton, the fibre of two worlds and many ages.* New York: Grosset & Dunlap, Publishers, xix + 24 pp.

> Originally published in 1924.

→ CRAWFORD, M. D. C. (1941) *The ways of fashion.* New York: G. P. Putnam's Sons, ix + 320 pp.

DYER, WALTER S. (1941) *A practical survey of chemistry.* New York: Henry Holt and Company, vii + 480 pp.

FARMER, E. H. (1944) Advances in the scientific knowledge of rubber. *Endeavour*, vol. 3, pp. 72–79.

★ FINDLAY, ALEXANDER. (1937) *A hundred years of chemistry*. New York: The Macmillan Company, 352 pp.

GARVEY, B. S., JR. (1941) Synthetic rubber. *The Scientific Monthly*, vol. 52, pp. 48–55.

GIBBONS, W. A. (1940) The rubber industry, 1839–1939. *Annual Report of the Board of Regents of the Smithsonian Institution*, pp. 193–214.
". . . Reprinted by permission from *Industrial and Engineering Chemistry*, vol. 31, p. 1199, October, 1939."

GIBBS, W. E. (1934) Chemical engineering and its industrial significance. *Science Progress*, vol. 28, pp. 405–419.

GORDY, EDWARD, L. *See* HAYNES & GORDY (1935).

HAYNES, WILLIAMS, and GORDY, EDWARD L., editors. (1935) *Chemical Industry's Contribution to the Nation: 1635–1935. A Record of Chemical Accomplishment, with an Index of the Chemicals Made in America*. New York: Chemical Markets, Inc., 176 pp. "A Supplement to *Chemical Industries*, May, 1935. Published in Celebration of the Tercentenary of the Founding of the American Chemical Industry by John Winthrop, Jr. . . ."

➤ HAYNES, WILLIAMS. (1942) *This chemical age, the miracle of man-made materials*. New York: Alfred A. Knopf, xi + 385 + 22 pp.
An extraordinarily lucid account of modern chemical achievement.

HOLMES, HARRY N. (1941) *General chemistry*. Fourth edition. New York: The Macmillan Company, viii + 720 pp.

➤ HUNT, JAMES K. (1943) Nylon: development, physical properties, and present status. *Textile Colorist*, vol. 65, pp. 10–12.

MAJOR, RANDOLPH T. (1940) Contribution of the chemical industry to science. *Scientific Monthly*, vol. 51, pp. 158–164.

MARK, H. (1943) Some scientific aspects of the synthetic rubber problem. *American Scientist*, vol. 31, pp. 97–141.

MAUERSBERGER, HERBERT R. (1941) The new synthetic textile fibers. *Annual Report of the Board of Regents of the Smithsonian Institution*, pp. 211–223.
". . . Reprinted by permission from *Rayon Textile Monthly*, November and December, 1940."

➔ MIALL, STEPHEN; and MIALL, LAURENCE MACKENZIE. (1937) *Chemistry, matter, and life*. New York: Longmans, Green and Co., ix + 296 pp.

➔ MORRISON, A. CRESSY. (1937) *Man in a chemical world; the service of chemical industry*. New York: Charles Scribner's Sons, xi + 292 pp.

PHILIP, J. C. (1937) The chemist in the service of the community. Ch. iii of *What science stands for*. London, George Allen & Unwin Ltd., pp. 39–71.

★ STINE, C. M. A. (1935) *The place of fundamental research in an industrial research organization*. 2 pp.
[Mimeographed copy of paper read "Before the Cleveland branch of the American Chemical Society at Cleveland, Ohio, Thursday evening, October 24."] Reprinted in *Chemical Engineering Congress of the World Power Congress*.

STINE, CHARLES M. A. (1938) *What laboratories of industry are doing for the world of tomorrow: chemicals and textiles*. 5 pp.
[Mimeographed copy of "An Address . . . to be delivered before the New York Herald Tribune Eighth Annual Forum on Current Problems, Thursday, October 27, 1938, 1:45 P.M., at the New York World's Fair Grounds."]

★ STINE, CHARLES M. A. (1940[1]) Rise of the organic chemical industry in the United States. *Annual Report of the Board of Regents of the Smithsonian Institution*, pp. 177–192.
". . . Reprinted by permission from *Industrial and Engineering Chemistry*, vol. 32, no. 2, February, 1940," pp. 137–144.

★ STINE, CHARLES M. A. (1940[2]) Chemical engineering and industry. *Transactions of American Institute of Chemical Engineers*, vol. 36, pp. 417–432.

★ STINE, CHARLES M. A. (1941) Fundamental research in industry. *Research — a national resource*. II: *Report of the National Resources Planning Board.* Washington: United States Government Printing Office, pp. 98–107.

★ STINE, CHARLES M. A. (1942) Molders of a better destiny. *Science,* vol. 96, pp. 305–311.

TAYLOR, HUGH S. (1941) Large molecules through atomic spectacles. *Proceedings of the American Philosophical Society,* vol. 85, pp. 1–12.

➙ TILDEN, SIR WILLIAM A. (1926) *Chemical discovery and invention in the twentieth century.* Fifth edition, London: George Routledge and Sons, Limited, xvi + 487 pp.

Chapter 8: Notes

1 *Coolidge* (1944), p. 1.
2 *Bolton* (1945), pp. 107–109.
3 *Stine* (1935), p. 1.
4 *Bolton* (1942²), p. 53.
5 Quoted in *Adams* (1939), p. 297.
6 *Adams* (1939).
7 *Findlay* (1937), pp. 195–196.
8 *Ibid.*
9 *Ibid.*
10 Quoted *ibid.*
11 *Haynes* (1942), p. 209.
12 *Ibid.*
13 *Ibid.,* p. 212; *Cramer* (1942).
14 Information from Du Pont Co.
15 *Ibid.*
16 *Ibid.*
17 *Conant, Compton, & Baruch* (1942), p. 68.
18 *Adams* (1939), p. 301.
19 *Crawford* (1941).
20 *Baldwin* (1944).
21 *Carlisle* (1943); *Haynes* (1942), ch. 16, ch. 17.
22 After *Bolton* (1942²), p. 53.
23 Quoted in *Adams* (1939), p. 301.
24 *Ibid.*
25 From *Conant* (1939), p. 585.
26 *Adams* (1939), p. 301.
27 *Bolton* (1942²), p. 53.
28 *Ibid.*
29 *Ibid.,* p. 56.
30 *Stine* (1938), p. 4.
31 Personal communication from Dr. Jas. K. Hunt.

CHAPTER 9: FUNDAMENTAL RESEARCH IN WHICH A PRACTICAL APPLICATION SEEMS LIKELY

Bibliography and Guide to Further Reading

ALLER, LAWRENCE. *See* GOLDBERG & ALLER (1943).

[BRITISH COUNCIL, THE.] (1944) The mineral requirements of plants. *MSN, Monthly Science News,* No. 37, pp. 1–3.

★ BROWNE, CHARLES A. (1944) A source book of agricultural chemistry. *Chronica Botanica,* vol. 8, no. 1, x + 290 pp.

> Despite its restrictive title this splendid work is a history of the subject as well as a "source book."

★ CHANDLER, W. H., HOAGLAND, D. R., and HIBBARD, P. L. (1931) Little-leaf or rosette in fruit trees. *Proceedings of the American Society for Horticultural Science,* vol. 28, pp. 556–560.

★ CHANDLER, W. H., HOAGLAND, D. R., and HIBBARD, P. L. (1932) Little-leaf or rosette of fruit trees. II. Effect of zinc and other treatments. *Proceedings of the American Society for Horticultural Science,* vol. 29, pp. 255–263.

➙ GOLDBERG, LEO, and ALLER, LAWRENCE H. (1943) *Atoms, stars, and nebulae.* Philadelphia: The Blakiston Company. (The Harvard Books on Astronomy), vi + 323 pp.

➙ HAMBIDGE, GOVE, Editor. (1941) *Hunger signs in crops, a symposium.* Washington, D. C.: The American Society of Agronomy and the National Fertilizer Association, xiii + 327 pp.

HIBBARD, P. L. *See* CHANDLER, HOAGLAND, & HIBBARD (1931) and (1932).

➙ HOAGLAND, D. R. (1944) General aspects of the study of plant nutrition. *Science in the University.* Berkeley and Los Angeles: University of California Press, pp. 279–292.

★ HOAGLAND, D. R. (1946) The nutrition and biochemistry of plants. *Currents in biochemical research,* edited David E. Green. New York: Interscience Publishers, Inc., pp. 6[?]–77.

HOAGLAND, D. R. *See* CHANDLER, HOAGLAND, & HIBBARD (1931) and (1932).

JEANS, J. H. (1904) A suggested explanation of radio-activity. *Nature*, vol. 70, p. 101.

JEANS, Sir JAMES H. (1929) *Astronomy and cosmogony*. Cambridge: At the University Press, x + 428 pp. Especially pp. 113–115.

McMURTREY, J. E., JR., and ROBINSON, W. O. (1938) Neglected soil constituents that affect plant and animal development. *Soils & Men, Year Book of Agriculture 1938* (United States Department of Agriculture), pp. 807–829.

NORDENSKIÖLD, ERIK. (1936) *The history of biology, a survey*. Translated from the Swedish by Leonard Bucknall Eyre. New York: Tudor Publishing Co., xii + 629 + xv pp.

REED, HOWARD S. (1942) *A short history of the plant sciences*. Waltham, Mass.: Chronica Botanica Company (A new series of plant science books, vol. 7), x + 320 pp.

ROBINSON, W. D. *See* McMURTREY & ROBINSON (1938).

SACHS, JULIUS VON. (1890) *History of botany (1530–1860)*. Authorized translation by Henry E. F. Garnsey, revised by Isaac Bayley Balfour. Oxford: At the Clarendon Press, xvi + 568 pp. Esp. "Third book," chap. 2, "History of the theory of the nutrition of plants, 1583–1860."

SHAPLEY, HARLOW. (1946) It's an old story with the stars. *One world or none*, edited by Dexter Masters and Katharine Way. New York: Whittlesey House, McGraw Hill Book Co., Inc., pp. 7–10.

SHIVE, JOHN W. (1940) Sketch of the development of the water culture method of growing plants. *The Scientific Monthly*, vol. 51, pp. 233–240.

STILES, WALTER. (1946) *Trace elements in plants and animals*. Cambridge: At the University Press, New York: The Macmillan Company, x + 189 pp.

WALLACE, T. (1943) *The diagnosis of mineral deficiencies in plants*. London: His Majesty's Stationery Office, vi + 116 pp.

Chapter 9: Notes

1 *Shive* (1940).
2 *Ibid.*; cf. *Stiles* (1946), ch. 1.
3 *Stiles* (1946), p. 3.
4 *Hoagland* (1944), p. 282.
5 *Stiles* (1946), ch. 2.
6 *Hoagland* (1944), p. 282.
7 *Chandler, Hoagland, and Hibbard* (1931); *Stiles* (1946), pp. 74–76.
8 *Stiles* (1946), pp. 76–77.
9 *Stiles* (1946), ch. 3.
10 *Shapley* (1946), p. 7.
11 This section is based wholly on *Shapley* (1946).
12 *Ibid.* See also *Jeans* (1904) and *Jeans* (1929).
13 *Shapley* (1946).
14 *Ibid.*

CHAPTER 10: BLOOD GROUPS AND BLOOD TRANSFUSION

Bibliography and Guide to Further Reading

★ BERNHEIM, BERTRAM M. (1942) *Adventure in blood transfusion*. New York: Smith & Durrell, xxxviii + 182 pp.

★ BOYD, WILLIAM C. (1939[1]) Blood groups. *Tabulae Biologicae*, vol. 17, pp. 113–240.

BOYD, WILLIAM C. (1939[2]) Blood groups of American Indians. *American Journal of Physical Anthropology*, vol. 25, pp. 215–235.

BOYD, WILLIAM C. (1940[1]) Blood groups in the Australian aborigines. *American Journal of Physical Anthropology*, vol. 27, pp. 69–90.

→ BOYD, WILLIAM C. (1940[2]) Critique of methods of classifying mankind. *American Journal of Physical Anthropology*, vol. 27, pp. 333–364.

→ [BOYD, WILLIAM C.]. (1944) Karl Landsteiner, 1868–1943. *Journal of Immunology*, vol. 48, pp. 1–16. Contains a bibliography of the writings of K. Landsteiner.

BOYD, WILLIAM C. (1945) Rh blood factors: an orientation review. *Archives of Pathology*, vol. 40, pp. 114–127.

BOYD, WILLIAM C. *See* SCHIFF and BOYD (1942).

➤ CASTIGLIONI, ARTURO, (1946) *A history of medicine*. Translated from the Italian and edited by E. B. Krumbhaar. New York: Alfred A. Knopf, xxviii + 1013 + xl pp.

DE BAKEY, MICHAEL. *See* KILDUFFE & DE BAKEY (1942).

FEINBLATT, HENRY M. (1926) *Transfusion of blood*. New York: The Macmillan Company, 137 pp.

★ FULTON, JOHN F. (1935) *A bibliography of two Oxford physiologists: Richard Lower, 1631–1691, John Mayow, 1643–1679*. Introduction by K. J. Franklin. Oxford: Printed at the University Press by John Johnson, 62 pp.

"Reprinted from the *Oxford Bibliographical Society Proceedings and Papers, 1935*. Volume IV, Part I, pp. 1–62."

➤ HOLMES À COURT, A. W. (1927) The history of blood transfusion. *The Medical Journal of Australia*, October 15, pp. 528–533.

HOWELL, KATHARINE M. *See* ZIMMERMAN & HOWELL (1932).

KALISKI, DAVID J. *See* OTTENBERG and KALISKI (1913).

➤ KERR, W. M. (1922) A history of blood transfusion. *United States Naval Medical Bulletin*, vol. 16, pp. 465–475.

★ KEYNES, GEOFFREY. (1922) *Blood Transfusion*. Oxford Medical Publications, vii + 166 pp.

KILDUFFE, ROBERT A., and DE BAKEY, MICHAEL. (1942) *The blood bank and the technique and therapeutics of transfusions*. St. Louis: The C. V. Mosby Company, 558 pp.

KRUMBHAAR, E. B. *See* CASTIGLIONI (1946).

★ LANDSTEINER, KARL. (1945) *The specificity of serological reactions*. Revised edition. With a chapter on molecular structure and intermolecular forces by Linus Pauling. Cambridge: Harvard University Press, xiv + 310 pp.

LIBMAN, E. *See* OTTENBERG & LIBMAN (1915).

➤ MONTAGU, M. F. ASHLEY. (1945) *An introduction to physical anthropology*. Springfield, Illinois: Charles C. Thomas, xiv + 325 pp.

★ OTTENBERG, REUBEN. (1911) Studies in isoagglutination. 1. Transfusion and the question of intravascular agglu nation. *Journal of Experimental Me icine*, vol. 13, pp. 425–438.

★ OTTENBERG, REUBEN, and KALISK DAVID J. (1913) Accidents in tra fusion: their prevention by prelin nary blood examination: based on experience of one hundred twen eight transfusions. *Journal of American Medical Association*, v 61, pp. 2128–2140.

OTTENBERG, R., and LIBMAN, E. (191 Blood transfusion: indications; sults; general management. *Ame can Journal of the Medical Scienc* vol. 150, pp. 36–69.

➤ OTTENBERG, REUBEN. (1937) Remir cences of the history of blood tra fusion. *Journal of the Mount Si Hospital*, vol. 4, pp. 264–271. With valuable bibliography.

SCHIFF, FRITZ, and BOYD, WILLIAM (1942) *Blood grouping technic: manual for clinicians, serologists, thropologists, and students of le and military medicine*. With a fo word by Karl Landsteiner. New Yo Interscience Publishers, Inc., xiv 248 pp.

SINGER, CHARLES. (1928) *A short h tory of medicine, introducing medi principles to students and non-medi readers*. New York: Oxford Univers Press, xxiv + 368 pp.

WIENER, ALEXANDER S. (1945) Rec advances in knowledge of the blood factors, with special refere to the clinical applications. *Trans tions & Studies of the College Physicians of Philadelphia*, vol. fourth series, pp. 105–122.

ZIMMERMAN, LEO M., and HOWE KATHARINE M. (1932) History blood transfusion. *Annals of Medi History*, vol. 4, new series, pp. 41 433.

Chapter 10: Notes

1 *Zimmerman and Howell* (193. pp. 415–416; *Holmes à Co* (1927), p. 528.

2 Quoted in *Zimmerman and Hou* (1932), p. 416.

3 Various versions of this tale are d

cussed in *Kerr* (1922), pp. 466–467; cf. *Keynes* (1922), p. 2.

4 *Kerr* (1922), p. 467.

5 *Holmes à Court* (1927), p. 528.

6 *Fulton* (1935), p. 14.

7 Quoted in *Keynes* (1922), p. 9; cf. *Kerr* (1922), pp. 468–469; *Holmes à Court* (1932), p. 529.

8 *Zimmerman and Howell* (1932), pp. 418–419.

9 *Feinblatt* (1926), p. 78.

10 Denys in the *Philosophical Transactions*, quoted in *Kilduffe and De Bakey* (1942), p. 484.

11 Quoted in *Zimmerman and Howell* (1932), p. 422.

12 *Keynes* (1922), p. 11.

13 *Ibid.*, p. 12.

14 *Boyd* (1944).

15 *Schiff and Boyd* (1942), p. 3.

16 *Zimmerman and Howell* (1932), p. 428.

17 From *Schiff and Boyd* (1942), p. 6.

18 Personal communication from Reuben Ottenberg.

19 *Ottenberg* (1911); summarized in *Ottenberg* (1937), p. 267.

20 *Zimmerman and Howell* (1932), p. 428.

21 *Bernheim* (1942).

22 *Kerr* (1922), p. 474.

23 Personal communication from Reuben Ottenberg.

24 *Bernheim* (1942), p. xxviii.

25 *Ottenberg* (1937).

26 *Ibid.*

27 *Bernheim* (1942), pp. xxviii–xxix.

28 Cited by *Bernheim* (1942).

29 *Ibid.*

30 *Ibid.*

31 *Ibid.*

32 *Ibid.*

33 *Ottenberg* (1937).

34 *Keynes* (1922), p. 15.

35 *Ibid.*, p. 17.

36 Personal conversation with Geoffrey Keynes.

37 *Keynes* (1922), p. 17.

38 *Schiff and Boyd* (1942), p. 199.

39 *Montagu* (1945), pp. 131–132.

40 *Boyd* (1939 [1]); *Boyd* (1940 [2]). Dr. Boyd is completing a book on physical anthropology based on the blood-group classification of mankind.

41 *Boyd* (1945).

CHAPTER 11: THE STORY OF HYBRID CORN

Bibliography and Guide to Further Reading

→ BULLER, A. H. REGINALD. (1919) *Essays on wheat, including the discovery and introduction of Marquis Wheat, the early history of wheat-growing in Manitoba, wheat in western Canada, the origin of Red Bobs and Kitchener, and the wild wheat of Palestine.* New York: The Macmillan Company, xv + 339 pp.

→ CRABB, A. RICHARD. (1947) *The hybrid-corn makers.* With a foreword by H. D. Hughes. New Brunswick, N. J.; Rutgers University Press, xxv + 331 pp.

★ CUNNINGHAM, J. C. (1941) Maize bibliography for the years 1917 to 1936, inclusive. *Contributions from Iowa Corn Research Institute*, vol. 2, 364 pp.

★ EAST, EDWARD MURRAY, and JONES, DONALD F. (1919) *Inbreeding and outbreeding, their genetic and sociological significance.* Philadelphia & London: J. B. Lippincott Company, 285 pp.

→ EAST, EDWARD M. (1929) *Heredity and human affairs.* New York, London: Charles Scribner's Sons, vii + 325 pp.

→ GILES, DOROTHY. (1940) *Singing valleys: the story of corn.* New York: Random House, 361 pp.

HAYWARD, HERMAN E. (1938) *The structure of economic plants.* New York: The Macmillan Company, x + 674 pp.

HUNTER, H., and LEAKE, H. MARTIN. (1933) *Recent advances in agricultural plant breeding.* With a foreword by Sir Rowland H. Biffen. Philadelphia: P. Blakiston's Son & Co., Inc., x + 361 pp.

★ ILTIS, HUGO. (1932) *Life of Mendel.* Translated by Eden and Cedar Paul. London: George Allan & Unwin Ltd., 336 pp.

→ JENKINS, MERLE T. (1936) Corn improvement. *Yearbook of Agriculture* (United States Department of Agriculture), pp. 455–522.

→ JONES, DONALD F. (1945) Biographical memoir of Edward Murray East,

1879–1938. *National Academy of Sciences of the United States of America. Biographical Memoirs*, vol. 23, 9th memoir, pp. 217–242.

★ MANGELSDORF, P. C., and REEVES, R. G. (1939) *The origin of Indian corn and its relatives.* Agricultural and Mechanical College of Texas (Texas Agricultural Experiment Station, Bulletin no. 574 [Monograph]), 315 pp.

★ MANGELSDORF, PAUL C. (1945) The origin and nature of the ear of maize. *Botanical Museum Leaflets* (Harvard University), vol. 12, pp. 33–75.

★ RICHEY, FREDERICK D. (1935) *The what and how of hybrid corn.* Washington, D. C.: U. S. Department of Agriculture (Farmers' Bulletin no. 1744), 13 pp.

SARTON, GEORGE. (1934) The artificial fertilization of date-palms in the time of Ashur-nasir-pal, B.C. 885–860. *Isis*, vol. 21, pp. 8–13.

SHULL, GEORGE HARRISON. (1907) Importance of the mutation theory in practical breeding. *Proceedings American Breeders' Association*, vol. 3, 60–67.

★ SHULL, GEORGE H. (1908) The composition of a field of maize. *Report American Breeders' Association*, vol. 4, pp. 296–301.

→ SHULL, GEORGE H. (1909) A pure-line method in corn breeding. *American Breeders' Association*, vol. 5, pp. 51–59.

★ SHULL, GEORGE H. (1910) Hybridization methods in corn breeding. *American Breeders' Magazine*, vol. 1, pp. 98–107.

→ SHULL, GEORGE H. (1912) A pilgrimage to Brünn. *The Antiochian*, vol. 2, pp. 1–7.

→ SHULL, GEORGE H. (1946) Hybrid seed corn. *Science*, vol. 103, pp. 547–550.

→ TRUE, ALFRED CHARLES. (1937) *A history of agricultural experimentation and research in the United States, 1607–1925, including a history of the United States Department of Agriculture.* Washington: United States Government Printing Office (Miscellaneous Publication no. 251, United States Department of Agriculture), vi + 321 pp.

Chapter 11: Notes

1 Jenkins (1936), p. 457.
2 Mangelsdorf (1945); Mangelsdorf and Reeve (1939).
3 Quoted in Jenkins (1936), p. 457
4 Giles (1940), p. 221.
5 Quoted in Buller (1919), p. v.
6 Jenkins (1936), pp. 464–466.
7 Crabb (1947), ch. 2; Jenkins (1936), p. 467.
8 Information supplied by P. Mangelsdorf.
9 Sarton (1934).
10 Hayward (1938), ch. 5.
11 Iltis (1932).
12 Information supplied by G. Shull.
13 Shull (1908).
14 Personal communication from G. Shull.
15 Personal communication from G. Shull.
16 Information supplied by P. Mangelsdorf.
17 Information supplied by P. Mangelsdorf.
18 Crabb (1947), ch. 4; all the information concerning East's early work on inbreeding derives from Crabb's book and from several conversations with P. Mangelsdorf.
19 East (1929), p. 153.
20 Crabb (1947), ch. 4.
21 Quoted in Crabb (1947), ch. 5.
22 Crabb (1947), ch. 7.
23 Jones (1945).
24 Information supplied by P. Mangelsdorf.
25 See Crabb (1947).
26 Jenkins (1936), p. 479.
27 Crabb (1947).
28 Ibid.
29 Giles (1940).
30 Giles (1940), p. 233.
31 Personal communication from Mangelsdorf.
32 Personal communication from Richard Crabb.
33 Crabb (1947), ch. 7.

CHAPTER 12: THE FORTUNE AT THE RAINBOW'S END

Notes

(There is no Bibliography for this chapter. The Notes refer to the Bibliography for Chapter 11.)

1 Personal communication from G. H. Shull.
2 Personal communication from G. H. Shull.
3 Personal communication from G. H. Shull.
4 *Shull* (1907).
5 *Shull* (1946).
6 Personal communication from G. H. Shull.
7 Personal communication from G. H. Shull.
8 Quoted in *Crabb* (1947), p. 66.
9 See *Crabb* (1947), p. 108.

CHAPTER 13: PRACTICAL INNOVATIONS BASED ON EXISTING FUNDAMENTAL KNOWLEDGE

Bibliography and Guide to Further Reading

BUCKLEY, OLIVER E. (1937) The evolution of the crystal wave filter. *Journal of Applied Physics*, vol. 8, pp. 40–47.
CAJORI, FLORIAN. (1938) *A history of physics in its elementary branches, including the evolution of physical laboratories*. Revised and enlarged edition. New York: The Macmillan Company, xiii + 424 pp.
CREW, HENRY. (1935) *The rise of modern physics*. Second edition. Baltimore: The Williams & Wilkins Company, xix + 434 pp.
CURIE, MARIE. (1923) *Pierre Curie*. Translated by Charlotte and Vernon Kellogg. With "autobiographical notes" by Marie Curie. New York: The Macmillan Company, 242 pp.
[CURIE, PIERRE]. (1908) *Oeuvres de Pierre Curie*. Publiées par les soins de la Société française de physique. Avec une préface par Mme. Pierre Curie. Paris: Gauthier-Villars, Imprimeur-Librairie, xxii + 661 pp.

→ DARROW, KARL K. (1926) *Introduction to contemporary physics*. New York: D. Van Nostrand Company, Inc., xxvi + 453 pp.
→ DARROW, KARL K. (1936) *The renaissance of physics*. New York: The Macmillan Company, 306 pp.
→ EVANS, RICHARD J. (1946) Echo ranging sonar. *Electronics*, vol. 19, pp. 88–93.
★ MCKEEHAN, L. W. (1926) Magnetostriction. *Journal of the Franklin Institute*, vol. 202, pp. 737–773.
    Contains a valuable bibliography and account of early history.
→ MILLIKAN, ROBERT A. (1920) Contributions of physical science. Ch. iii of *The new world of science, its development during the war*, edited by Robert M. Yerkes. New York: The Century Co., pp. 33–48.
PIERCE, GEORGE W. (1928) Magnetostriction oscillators, an application of magnetostriction to the control of frequency of audio and radio electric oscillations, to the production of sound, and to the measurement of the elastic constants of metals. *Proceedings of the American Academy of Arts and Sciences*, vol. 63, pp. 1–47.

Chapter 13: Notes

1 *McKeehan* (1926).
2 Personal communication from G. W. Pierce.
3 *Evans* (1946).
4 *Curie* (1908); *Curie* (1923), ch. 2.
5 *Curie* (1923), p. 47.
6 *Curie* (1923), p. 47, footnote; *Millikan* (1920), pp. 41–42.
7 *Buckley* (1937).
8 *Cajori* (1938), p. 339; *Darrow* (1926), p. 117; *Darrow* (1936), pp. 175–181.

CHAPTER 14: FORAMINIFERA AND OIL PROSPECTING

Bibliography and Guide to Further Reading

BRUCKSHAW, J. McG. (1943) Physics and the search for oil. *Reports on progress in physics,* vol. 9, pp. 198–227.

➤ BRUES, CHARLES T. (1923) Ancient insects; fossils in amber and other deposits. *The Scientific Monthly,* vol. 17, pp. 289–304.

★ CRONEIS, CAREY. (1941) Micropaleontology — past and future. *Bulletin of the American Association of Petroleum Geologists,* vol. 25, pp. 1208–1255.
Contains an excellent and extensive bibliography.

★ CUSHMAN, JOSEPH A. (1924) The use of foraminifera in geologic correlation. *Bulletin of the American Association of Petroleum Geologists,* vol. 8, pp. 485–491.

➤ CUSHMAN, JOSEPH A. (1928) Natural history by radio; fossils — what they are and their uses to man. *The Scientific Monthly,* vol. 27, pp. 346–348.

★ CUSHMAN, JOSEPH A. (1938) The future of Paleontology. *Bulletin of the Geological Society of America,* vol. 49, pp. 359–366.
Address as retiring president of the Paleontological Society, 1937.

★ CUSHMAN, JOSEPH A. (1940) *Foraminifera, their classification and economic use.* Third edition, revised and enlarged, with an illustrated key to the genera. Cambridge: Harvard University Press, ix + 535 pp.

DRACHMANN, A. G. (1932) *Ancient oil mills and presses.* København: Hovedkommissioner: Levin & Munksgaard (Det Kgl. Danske Videnskabernes Selskab. Archaeologisk-Kunsthistoriske Meddelelser. 1, 1) 181 pp.

➤ EGLOFF, GUSTAV. (1933) *Earth Oil.* Baltimore: The Williams & Wilkins Company (A Century of Progress Series), xi + 158 pp.

ELLIS, BROOKS F. (1936) The master key to oil. *Natural History,* vol. 38, pp. 369–381, 442.

FORBES, R.-J. (1937) *Sketch of the history of the petroleum industry.* Paris: Deuxième Congrès Mondial du Pétrole, 6 pp.

FROLICH, PER K. (1943) Petroleum, past, present and future. *Science,* vol. 98, pp. 457–463, 484–487.
". . . printed in the November issue of *Industrial and Engineering Chemistry* . . ."

GALLOWAY, J. J. (1933) *A manual of foraminifera.* Bloomington, Indiana: The Principia Press, Inc., xiv + 4[ ] pp.

➤ GOULD, CHAS. N. (1929) The usefulne[ ] of the useless. *Scientific Monthly,* v[ ] 29, pp. 440–446.
Discusses 2 "new" methods us[ ] to discover supplies of petroleu[ ] petrography and micro-palaeont[ ] ogy.

★ HAGER, DORSEY. (1926) *Practical oil [ ] ology, the application of geology [ ] oil field problems.* Fourth editio[ ] New York: McGraw-Hill Book Co[ ] pany, xii + 309 pp.

➤ KETTERING, CHARLES F., and ORTH, A[ ] LEN. (1932) *The new necessity, t[ ] culmination of a century of progr[ ] in transportation.* Baltimore: The W[ ] liams & Wilkins Company (A Centu[ ] of Progress Series), x + 124 pp.

LEES, G. M. (1940) The search for [ ] *Annual Report of the Board of [ ] gents of the Smithsonian Instituti[ ]* pp. 231–248.
"Reprinted by permission from [ ] Geographical Journal, vol. 95, no.[ ] January, 1940."

➤ MATHER, KIRTLEY F. (1944) *Enou[ ] and to spare. Mother earth can no[ ] ish every man in freedom.* New Yo[ ] and London: Harper & Brothers, [ ] pp.
Especially valuable for the app[ ] dices, containing data on "pe[ ] leum reserves in the United State[ ] and other natural resources both [ ] the U. S. and the world.

MISER, HUGH D. (1939) Our petrole[ ] supply. *Annual Report of the Bo[ ] of Regents of the Smithsonian In[ ] tution,* pp. 303–318.
"Reprinted by permission from [ ] Journal of the Washington Acade[ ] of Sciences, vol. 29, no. 3, pp. [ ] 109, March 15, 1939."

ORTH, ALLEN. *See* KETTERING [ ] ORTH (1932).

➤ PEABODY, ERNEST H. (1942) *Oil F[ ] a world-wide adventure.* New Yo[ ] The Newcomen Society, Ameri[ ] Branch, 96 pp.

PRATT, WALLACE E. (1944) Our pe[ ] leum resources. *Annual Report of [ ] Board of Regents of the Smithson[ ] Institution,* pp. 297–306, also *Am[ ] ican Scientist,* vol. 32, pp. 120–128[ ]

RANKINE, A. O. (1945) Sounding the earth's crust. *Science at your service,* by Julian S. Huxley *et al.* London: George Allen & Unwin Ltd., pp. 50–55.

RAYMOND, PERCY E. (1939) *Prehistoric life.* Cambridge: Harvard University Press, ix + 324 pp.
A splendid accurate and charmingly written introduction to the subject of paleontology.

SAGUI, CORNELIO L. (1930) Economic geology and allied sciences in ancient times. *Economic Geology,* vol. 25, pp. 65–86.

SAGUI, CORNELIO L. (1933) Economic geology and its allied sciences in ancient times; ancient literature. *Economic Geology,* vol. 28, pp. 20–40.

SCHUCHERT, CHARLES. (1924) The value of micro-fossils in petroleum exploration. *Bulletin of the American Association of Petroleum Geologists,* vol. 8, pp. 539–553.

STIGAND, I. A. (1925) *Outlines of the occurrence and geology of petroleum, an introductory handbook.* With an appendix on geophysical methods as applied to oil-finding. London: Charles Griffin and Company, Limited, x + 246 pp.

WILMARTH, M. GRACE. (1925) *The geologic time classification of the United States Geological Survey compared with other classifications accompanied by the original definitions of era, period and epoch terms.* Washington: Government Printing Office (United States Geological Survey, Bulletin 769), vi + 138 pp.

Chapter 14: Notes

1 *Cushman* (1940), p. 3.
2 *Raymond* (1939), ch. 1.
3 *Brues* (1923), p. 299.
4 *Cushman* (1928), p. 346.
5 *Hager* (1926), p. 50.
6 *Croneis* (1941), p. 1209, 1212, 1215.
7 *Ellis* (1936).
8 *Croneis* (1941), p. 1219.
9 *Mather* (1944), p. 155; cf. *Lees* (1940), p. 237; also *Pratt* (1944); *Miser* (1939).

10 Personal communication from K. F. Mather.
11 *Egloff* (1933), p. 80.
12 Personal communication from K. F. Mather.
13 *Egloff* (1933), p. 23.
14 *Ibid.,* p. 25.
15 *Ellis* (1936), p. 370.
16 *Hager* (1926), p. 81.
17 *Schuchert* (1924), p. 548.
18 Quoted *ibid.,* p. 549.
19 *Croneis* (1941), p. 1230–1236.
20 *Ibid.*
21 *Cushman* (1940), ch. 5.
22 *Ibid.*
23 *Egloff* (1933), pp. 125–128; *Kettering and Orth* (1932), pp. 4–5.
24 *Gould* (1929), p. 442.
25 *Egloff* (1933), pp. 17–34; *Gould* (1929), *Miser* (1939), pp. 308–309. *Lees* (1940), pp. 239–241; *Stigand* (1925), appendix, pp. 200–224; *Bruckshaw* (1943); *Rankine* (1945).

CHAPTER 15: THE CHEMIST'S JOB OF WORK

Bibliography and Guide to Further Reading

ARMSTRONG, E. F., editor. (1924) *Chemistry in the twentieth century; an account of the achievement and the present state of knowledge in chemical science.* London: Ernest Benn Limited, viii + 281 pp.

→ BAEKELAND, LEO HENDRIK. (1935) Impress of chemistry upon industry; bakelite, an example. *Industrial and Engineering Chemistry,* vol. 27, pp. 538–543.

→ BAEKELAND, L. H. (1938) Science and industry. *Chemistry & Industry,* vol. 57, pp. 679–682.

★ BOYD, T. A. (1935) *Research, the pathfinder of science and industry.* New York: D. Appleton-Century Company, xv + 319 pp.

CHAPMAN, A. CHASTON. (1927) *The growth of the profession of chemistry during the past half-century (1877–1927).* London: The Institute of Chemistry of Great Britain and Ireland, 23 pp.

→ DEMING, HORACE G. (1930) *In the realm of carbon, the story of organic chemistry*. New York: John Wiley & Sons, Inc., x + 365 pp.

→ DYER, WALTER S. (1941) *A practical survey of chemistry*. New York: Henry Holt and Company, vii + 480 pp.

FARRELL, HUGH. (1925) *What price progress? The stake of the investor in the development of chemistry*. New York: The Chemical Foundation, Inc., 102 pp.

FINDLAY, ALEXANDER. (1916) *Chemistry in the service of man*. London: Longmans, Green and Co., xiv + 255 pp.

★ FINDLAY, ALEXANDER. (1937) *A hundred years of chemistry*. New York: The Macmillan Company, 352 pp.

GOOD, H. G. (1936) On the early history of Liebig's laboratory. *Journal of Chemical Education*, vol. 13, pp. 557–562.

GIBBS, W. E. (1934) Chemical engineering and its industrial significance. *Science Progress*, vol. 28, pp. 405–419.

HALE, WILLIAM J. (1932) *Chemistry triumphant, the rise and reign of chemistry in a chemical world*. Baltimore: The Williams & Wilkins Company (A Century of Progress Series), x + 151 pp.

HALE, HARRISON. (1940) America's chemical heritage. *The Scientific Monthly*, vol. 51, pp. 269–276.

HARROW, BENJAMIN. (1920) *Eminent chemists of our time*. New York: D. Van Nostrand Company, pp. xvi + 248.

→ HAYNES, WILLIAMS, and GORDY, EDWARD L., editors. (1935) *Chemical Industry's Contribution to the Nation: 1635–1935. A Record of Chemical Accomplishment, with an Index of the Chemicals Made in America*. New York: Chemical Markets, Inc., 176 pp.

"A Supplement to *Chemical Industries*; May, 1935. Published in Celebration of the Tercentenary of the Founding of the American Chemical Industry by John Winthrop, Jr. . . ."

→ HAYNES, WILLIAMS. (1942) *This chemical age, the miracle of man-made materials*. New York: Alfred A. Knopf, xi + 385 + 22 pp.

An extraordinarily lucid account modern chemical achievement.

HOLMYARD, E. J. (1925) *Chemistry the time of Dalton*. London: Oxfo University Press (Chapters in the H tory of Science, 3); 128 pp.

HOLMYARD, ERIC JOHN. (1931) *Makers chemistry*. Oxford: At the Clarend Press, xv + 314 pp.

JAPP, FRANCIS R. (1910) Kekulé m morial lecture. In *Memorial lectu delivered before the Chemical Soci 1893–1900*. London: Gurney a Jackson, pp. 97–138.

Kekulé's two dreams are given his own words on p. 100.

★ KELLY, FRED C. (1936) *One thing le to another: the growth of an indust* Boston and New York: Hough Mifflin Company, 104 pp.

KETTERING, CHARLES F. (1944) Thom Midgley, Jr., an appreciation. *Scien* vol. 100, pp. 562–564.

KETTERING, CHARLES F. (1947) B graphical memoir of Thomas Midg Jr. *National Academy of Sciences the United States of America, B graphical Memoirs*, vol. 24, pp. 3 380.

→ LACHMAN, ARTHUR. (1899) *The sp of organic chemistry. An introduct to the current literature of the subj* With an introduction by Paul C. Fr New York: The Macmillan Compa xviii + 229 pp.

→ LIEBIG, JUSTUS VON. (1851) *Fami letters on chemistry, in its relation physiology, dietetics, agriculture, co merce and political economy*. Th edition. London: Taylor, Walton Maberly, xx + 536 pp.

→ LOWRY, T. M. (1915) *Historical in duction to chemistry*. London: M millan and Co., Limited, xv + pp.

MAJOR, RANDOLPH T. (1940) Contri tion of the chemical industry science. *The Scientific Monthly*, 51, pp. 158–164.

★ MASON, HOWARD S. (1943) History the use of graphic formulas in org chemistry. *Isis*. vol. 34, pp. 3 354.

★ McKIE, DOUGLAS. (1944) Wöhl "synthetic" urea and the rejection vitalism: a chemical legend. *Natu* vol. 153, pp. 608–610.

MEYER, ERNST VON. (1906) *A history of chemistry from earliest times to the present day, being also an introduction to the study of the science.* Translated by George McGowan. Third edition. London: Macmillan and Co., Limited, xxvii + 691 pp.

MIALL, STEPHEN; and MIALL, LAURENCE MACKENZIE. (1937) *Chemistry, matter, and life.* New York: Longmans, Green & Co., ix + 296 pp.

MORRISON, A. CRESSY. (1937) *Man in a chemical world; the service of chemical industry.* New York: Charles Scribner's Sons, xi + 292 pp.

MUIR, M. M. PATTISON. (1909) *A history of chemical theories and laws.* New York: John Wiley & Sons, xx + 567 pp.

PALMER, HENRY F., and SHITH, GEORG E. P., JR. (1944) *Some aspects of the American chemical industry.* Akron: The Firestone Tire & Rubber Co. (Firestone Chemical Research Laboratories); 56 pp.

PARTINGTON, J. R. (1935) *Origins and development of applied chemistry.* London: Longmans, Green and Co., xii + 597 pp.

PARTINGTON, J. R. (1936) The origin of modern chemical symbols and formulae. *Journal of the Society of Chemical Industry,* vol. 55, pp. 759–762.

PARTINGTON, J. R. (1937) *A short history of chemistry.* New York: The Macmillan Company, xiv + 386 pp.

PAULING, LINUS. (1947) *General chemistry: an introduction to descriptive chemistry and modern chemical theory.* San Francisco: W. H. Freeman and Company, vii + 599 pp.

ROBERTSON, G. ROSS. (1944) The task of the organic chemist. *Science in the University.* Berkeley and Los Angeles: University of California Press, pp. 67–79.
A brilliant essay.

SCHORLEMMER, CARL. (1894) *The rise and development of organic chemistry.* Revised edition, edited by Arthur Smithells. London: Macmillan and Co., xxvii + 280 pp.

THORPE, SIR EDWARD. (1921) *History of chemistry.* London: Watts & Co., vol. 1, 148 pp.; vol. 2, 152 pp.

TILDEN, SIR WILLIAM A. (1926) *Chemical discovery and invention in the twentieth century.* Fifth edition. London: George Routledge and Sons, Limited, pp. xvi + 487.

→ WEIGSAL, MEYER W., editor. (1944) *Chaim Weizmann, statesman, scientist, builder of the Jewish Commonwealth.* With a foreword by Felix Frankfurter. New York: Dial Press, 340 pp.
Of special interest is part iv, "The scientist," with chapters by Ernst Bergmann, H. B. Speakman, Vladimir N. Ipatieff, and Louis B. Fieser.

WILLIAMS, ROBERT R. (1930) Chemistry in the telephone industry. *Industrial and Engineering Chemistry;* vol. 22, pp. 316–322.

Chapter 15: Notes

1 *Robertson* (1944), p. 67.
2 *Ibid.*
3 *Partington* (1935).
4 *Partington* (1937), p. 1.
5 *Ibid.,* p. 20.
6 *McKie* (1944), p. 608.
7 *Tilden* (1926), p. 334.
8 *Ibid.*
9 *Partington* (1937), p. 229.
10 *Partington* (1937), pp. 203–204.
11 Quoted *ibid.*
12 Quoted in *Japp* (1910), p. 100.
13 *Partington* (1937), p. 286.
14 *Robertson* (1944), p. 68.
15 *Kelly* (1936), p. 9.
16 *Ibid.,* p. 10.
17 *Ibid.,* pp. 11–12; cf. *Weigsal* (1944), pp. 266–267.
18 *Haynes* (1942), p. 329.
19 *Kelly* (1936), p. 12.
20 *Haynes* (1942), pp. 331–332.
21 *Ibid.*
22 *Robertson* (1944), pp. 75–76.
23 *Ibid.*
24 *Pauling* (1947), p. 494.
25 *Robertson,* p. 77.
26 *Ibid.,* p. 76.

CHAPTER 16: THE SOLAR CORONA

Bibliography and Guide to Further Reading

BUSH, VANNEVAR. (1941) Biographical memoir of Arthur Edwin Kennelly 1861–1939. *National Academy of Sciences of the United States of America, biographical memoirs*, vol. 22, pp. 83–119.

→ DELLINGER, JOSEPH. (1947) The ionosphere. *Scientific Monthly*, vol. 65, pp. 115–126.

★ DE SOTO, CLINTON B. (1936) *Two hundred meters and down: the story of amateur radio*. West Hartford, Conn.: The American Radio Relay League, Inc., ix + 184 pp.

FLEMING, J. A. (1942) The sun and the earth's magnetic field. *Annual Report of the Smithsonian Institution*, pp. 173–208.

GOLDBERG, LEO. (1940) Patrolling the corona. *The Telescope*, vol. 7, pp. 45–47.

LYOT, BERNARD. (1945) Planetary and solar observations on the Pic du Midi in 1941, 1942, and 1943. *The Astrophysical Journal*, vol. 101, pp. 255–259.

→ MENZEL, DONALD H. (1939) The relationship of chemistry and astronomy. *The Telescope*, vol. 6, pp. 130–132, 143.

→ MENZEL, DONALD H. (1941 [1]) What is the solar corona? *The Telescope*, vol. 8, pp. 64–67.

★ MENZEL, DONALD H. (1941 [2]) A preface to solar research. *The Scientific Monthly*, vol. 52, pp. 320–336.

★ MENZEL, DONALD H. (1945) The sun and radio communication. (An unpublished manuscript).

This material will be included in Dr. Menzel's forthcoming book, *Our sun*, in the series of Harvard Astronomical Books, published by Blakiston.

★ MIMNO, HARRY ROWE. (1937) The physics of the ionosphere. *Reviews of Modern Physics*, vol. 9, pp. 1–43.

★ MIMNO, HARRY ROWE. (1945) Wave propagation. Chapter 4 of *Transmission lines, antennas, and wave guides*, by Ronald W. P. King, Harry Rowe Mimno and Alexander H.

Wing. New York: McGraw-Hill Book Company, Inc., pp. 300–320.

PECK, JAMES L. H. (1946) Out of the world; the story of the ionosphere. *Harper's Magazine*, vol. 192, pp. 50 509.

★ PIERCE, GEORGE W. (1910) *Principles wireless telegraphy*. New Yor McGraw-Hill Book Company, ix 350 pp.

Contains a splendid account of ea history.

RATCLIFFE, J. A. (1940) *The physic principles of wireless*. With a for word by E. V. Appleton. Fourth ed tion, revised. London: Methuen & C Ltd. (Methuen's Monographs on Ph sical Subjects), vi + 110 pp.

→ ROBERTS, WALTER O. (1945) Artifici eclipses of the sun. *Sky and Telesco* vol. 4 (No. 4, February), pp. 3–6.

RUEHLE, A. E. (1940) Spectrochemic analysis. *Scientific Monthly*, vol. 5 pp. 41–44.

SKELLETT, A. M. (1940) The coron viser. *The Telescope*, vol. 7, pp. 54–5

★ TUSKA, C. D. (1944) Historical notes the determination of distance by tim radio waves. *Journal of the Frankl Institute*, vol. 237, pp. 1–20, 83–10

VYVYAN, R. N. (1933) *Wireless ov thirty years*. London: George Rou ledge & Sons, Ltd., xiv + 256 p

★ WHIPPLE, FRED L. (1943) Meteors a the earth's upper atmosphere. *Revie of Modern Physics*, vol. 15, pp. 24 264.

Chapter 16: Notes

1 Mimno (1937), p. 1.
2 Ibid., pp. 1–2.
3 Vyvyan (1933), p. 22.
4 Ibid., p. 25.
5 Mimno (1945), p. 305.
6 De Soto (1936), p. 24.
7 Mimno (1937), p. 4; De Sc (1936).
8 Mimno (1937), p. 4.
9 Ibid., p. 5.
10 Ibid.
11 Ibid.
12 Ibid.
13 Ibid.
14 Whipple (1943).

15 After *Mimno* (1945), p. 6.
16 The remainder of this chapter is based almost entirely on *Menzel* (1936).
17. *Roberts* (1945).

CHAPTER 17: SCIENCE, SERVANT OF MAN

Bibliography and Guide to Further Reading

AMES, JOSEPH SWEETMAN. (1918) The trained man of science in the war. *Science,* vol. 48, pp. 401–410.

[ANON.] (1940) *Science in war.* Harmondsworth, England: Penguin Books Ltd. (Penguin Special, S74), 140 pp.

BAXTER, JAMES PHINNEY, 3RD. (1946) *Scientists against time.* With a foreword by Vannevar Bush. Boston: Little, Brown and Company, xv + 473 pp.
A layman's account of the work of the Office of Scientific Research and Development.

BLAKESLEE, ALBERT F. (1940) Ideals of science. *Science,* vol. 92, pp. 589–592.

BRAGG, SIR WILLIAM. (1921) *The world of sound: six lectures delivered before a juvenile auditory at the Royal Institution, Christmas, 1919.* London: G. Bell and Sons Ltd., vii + 196 pp.

BRIDGMAN, P. W. (1947) Scientists and social responsibility. *Scientific Monthly,* vol. 65, pp. 148–154.

CALL, L. E., et al. (1943) Science and the war: a symposium presented at the seventy-fifth anniversary meeting of the Kansas Academy of Science, Lawrence, Kansas, April 10, 1943. Reprinted from *Transactions of the Kansas Academy of Science,* vol. 46, 47 pp.

COHEN, I. BERNARD. (1943) Benjamin Franklin as scientist and citizen. *American Scholar,* vol. 12, pp. 474–481.

COHEN, I. BERNARD. (1945[1]) American physicists at war: from the Revolution to the World Wars. *American Journal of Physics,* vol. 13, pp. 223–235.

COHEN, I. BERNARD. (1945[2]) American physicists at war: from the first World War to 1942. *American Journal of Physics,* vol. 13, pp. 333–346.

COHEN, I. BERNARD. (1945[3]) Science and the Revolution; the vital interplay of engineering and science with government had its beginning in war necessities. *Technology Review,* vol. 47, pp. 367–368, 374–378.

COHEN, I. BERNARD. (1946) Science and the Civil War. First large-scale organization of technical and scientific resources of man power during the Civil War marks that conflict as the turning point in the technology of warfare. *Technology Review,* vol. 48, pp. 167–170, 192–193.

[COMPTON, KARL T.] (1942) *Scientists face the world of 1942.* Essays by Karl T. Compton, Robert W. Trullinger, Vannevar Bush. New Brunswick: Rutgers University Press, 80 pp.

DUBRIDGE, L. A., and RIDENOUR, L. N. (1945) Expanded horizons: in developing microwave radar systems for military purposes the radiation laboratory bequeaths to civilian use a wide range of developments in electronics and radio techniques. *The Technology Review,* vol. 48, pp. 23–26, 62, 64, 66.

→ EIDINOFF, MAXWELL LEIGH, and RUCHLIS, HYMAN. (1947) *Atomics for the millions.* With an introduction by Harold C. Urey. New York: Whittlesey House, McGraw-Hill Book Company, Inc., xiv + 281 pp.

EISENSCHIML, OTTO. (1942) The chemist in three wars. *Science,* vol. 96, pp. 347–352, 367–373.

★ GILCHRIST, H. L. (1928) *A comparative study of World War casualties from gas and other weapons.* Washington: United States Government Printing Office, vi + 51 pp.

★ GORAN, MORRIS. (1941) The myth of poison gas. *The Scientific Monthly,* vol. 53, pp. 374–376.

GOUDSMIT, SAMUEL A. (1947) *Alsos.* New York: Henry Schuman, Inc., xiv + 259 pp.
The account of the mission sent to find out whether the Nazis had an atom bomb — and the only documented case history of science under totalitarianism.

→ GRAY, GEORGE W. (1943) *Science at War.* New York, London: Harper & Brothers Publishers, xii + 296 pp.

→ HALDANE, J. B. S. (1925) Callinicus, a defense of chemical warfare. New York: E. P. Dutton & Company, 84 pp.

→ HECHT, SELIG. (1947) *Explaining the atom.* New York: The Viking Press, xiv + 205 pp.

HOPKINS, NEVIL MONROE. (1919) *The outlook for research and invention, with an appendix of problems awaiting solution.* New York: D. Van Nostrand Company, x + 241 pp.

HUME, EDGAR ERSKINE. (1943) Contributions of the medical corps of the army to the public health laboratory. *Science,* vol. 97, pp. 293–300.

HUXLEY, JULIAN SORELL. (1940) Science, war and reconstruction. *Science,* vol. 91, pp. 151–158.

[JOHN CRERAR LIBRARY, THE.] (1917) *A selected list of books on military medicine and surgery, September 24, 1917.* Chicago: Printed by Order of the Board of Directors, 58 pp.

KAEMPFFERT, WALDEMAR. (1931) Communication and world peace. *Proceedings of the American Philosophical Society,* vol. 70, pp. 273–284.

KAEMPFFERT, WALDEMAR. (1942) *Science and technology — offspring of war, a lecture delivered on the Nellie Heldt Lecture Fund.* Oberlin: Oberlin College (The Nellie Heldt Lectures, 2), 46 pp.

KAEMPFFERT, WALDEMAR. (1943) Science and war. *Science,* vol. 97, pp. 532–533.

LEET, D. DON. (1946) Earth motion from the atomic bomb test. *American Scientist,* vol. 34, pp. 198–211.

LEROUX, LUCIEN. (1933) *La guerre chimique.* Deuxième édition revue et augmentée. Paris: Éditions Spes, 163 pp.

MONTAGU, M. F. ASHLEY. (1943) Four on war: from the writings of earlier scientists is culled proof of their efforts for life rather than destruction. *The Technology Review,* vol. 45, pp. 315–316, 334, 336, 338.

→ RABI, I. I. (1945) The physicist returns from the war. *The Atlantic Monthly,* vol. 176, October, pp. 107–114.

★ RAYLEIGH, LORD. (1938) Vision in nature and vision aided by science; science and warfare. *Science,* vol. 88, pp. 175–181, 204–208.

→ RIDENOUR, LOUIS N. (1947) The scientist fights for peace. *Atlantic Monthly,* vol. 179 (May), pp. 80–83.

RUCHLIS, HYMAN. *See* EIDINOFF RUCHLIS (1947).

→ SHAPLEY, HARLOW. (1945) A desi for fighting. *American Scientist,* v 33, pp. 84–102.

SIGERIST, HENRY E. (1942) War a culture. *Bulletin of the History Medicine,* vol. 11, pp. 1–11.

SIGERIST, HENRY E. (1943) War a medicine. *The Journal of Laborato and Clinical Medicine,* vol. 28, 531–538.

→ SMYTH, HENRY DEWOLF. (1945) *Aton energy for military purposes. T official report on the development the atomic bomb under the auspi of the United States Governme 1940–1945.* Princeton: Princeton U versity Press, ix + 264 pp.

STONE, M. H. (1944) American matl matics in the present war. *Science,* v 100, pp. 529–535.

SWENSON, T. L. (1944) Agricultu chemical research for war and pea *American Scientist,* vol. 32, pp. 19 204.

→ THIMANN, K. V. (1947) The role biologists in warfare. *Bulletin of t Atomic Scientists,* vol. 3, pp. 211–2

→ YERKES, ROBERT M., editor. (1920) *T new world of science; its developme during the war.* Introduction George Ellery Hale, New York: T Century Co. (The Century N World Series), xix + 443 pp.

Chapter 17: Notes

1 *Hecht* (1947); *Eidinoff and Ruch* (1947).
2 *Smyth* (1945), ch. xiii.
3 *Goudsmit* (1947), pp. 168–170.
4 *Haldane* (1925), pp. 28–29.
5 *Ibid.,* p. 30.
6 *Ames* (1918).
7 *Bridgman* (1947), p. 150.
8 *Rayleigh* (1938), p. 207.
9 *Ibid.*
10 *Gilchrist* (1928); *Goran* (1941).
11 Cf. *Yerkes* (1920), *passim.*
12 *Rayleigh* (1938), pp. 207–208.
13 *Ibid.*
14 *Ibid.*
15 *Blakeslee* (1940).
16 Cf. comments in *Ridenour* (1947).

CHAPTER 18: HOW TO GET THE MOST OUT OF SCIENCE

Bibliography and Guide to Further Reading

BAILEY, I. W., and SPOEHR, H. A. (1929) *The rôle of research in the development of forestry in North America.* New York: The Macmillan Company, xiii + 118 pp.

BAKER, JOHN R. (1942) *The scientific life.* London: George Allen & Unwin Ltd., 154 pp.

BAKER, JOHN R. (1945) *Science and the planned state.* London: George Allen & Unwin Ltd., 120 pp.

BERNAL, J. D. (1939) *The social function of science.* London: George Routledge & Sons Ltd., xvi + 482 pp.

BLACKWELDER, ELIOT. (1941) Science and human prospects. *Annual Report of the Board of Regents of the Smithsonian Institution,* pp. 267–283. ". . . Reprinted by permission from the *Bulletin of the Geological Society of America,* vol. 52, Mar. 1, 1941."

BRIDGMAN, P. W. (1940) Science: public or private? *Philosophy of Science,* vol. 7, pp. 36–48.

BRIDGMAN, P. W. (1943) Science, and its changing social environment. *Science,* vol. 97, pp. 147–150.

BRIDGMAN, P. W. (1945) The prospect for intelligence. *Yale Review,* vol. 34, pp. 444–461.

BRIDGMAN, P. W. (1947) Scientists and social responsibility. *Scientific Monthly,* vol. 65, pp. 148–154.

BUCKLEY, OLIVER E. (1945) "Planned" research opposed. [A letter to the editor of *The New York Times,* dated 21 August 1945.] An important corrective to the opinion that industrial research is completely "planned."

BUSH, VANNEVAR. (1945) *Science the endless frontier, a report to the president.* Washington: United States Government Printing Office, ix + 184 pp.

BUSH, VANNEVAR. (1946) *Endless horizons.* Introduction by Dr. Frank B. Jewett. Washington: Public Affairs Press, viii + 182 pp.

CANNON, WALTER B., and FIELD, RICHARD M. (1945) International relations in science; a review of their aims and methods in the past and in the future. *Chronica Botanica,* vol. 9, pp. 255–298.

CARLSON, A. J. (1940) The role of the fundamental sciences in medical progress. *Scientific Monthly,* vol. 50, pp. 59–64.

→ CONANT, JAMES B. (1943) Science and society in the postwar world. *Technology Review,* vol. 45, pp. 366–367, 388, 390, 392, 394.

→ CONANT, JAMES B. (1944) The advancement of learning in the United States in the postwar world. *Proceedings of the American Philosophical Society,* vol. 87, pp. 291–298.

→ CONANT, JAMES BRYANT. (1944) Science and the national welfare. *Harvard Alumni Bulletin,* vol. 47, pp. 56–59. Address on acceptance of the Priestley Medal of the American Chemical Society.

★ CONANT, JAMES BRYANT. (1945) National research argued. [A letter to the editor of *The New York Times,* dated 10 August 1945.]

★ CONANT, JAMES B. (1947 [1]) *On understanding science, an historical approach.* New Haven: Yale University Press, xv + 145 pp. The Terry Lectures.

→ CONANT, JAMES B. (1947 [2]) Science and the practical arts. *Harvard Business Review,* vol. 25, pp. 545–553.

→ CONANT, JAMES B. (1947 [3]) *America's fitness to survive.* Boston: Retail Trade Board, Boston Chamber of Commerce, 13 pp. An address delivered before the Boston Conference on Distribution, 21 October 1947.

CONKLIN, EDWIN GRANT. (1935) *Freedom and responsibility, a biological view of some problems of democracy.* Boston: Houghton Mifflin Company, vii + 88 pp.

CROWTHER, J. G. (1941) *The social relations of science.* New York: The Macmillan Company, xxxii + 665 pp. Advocates planning and condemns scientific research of the past because it was removed "from welfare." To be taken *cum grano salis.*

DuBRIDGE, L. A. (1946) Science and national policy. *American Scientist,* vol. 34, pp. 226–238.

FIELD, RICHARD M. *See* CANNON (1945).

→ FULTON, JOHN F. (1945) Penicillin, plasma fractionation, and the physician. *Atlantic Monthly*, vol. 176 (September), pp. 107–114.

→ GEORGE, WILLIAM H. (1936) *The scientist in action, a scientific study of his methods.* London: Williams & Norgate Ltd., 355 pp.

★ GREGG, ALAN. (1944) A critique of medical research. *Proceedings of the American Philosophical Society,* vol. 87, pp. 313–320.

→ GREGORY, SIR RICHARD. (1938) *Cultural contacts of science.* Washington: Carnegie Institution of Washington, 56 pp.

Elihu Root Lectures of Carnegie Institution of Washington on the influence of science and research on current thought, fifth lecture, delivered December 8, 1938.

GREGORY, SIR RICHARD. (1941) Scientific knowledge and action. *Nature,* vol. 148, pp. 612–616.

GREGORY, SIR RICHARD. (1941) *Science in chains.* London: Macmillan & Co., Ltd., 32 pp.

"Macmillan War Pamphlets," no. 12.

★ HALE, GEORGE ELLERY. (1913, 1914, 1915) National academies and the progress of research. *Science,* vol. 38 (1913), pp. 681–698; vol. 39 (1914), pp. 189–200; vol. 40 (1914), pp. 907–919; vol. 41 (1915), pp. 12–23.

HALE, GEORGE ELLERY. (1922) A national focus of science and research. *Scribner's Magazine,* vol. 72, pp. 515–531.

HENDERSON, LAWRENCE J. (1941) *The study of man.* Philadelphia: University of Pennsylvania Press, 22 pp.

"University of Pennsylvania Bicentennial Conference."

★ HILL, A. V. (1941 [1]) Science, national and international, and the basis of cooperation. *Science,* vol. 93, pp. 579–584.

★ HILL, A. V. (1941 [2]) The use and misuse of science in government. *Science,* vol. 94, pp. 475–477.

→ HILL, DOUGLAS W. (1944–?) *The impact and value of science.* London: Hutchinson's Scientific & Technical Publications, 88 pp.

HOAGLAND, HUDSON. (1947) Scienti capital and the dividends of appli science. *Diseases of the nervous s tem,* vol. 8, pp. 106–110.

HUXLEY, JULIAN. (1935) *Science a social needs.* With an introducto chapter by Sir William Bragg, a discussions with Professor H. Le Sir Thomas D. Barlow, and P fessor P. M. S. Blackett. New Yo and London: Harper & Brothers Pu lishers, xvi + 287 pp.

Based on a "tour" of British cent of research.

HUXLEY, J. S., et al. (1944) *Reshapi man's heritage: biology in the serv of man.* London: George Allen Unwin, Ltd., 96 pp.

★ HUXLEY, THOMAS H. (1893) *Method a results.* London: Macmillan and C (Collected Essays, vol. 1), viii + 4 pp.

Especially "The progress of scien 1837–1887," a moving and eloque plea for pure science.

JEWETT, FRANK B., and KING, ROBE W. (1941) *Engineering progress a the social order.* Philadelphia: U versity of Pennsylvania Press, pp.

"University of Pennsylvania Bice tennial Conference."

KAEMPFFERT, WALDEMAR. (194 *Should the government support s ence?* New York: Public Affairs Co mittee, Inc. (Public Affairs Pamph No. 119), 32 pp.

★ [KAPITSA, P. L.] (1943) *Address academician P. L. Kapitsa on t organization of scientific work in t Institute for Physical Problems of t Academy of Sciences of the USS* London, Society for Cultural Re tions with the U.S.S.R. [98, Gow Street], 17 pp. + 10 pp., mime graphed.

"Translated from the reprint *Vestnik Akademii Nauk S.S.R.,* N 6, 1943." The 10 pp. supplement devoted to a discussion of Kapits address by other academicians. I dicates that the point of view towa over-all planning advocated many leading Soviet scientists quite different from that of Ame can and British fellow-travelers Russophiles.

KING, ROBERT W. *See* JEWETT (1941).

LANGMUIR, IRVING. (1934) Science as a guide in life. *General Electric Review,* vol. 37, pp. 312–317.

LANGMUIR, IRVING. (1943) Science, common sense and decency. *Science,* vol. 97, pp. 1–7.

LEHMAN, HARVEY C. (1943) Man's most creative years: then and now. *Science,* vol. 98, pp. 393–399.

MEES, C. E. KENNETH. (1920) *The organization of industrial scientific research.* New York: McGraw-Hill Book Company, Inc., ix + 175 pp.

MEES, C. E. KENNETH. (1946) *The path of science.* With the co-operation of John R. Baker. New York: John Wiley & Sons, Inc., xii + 250 pp.
> An important book — to be read by all who are interested in the planning of both fundamental and applied research.

MELLANBY, SIR EDWARD. (1939) *Recent advances in medical science, a study of their social and economic implications. The Rede Lecture delivered before the University of Cambridge on 28 April 1939.* Cambridge, England: At the University Press, 62 pp.

MERTON, ROBERT K. (1935) Fluctuations in the rate of industrial invention. *The Quarterly Journal of Economics,* vol. 49, pp. 454–474.

MERTON, ROBERT K. (1947) The machine, the worker and the engineer. *Science,* vol. 105, pp. 79–84.

MITCHELL, WESLEY C. (1939) The public relations of science. *Science,* vol. 90, pp. 599, 607.

MUNRO, WILLIAM B. (1940) Some economic repercussions of medical progress. *The Scientific Monthly,* vol. 51, pp. 172–178.

NAGEL, ERNEST. (1945) Science — with and without wisdom. Is there any chance that science can help solve social problems? *The Saturday Review of Literature,* vol. 28, pp. 7–8, 22, 24–25.

POLANYI, M. (1940) *The contempt of freedom, the Russian experiment and after.* London: Watts & Co., ix + 116 pp.
> Esp. "The rights and duties of science," pp. 1–26.

POLANYI, MICHAEL. (1946) The planning of science. *Society for Freedom in Science: Occasional pamphlet no. 4,* 14 pp.

★ ROLLER, DUANE. (1945) The crucial postwar need for an international, auxiliary language for the sciences. *Science,* vol. 101, pp. 299–300.

→ SARTON, GEORGE. (1937) *The history of science and the new humanism.* Cambridge: Harvard University Press, xx + 196 pp.

→ SAX, KARL. (1947) Soviet science and political philosophy. *Scientific Monthly,* vol. 65, pp. 43–47.

★ SCHLESINGER, ARTHUR M. (1946) An American historian looks at science and technology. *Isis,* vol. 36, pp. 162–166.

→ SHAPLEY, HARLOW. (1945) Status quo or pioneer? The fate of American science. *Harper's Magazine,* vol. 191, pp. 312–317.

SIGERIST, HENRY E. (1941) *Medicine and human welfare.* New Haven: Yale University Press, ix + 148 pp.
> The Terry Lectures.

★ SIGERIST, HENRY E. (1943) *Civilization and Disease.* Ithaca: Cornell University Press, xii + 255 pp.
> The Messenger Lectures.

SPOEHR, H. A. *See* BAILEY (1929).

★ STEELMAN, JOHN R. (1947) *Science and public policy.* Vol. 1. A program for the nation. Washington, D. C.: U. S. Government Printing Office, x + 73 pp.

→ TANSLEY, A. G. (1942) *The values of science to humanity.* London: George Allen & Unwin Ltd., 32 pp.
> The Herbert Spencer Lecture, Oxford University, 2 June 1942.

→ TAYLOR, F. SHERWOOD. (1945) *Science past and present.* London, Toronto: William Heinemann Ltd., 275 pp.

★ VON PETTENKOFER, MAX. (1941) *The value of health to a city; two lectures delivered in 1873.* Translated from the German, with an introduction by Henry E. Sigerist. Baltimore: The Johns Hopkins Press, 52 pp.
> "Reprinted from *Bulletin of the History of Medicine, . . .*" vol. 10, pp. 473–503, 593–613.

WEAVER, WARREN. (1945) Free science sought. [A letter to the editor of *The New York Times,* dated 28 August 1945.]

★ WOODWARD, S. B., and FEEMSTER, ROY F. (1933) The relation of smallpox morbidity to vaccination laws. *New England Journal of Medicine*, vol. 208, pp. 317–318.

Chapter 18: Notes

1 *Bernal* (1939); *Crowther* (1941).
2 *Baker* (1942); *Baker* (1945); *Polanyi* (1940).
3 *Woodward and Feemster* (1933).
4 See chapter 5.
5 *Schlesinger* (1946), p. 165.
6 *Buckley* (1945).
7 *Mees* (1946), pp. 186 ff.
8 *Conant* (1945).
9 *Ibid.*
10 *Bernal* (1939), p. 343.
11 *Fulton* (1945).
12 *Conant* (1947 [1]).
13 *Polanyi* (1946).
14 *Fulton* (1945).
15 *Crowther* (1941), p. 352.
16 *Crowther* (1941), p. 522.
17 *Bernal* (1939), p. 98.
18 Conant (1943).

Acknowledgments

THE PLEASANTEST task of the author of a scientific or historical book is that of acknowledging his indebtedness to the many kind persons who have helped him. Not only does the opportunity of expressing gratitude in a more pronounced way than the personal letter make the writing of the "acknowledgments" section a joy, but the very fact of writing it symbolizes the end of the job. The research upon which this book is built was begun in spring 1942; the manuscript has been completed five and a half years later, in fall 1947.

The reader should appreciate the difficulties in the way of any single individual who attempts to write a book dealing with aspects of all the sciences, as this one does. The preparation of each chapter demands serious study, not only of the special subject dealt with, such as the nutritional requirements of plants, but also of the relation of that subject to the branch of science to which it belongs, plant science as a whole. So closely intertwined are the paths of modern science that each subject has to be viewed in relation to other sciences as well, chemical techniques, data from physics, etc. Although each of the case histories forms a separate story (one that may be read with profit apart from the rest of the book) I have tried in so far as possible to show the reader not only the continuity of scientific history from early days to the present within each chapter, but also how the story there presented is related to the life of science as a whole.

During the five and a half years which the writing of this book has required, many subjects of promise proved disappointing. They represented "dead ends" from the special viewpoint adopted because, in many cases, the pattern of the application was not so clearly defined as another; or, because the published literature concerning it was not so abundant as at first seemed to be the case; or, even if the literature was satisfactory and the pattern clear, the very nature of the subject did not lend itself to a simple exposition for the layman who has no adequate scientific background. Although the case histories are representative of the several branches of science, they make no attempt to give the reader an overall view of the present state of knowledge in all of them, but give the reader a sufficient basis for understanding only the *nature* of the scientific enterprise (as explained in Chapter 1) rather than a summary of all the results obtained by scientists.

When Dr. Harlow Shapley first broached the subject of the book to me, the only reservation I held was the accuracy of the chapters falling outside my own special competence as an historian of science trained chiefly in mathematics and physics. This obstacle has, I hope, been overcome by the willingness of experts to read critically the chapter or chapters dealing with their individual specialties.

In addition to those who read individual chapters for me, I am under the greatest debt to many friends and colleagues who willingly gave of their time to explain to me the basic principles of their subject, who suggested reading, and answered many questions. There is an equal debt to the authors of the many excellent and informative books, monographs, and articles which are listed above in the section of "Bibliography and Guide to Further Reading." I feel much as the physician Sir Thomas Mayerne must have felt when he wrote: "It is easy to swell out books when half is the work of others."[1] Yet I must admit to a considerable satisfaction in being able to make available to the lay reader the contents of many publications which he would not otherwise have encountered.

I gratefully acknowledge my obligation to the following persons for having read, in an earlier form, one or more chapters of the manuscript; for having, in the midst of a busy schedule of teaching and research, taken out time to give me critical comments which have ensured a higher degree of accuracy and understanding than would otherwise have been possible.

Chapter 2: Conditions of Scientific Discovery
  DR. IAGO GALDSTON, New York Academy of Medicine
  DR. JOHN F. FULTON, Director of the Historical Library, and Sterling Professor of Physiology, Yale University School of Medicine

[1] As quoted by Miss Marjorie Hope Nicolson in her charming preface to the *Conway Letters*.

Professor George Sarton, Harvard University, Associate of the Carnegie Institution of Washington, and editor of *Isis*

Chapter 3: The "Happy Accident" and Its Consequences
Dr. Iago Galdston
Professor George Sarton

Chapter 4: The "Spectrum" of Scientific Activity
Dr. Philippe Emmanuel Le Corbeiller, Lecturer on Engineering Sciences and Applied Physics, Harvard University
Dr. Iago Galdston
Professor George Sarton

Chapter 5: Fundamental Research and Its Applications
Dr. Karl K. Darrow, Bell Telephone Laboratories (only that portion dealing with electron diffraction)
Dr. Philippe E. Le Corbeiller

Chapter 6: Auxins and Agriculture
Professor Kenneth V. Thimann, Harvard University [2]
Professor F. W. Went, California Institute of Technology

Chapter 7: The Electric Current and Radio
Dr. Philippe E. Le Corbeiller
Professor George Sarton

Chapter 8: Synthetic Rubber and Nylon
Dr. Jas. K. Hunt, Director of Public Relations, E. I. DuPont de Nemours and Co. [3]
Professor Robert Woodward, Harvard University

Chapter 9: Fundamental Research in Which a Practical Application Seems Likely
Professor K. V. Thimann

Chapter 10: Blood Groups and Blood Transfusion [4]
Dr. William C. Boyd, Boston University School of Medicine [5]

[2] Who, also, in many conversations, gave me what amounted to a private course in plant physiology.

[3] Who also supplied me with reprints and photostats of many articles I needed for writing that chapter, who answered many questions, and who furnished information about the discovery of 2,4-D.

[4] A chance meeting with Dr. Geoffrey Keynes in the office of our mutual friend, Mr. Philip Hofer, in the Houghton Library, enabled me to clear up a vexing point on the introduction of blood transfusion into the British Army in World War I.

[5] With whom, also, on many occasions, I was able to discuss the technique of blood group determinations and the applications of blood groups to anthropology.

Mrs. William C. Boyd

Dr. Bertram M. Bernheim, Associate Professor of Surgery, the Johns Hopkins Medical School [6]

Dr. Reuben Ottenberg, New York City [7]

Chapter 11: The Story of Hybrid Corn; and Chapter 12: The Fortune at the Rainbow's End

Professor (emeritus), George Harrison Shull, Princeton University [8]

Mr. A. Richard Crabb, Naperville, Illinois [9]

Professor Paul C. Mangelsdorf, Harvard University [10]

Chapter 13: Practical Innovations Based on Existing Fundamental Knowledge

Professor (emeritus) G. W. Pierce, Harvard University [11]

Professor Theodore V. Hunt, Harvard University [12]

Chapter 14: Foraminifera and Oil Prospecting

Dr. Joseph C. Cushman, Founder and Director of the Cushman Laboratory for Foraminiferal Research, Sharon, Mass. [13]

Professor Kirtley F. Mather, Harvard University

Chapter 15: The Chemist's Job of Work

Professor Robert Woodward

Dr. Leonard Nash, Harvard University

[6] Who drew my attention to the great importance of sodium citrate which, at first, I had slighted.

[7] Who also kindly sent me reprints of his early publications and supplied a considerable amount of personal information.

[8] Who also sent me much valuable personal information, supplied the photograph of his exhibition in Omaha, and who drew my attention first to the significance of the work of Donald F. Jones.

[9] Who also very generously sent me the galleys of his book, *The Hybrid Corn Makers*, so that I might incorporate his own findings in my chapter.

[10] Who also patiently explained to me the techniques of, and the problems in, corn breeding, showed me the significance of the work of Edward Murray East, and allowed me to photograph the exhibit of the double cross in the Botanical Museum, Harvard University.

[11] Who also kindly supplied me with information concerning his own early work in the field of magnetostriction and who made available to me copies of his early correspondence with Lee De Forest (for Chapter 16).

[12] Who also drew my attention to the diagram showing the construction of a magnetostriction underwater sound oscillator.

[13] Who generously allowed me to visit him and ask him questions about his own early research and the history of the subject in general, and who supplied me with most of the illustrations for Chapter 14.

Chapter 16: The Solar Corona and Radio Communication [14]
  MR. JOHN ALVIN PIERCE, Research Fellow in Electronics, Harvard University [15]
  DR. PHILIPPE E. LE CORBEILLER
  DR. WALTER O. ROBERTS, Superintendent of the High Altitude Observatory at Climax, Colorado [16]

When the manuscript was completed, it was read in its entirety by MR. THOMAS KUHN, who made many valuable comments; and the chapters dealing with biological subjects (Chapters 2, 3, 6, 9, 10, 11, and 12) were read by MRS. WALLES T. EDMONDSON, who saved me from several bad slips.

I should like to acknowledge the kindness of the officers of the National Science Fund (National Academy of Sciences): DR. WILLIAM J. ROBBINS, Director of the New York Botanical Garden, and first chairman of the National Science Fund, who, especially during the first year of research, made many helpful suggestions and helped me to organize my ideas about the book, and who read the galleys of the book; MR. HOWLAND SARGEANT, Secretary of the National Science Fund, who has assisted me in innumerable ways and who very kindly read the whole book in manuscript in an earlier draft; and, finally, DR. HARLOW SHAPLEY, Director of the Harvard Observatory, and present chairman of the National Science Fund, with whom I have had the opportunity of talking over many aspects of the book, and who has written such a splendid preface to it.

To PROFESSOR GEORGE SARTON, DR. PHILIPPE E. LE CORBEILLER, and especially DR. IAGO GALDSTON, I extend grateful thanks for many discussions I have had with them of the central problems of the book from its inception — and to all three for having carefully read the manuscript in an earlier draft. I should also like to thank MR. HARRY JOHNSON of Simmons College and PROFESSOR M. F. ASHLEY MONTAGU of Hahnemann Medical School for criticism of an early outline.

In addition to reading the chapters devoted to their respective specialties, PROFESSOR K. V. THIMANN and PROFESSOR KIRTLEY F.

[14] PROFESSOR DONALD H. MENZEL of the Harvard Observatory gave me a private course of instruction on this subject and presented me with an unpublished manuscript on the sun and radio communication. PROFESSOR FRED L. WHIPPLE, also of the Harvard Observatory, answered many questions about the upper atmosphere.
[15] Who also provided the information on the dynamical model of the ionosphere.
[16] Who also supplied the diagram showing coronal activity.

MATHER, both of Harvard University, allowed me time to discuss with them the general problems of the book; PROFESSOR MATHER read the last chapter and made valuable suggestions for its improvement.

An opportunity to discuss the major theme of the book at a meeting of the Tannery Club for the History of Science and of the Harvard Inter-Scientific Discussion Group enabled me to clarify several important ideas.

DR. J. B. F. SCHONLAND of South Africa, PROFESSOR REINHOLD RÜDENBERG of Harvard University, and DR. CLAUDE ZOBELL of the Scripps Institute of Oceanography kindly supplied me with information on their own work; but alas!, those chapters have not been included in the final version of the book.

I gladly acknowledge two special debts: one to the Harvard Library where most of the research was done, to its staff for locating books and articles when the reference was incomplete and for obtaining books not in Harvard's own extensive collection; the other to MR. PAUL DONALDSON of Cruft Laboratory, Harvard University, Master Photographer, for his help in preparing the illustrations.

A grant from the Milton Fund of Harvard University provided funds for research and bibliographical assistance, for travel, and for secretarial and other expenses necessary to the writing of this book.

I wish to thank the following assistants for help given me in surveying areas for possible case histories and for gathering materials (especially in the fields of medicine and biology), and for assembling bibliographies: MISS SYBIL BECKETT, MRS. MARY ELINOR McMULLEN BROWN, MISS BARBARA EWING, MRS. HELEN LEWIS THOMAS, and MISS CHRISTINA VAN DEUSEN. And to the stenographers who prepared outlines, early drafts, and final copy — especially MRS. ELIZABETH C. CABOT, MISS MIMI CHAMIAN, MRS. GEORGE HAWLEY, MRS. BENJAMIN LAX, and MRS. JOHN McCOMB — I hereby express my most grateful appreciation.

A special debt is owing MR. RANALD HOBBS of New York City.

I acknowledge with thanks the kindness of MR. ROGER SCAIFE and MR. ANGUS CAMERON of Little, Brown and Company, who made many helpful suggestions that have vastly improved the book.

My wife, FRANCES PARSONS DAVIS, stopped work on her own book, *Look Unto The Rock*, in order to be able to help me complete and revise the manuscript. Particularly she saw to it that I held by John Ray's admonition to authors: "He that useth many words for the explaining of any subject, doth, like the cuttle-fish, hide himself for the most part in his own ink." My best critic and most faithful reader — so much of this book is hers that to acknowledge it were supererogation.

I. Bernard Cohen

Index